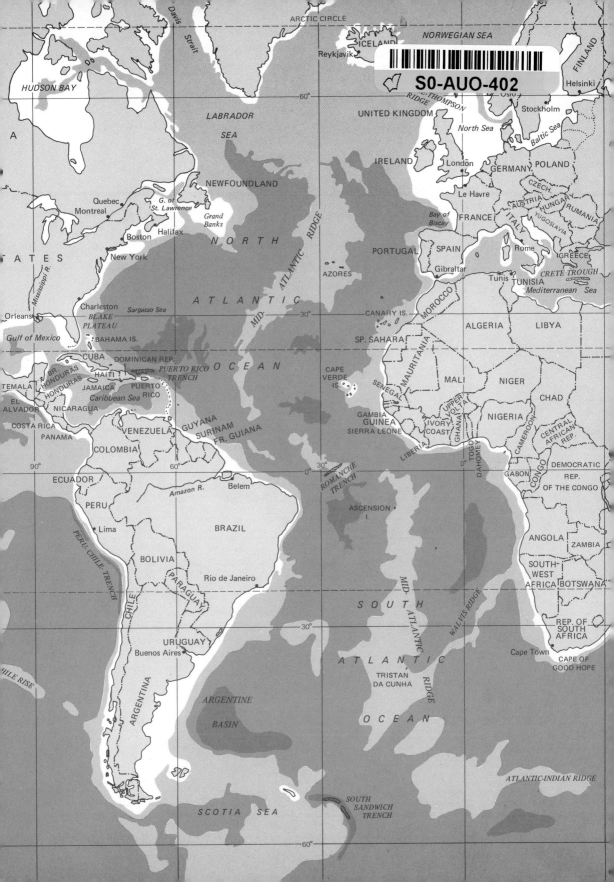

ARCTIC CIRCLE

NORWEGIAN SEA

ICELAND

FINLAND

Davis Strait

HUDSON BAY

Reykjavik

S0-AUO-402

Helsinki

LABRADOR SEA

THOMPSON RIDGE

UNITED KINGDOM

Oslo

Stockholm

60°

North Sea

Baltic Sea

NEWFOUNDLAND

IRELAND

London

GERMANY POLAND

Quebec

Montreal

G. of St. Lawrence

Grand Banks

Le Havre

FRANCE

CZECH.

AUSTRIA HUNGARY

RUMANIA

YUGOSLAVIA

Boston

Halifax

N O R T H

PORTUGAL

Bay of Biscay

ITALY

New York

SPAIN

Rome

GREECE

CRETE TROUGH

MID-

ATLANTIC

RIDGE

A T L A N T I C

AZORES

Gibraltar

Tunis

TUNISIA

Mediterranean Sea

Charleston

Sargasso Sea

30°

CANARY IS.

MOROCCO

ALGERIA

LIBYA

Orleans

BLAKE PLATEAU

SP. SAHARA

Gulf of Mexico

BAHAMA IS.

O C E A N

MAURITANIA

MALI

NIGER

CUBA

DOMINICAN REP.

PUERTO RICO TRENCH

CAPE VERDE IS.

CHAD

TEMALA

BR. HONDURAS

HAITI

JAMAICA

PUERTO RICO

SENEGAL

UPPER VOLTA

NIGERIA

HONDURAS

EL ALVADOR

NICARAGUA

Caribbean Sea

GAMBIA

GUINEA

SIERRA LEONE

IVORY COAST

GHANA

CAMEROON

CENTRAL AFRICAN REP.

COSTA RICA

PANAMA

VENEZUELA

GUYANA

SURINAM

FR. GUIANA

LIBERIA

TOGO

DAHOMEY

GABON

CONGO

DEMOCRATIC

90°

COLOMBIA

60°

0°

30°

0°

REP.

OF THE CONGO

ECUADOR

Amazon R.

Belem

ROMANCHE TRENCH

PERU

Lima

BRAZIL

ASCENSION I.

BOLIVIA

ANGOLA

ZAMBIA

PARAGUAY

Rio de Janeiro

S O U T H

SOUTH-WEST AFRICA

BOTSWANA

MID-

ATLANTIC

RIDGE

WALVIS RIDGE

30°

REP. OF SOUTH AFRICA

URUGUAY

Buenos Aires

A T L A N T I C

Cape Town

CAPE OF GOOD HOPE

HILE RISE

ARGENTINA

ARGENTINE BASIN

TRISTAN DA CUNHA

O C E A N

ATLANTIC-INDIAN RIDGE

SCOTIA SEA

SOUTH SANDWICH TRENCH

60°

PERU-CHILE TRENCH

CHILE

Mississippi R.

TATES

A

SECOND EDITION

the world ocean

AN INTRODUCTION TO OCEANOGRAPHY

WILLIAM A. ANIKOUCHINE
*Consultant Oceanographer
and
Research Associate
Marine Science Institute
University of California, Santa Barbara*

RICHARD W. STERNBERG
*Professor of Oceanography
Department of Oceanography
University of Washington
Seattle, Washington*

Prentice-Hall, Inc., Englewood Cliffs, New Jersey 07632

Library of Congress Cataloging in Publication Data

ANIKOUCHINE, WILLIAM A. (DATE)
   The world ocean.

   Includes bibliographies and index.
   1. Oceanography. I. Sternberg, Richard W.,
(date)   joint author. II. Title.
GC16.A5 1981   551.46   80-24473
ISBN 0-13-967778-X

Editorial/production supervision
and interior design by Ellen W. Caughey
Cover design by Lorraine Mullaney
Cover photograph by Four by Five
Manufacturing buyer: John Hall

Printed in the United States of America

10 9 8 7 6 5 4 3 2 1

Prentice-Hall International, Inc., *London*
Prentice-Hall of Australia Pty. Limited, *Sydney*
Prentice-Hall of Canada, Ltd., *Toronto*
Prentice-Hall of India Private Limited, *New Delhi*
Prentice-Hall of Japan, Inc., *Tokyo*
Prentice-Hall of Southeast Asia Pte. Ltd., *Singapore*
Whitehall Books Limited, *Wellington, New Zealand*

contents

10

11

12

13

preface
to the second edition

Nearly a decade has elapsed between the editions of *The World Ocean*. Advances in oceanography and related sciences during that time have expanded our understanding of some of the topics treated in the first edition and revisions were in order. At the same time an attempt was made to clarify seemingly obscure or erroneous passages in the narrative and to improve those drawings and illustrations that were not as lucid as desired. The suggestions offered by users and reviewers of the first edition were incorporated to the fullest possible extent.

In correcting and bringing to date the first edition we recognized that certain topics were omitted or treated too sketchily. New material and expansion or elaboration of preexisting text were introduced into the second edition to rectify those perceived deficiencies. The result is a text that is somewhat more developed than the first edition. To preserve the intent to produce a text having the attributes described in the preface to the first edition, we endeavored to maintain a modular structure in elaborating material so that the reader need go only as far into a subject as is appropriate. For classroom use the instructor can provide the student with guidance in this regard.

Changes to several chapters in this edition have been minor. Chapters on tides, biological oceanography, instrumentation, and the Appendix were given only small additions of text and a few new illustrations. Elsewhere in the text changes and additions have been substantial. The treatment of plate tectonics has been expanded to reflect our current knowledge. The principles of plate tectonics and sea-floor spreading have been introduced into other sections of the text where such principles apply. The history of the ocean basins and the origin and morphology of coasts are notable examples. Material has been added on the structure of water, chemical transport, the carbonate equilibrium, sound in the sea, ice in the ocean, storms at sea, turbulence, wave spectra, wave prediction, ecosystem modeling, particles suspended in the sea, petroleum and mineral genesis, positioning systems, and certain state-of-the-art instruments.

A guiding principle in deciding what material to introduce into the second edition was whether it provides an insight into the application of ocean sciences or presents a new topic in oceanography rather than just amplifying a subject considered to be adequately treated in the first edition. We hope that we have succeeded in producing a fresh treatment of our text while preserving those qualities found desirable by past readers.

WILLIAM A. ANIKOUCHINE
RICHARD W. STERNBERG

preface
to the first edition

This text is a compilation of lectures that the authors have used for several years in a beginning oceanography course for students without backgrounds in science.

A tremendous interest in using the world ocean for many purposes has been generated in recent years. This interest has accelerated the growth of the science of oceanography and has stimulated the inquiry of nonscientists. At present this country has many institutions that provide courses in basic oceanography. These courses are often crowded with individuals who have been made aware of the potential use of the sea, who are curious about the sea, or who just want to increase their general knowledge.

We have found that most students, science majors or not, are gratified if they gain an understanding of the principles of oceanographic science. It has been our experience that the principles of oceanography can be assimilated by students having practically no background in science or mathematics provided these subjects are introduced in context at the appropriate point in the course. Accordingly we have designed this text to acquaint lower-division university students with certain basic facts and the physical concepts needed to give a feeling for the general makeup of the world ocean and how it is investigated by oceanographers. Chapters are included to provide the students with a limited background in physics and chemistry as they proceed through the text. These chapters are not intended to replace the many fine lower-division physics and chemistry texts available; they reflect what the authors consider necessary so that the text can stress concepts as well as descriptions of oceanographic phenomena. We have attempted to retain rigorousness and veracity as a necessary accompaniment to simplicity so that students proceeding in oceanography will have a valid and useful book upon which to build their knowledge.

The authors have avoided including material that usually is put in introductory texts to provide a "balanced" or "comprehensive" treatment of the subject. Historical details, repetitive examples, and nonessential facts and descriptions to which a reader is expected to "relate" or "identify" are absent. The persevering student will encounter this sort of information elsewhere at a propitious time. At the level of this text, the student would only have to labor through such passages in search of the words and phrases important enough to underline with his or her colored pencil. It is our intent that a judiciously rubricated copy of this text contain virtually all underlined words.

A person having little or no scientific background can study this text with the aid of a qualified instructor and gain not merely a myriad of facts and figures about the world ocean but some feeling for the sea as an entity, a "consistent thing," that is shaped and controlled by its surroundings and in turn modifies all with which it is in contact. If the student comes to realize the complexity of the world ocean and our transitory understanding of it, one important aim of this book will have been attained.

WILLIAM A. ANIKOUCHINE
RICHARD W. STERNBERG

acknowledgments

Writing about the many disciplines comprising oceanography required that many people help in providing factual information, illustrations, photographs, critiques, and typing services. We are grateful for this assistance and lament that we cannot list every one of the many persons involved. Still, we would like to acknowledge those who helped in a major way.

We are pleased to acknowledge the influence of Professor Richard H. Fleming of the University of Washington who is a pioneer in the field of teaching undergraduate oceanography in the United States. Although Professor Fleming had no direct contact with this book, a number of his approaches to the study of oceanography appear in its pages.

We are indebted to those institutions and individuals that permitted us to use their data and illustrations. Individual credits are given in the captions of tables and figures. Original photographic material was obtained through the courtesy of Mr. Bernard Nist, Dr. Peter B. Taylor, Dr. Billy P. Glass, Mr. Walter Brundage, Dr. William McLeish, and Kent Cambridge Scientific Incorporated.

We acknowledge Professors Grant Bartlett, Queen's University; James Drever, University of Wyoming; Gerald Fowler, University of Wisconsin (Parkside); Rodney Feldmann, Kent State University; L.J. Charlesworth, University of Toledo; Thomas Wolcott, North Carolina State University; and Dr. Robert S. Dischel, consulting environmental scientist, New York, for their helpful reviews.

A foremost acknowledgment of gratitude is extended to our wives, Joan and Lois, for their continued encouragement and patience during the preparation of this book. Their support made the job much easier.

introduction

1

About 71 percent of the earth's surface is covered by a film of water that fills a system of ocean basins that we call the *world ocean*. If the earth were the size of a grapefruit, the film of water would be the thickness of this sheet of paper. The world ocean is marked by diversity and similarity; by extremes of change that are predictable in some respects, unpredictable in many others. Many aspects are overwhelmingly complex; some are very simple. The nature of the world ocean governs much of the character of the earth and its atmosphere; and, in turn, much of the character of the ocean is determined by the earth's history, composition, and place in the solar system. The ocean was the cradle of life on this planet. In recent years, however, humankind itself—which evolved out of these primeval forms of life—has been modifying the ocean's character. Nevertheless, the ocean remains what poets have called it for centuries: a vast and beautiful mystery.

The study of the world ocean is called oceanography (from the Greek *graphos*, drawn). Oceanology (from the Greek *logos*, discourse) might be a better word, but that term has not taken precedence in this country. It is difficult to separate the study of the world ocean into distinct descriptive, investigative, predictive, or other phases. It is just as hard to identify a purely physical aspect from a chemical aspect of oceanography. Therefore, the science of oceanography consists of many scientific disciplines brought to bear on one broad topic: the sea.

An interdisciplinary science is bound to be composed of many, often curious, fragments of the purer sciences. We find much of the description of

1

seawater motion taken from a meteorologist's notion of winds. The study of chemistry of lakes has been adapted to learn about the fertility of seawater and its seasonal changes. Many soil bacteria live on the surface of ocean sediment; therefore, marine microbiology has roots deep in soil science. Soil mechanics, a discipline typically associated with civil engineering, has been used to study properties of materials covering the ocean bottom. The list could be extended, but it should be clear that oceanographers are persons with a variety of backgrounds who must have a substantial knowledge of most of the physical and natural sciences.

1.1   *The Principle of Unity*

The concept of the world ocean held by a marine scientist is somewhat different from that of the nonscientist. All of us learn in grade school to identify the names and placement of the continents and oceans. This exercise reveals that the oceans completely surround the land masses, but it is slightly misleading because it suggests that the oceans are separated geographically. From an oceanographer's point of view, the emphasis should be on a world ocean that is completely intercommunicating. This body of water extends from the Arctic to the Antarctic; although it is forced to twist its way around the continental masses and forms distinct basins (each of which possesses a name), all of the basins are interconnected.

Geological oceanographers, attempting to trace the history of the earth, have discovered that the world ocean is also connected in time. The shapes of the ocean basins and the positions of the continental masses have changed continually for hundreds of millions, possibly billions, of years; however, their physical connection appears to span their history. Oceanographers in the 1800's and early 1900's observed the effects of these connections. In the 1870's, seawater samples collected from all ocean basins and all depths revealed striking similarities in their relative chemical content. This fact implied that the oceans were well mixed and that differences in relative proportions of various chemicals flowing in from rivers were removed by the stirring processes. Further investigation has revealed that the mixing time is about 1,000 years. It is important to remember this unity in space and time when we consider the sea as a resource, because any change that we cause in one area will eventually influence all areas.

1.2   *The Sea and the Environments of the Earth*

The interaction between land, sea, and atmosphere covers such a wide range of phenomena that it is difficult to comprehend it completely. Anyone who has visited a shoreline is aware of the constant struggle between land and sea. In some places, the land dominates and extends seaward in the form of river deltas, mangrove swamps, or coral reefs. In other places, the sea dominates, eroding and shaping coastal features. A shoreline reveals only one way that the sea influences our environment. Actually, the world ocean influences almost every aspect of our lives; it affects our weather, our food and water, our recreation, international travel, and commerce. The world ocean is also an important part of the global environment; because of its size and shape, it interacts with the earth's atmosphere and land masses so that it is vital to our existence.

1.3 *Oceanography in the Past and Present*

The study of the sea has changed in its emphasis, scope, and complexity throughout history. The ancient mariners traversed the sea in search of new lands or to transport goods from one port to another. Their knowledge of the sea was oriented toward winds, currents, sailing conditions, and other elements of navigation that determined the success of their voyages. In the late nineteenth century, however, scientists began to seek knowledge of the world ocean for its own sake.

The early scientists accomplished the first oceanwide survey of the marine environment. Probably the most famous expedition, which opened the era of ocean exploration, was made between 1872 and 1876 by *H.M.S. Challenger* (pictured in Fig. 1-1). The *Challenger*, with its crew and seven scientists, crossed the Atlantic, Pacific, and Antarctic oceans, traveling over 125,000 km* (or 68,900 nautical miles). The expedition observed weather, currents, water chemistry at all depths, temperature, bottom topography, sediments, and marine life on a global scale. These measurements provided the factual foundation for the science of oceanography.

Nowadays, an oceanographer is often a specialist whose research effort is concentrated in a specific area of study, such as biological oceanography, chemical oceanography, geological oceanography, physical oceanography, or oceanographic engineering. We have said that it is difficult to separate the study of the world ocean into phases, so naturally there is significant overlap among these categories. For example, a scientist investigating the transport of sand near the sea floor must understand both the characteristics of the sand (geological oceanography) and the nature of ocean currents (physical oceanography). Modern oceanographic institutions house a variety of scientists whose common bond is the ocean. Their background, theoretical approach, and analytical techniques may be completely different; yet, their combined research leads toward a better understanding of the sea. These scientists use equipment that may be very sophisticated or very crude. Some of the simplest

---

*Metric units are used throughout this text. See the Appendix for a discussion of the metric system.

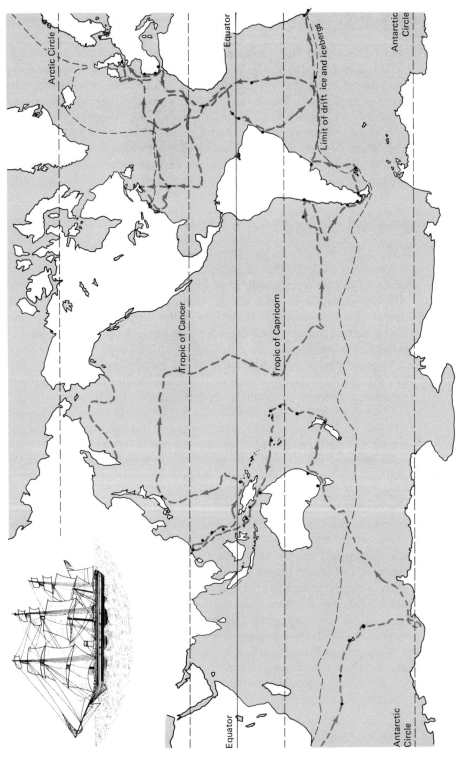

Figure 1-1 The voyage of *H.M.S. Challenger.*

Figure 1-2 Oceanographic vessel of the University of Washington, the *Thomas G. Thompson*, on an oceanographic expedition in the Arctic Ocean. (Photograph courtesy Joe S. Creager)

equipment includes the means for determining water clarity (a white-painted disc on a rope) and surface currents (buoyant chips or confetti sprinkled on the surface). Oceanographic research vessels are as small as rowboats or as large as ships 150 m (500 ft) long (Fig. 1-2), and there are more than 500 of them under the sponsorship of 66 nations. The rate of increase of the world's oceanographic research facilities is accelerating, yet, even with this total effort, our knowledge of the world ocean is still inadequate to solve many of the practical problems that exist (e.g., the prediction of weather, tsunamis, and hurricanes, or the biological and geochemical effects of waste disposal).

1.4 *The World Ocean as a Natural Resource*

The world ocean represents an incredibly large natural resource for all humankind. Although this resource is now relatively untapped, as population pressures increase, so will the demand for chemicals, minerals, food, and energy. The ocean basins contain approximately 1,370 × 10^6 cu km (328 million cubic miles) of seawater, which in itself is an important resource. The production of drinking water from the sea is still more expensive than naturally occurring fresh water, although desalination plants are used in water-deficient areas. Many techniques for removing the chemicals from seawater have been used, including distillation, freezing, osmosis, and ion exchange. Distillation seems to be the most economical. Approximately 700 desalination plants, each purifying over 85,000 liters (25,000 gal) of seawater per day, are in operation (or under construction) around the world, and this number will increase rapidly.

Every cubic kilometer of seawater contains about 39 million metric tons of dissolved solids, of which only common table salt (sodium chloride), magnesium, and bromine are being extracted in large quantities. Seawater probably contains chemical elements having a potential value of about 1 billion dollars per cu km; however, the economic feasibility of extracting many of these elements is highly questionable because of low concentrations. Nevertheless, the world's seawater represents a large source of materials.

Other valuable ocean resources are found on or under the sea floor. Deposits under the bottom include gas, oil, sulfur, potash, and coal. Bottom deposits include minerals precipitated from seawater, as well as sand, gravel, and oyster shells. Offshore oil wells, for example, accounted for 12 percent of the world production of oil in 1968 and 18.5 percent in 1978 (11.6×10^6 barrels per day). Exploitation so far has been confined to about 360 drilling platforms located around the continental margins in depths less than 230 m (750 ft). By 1985 the number of drilling platforms is expected to increase to about 700 with operating depths of 400 m (1,300 ft).

Far from shore on the deep-sea floor, oceanographers have discovered and mapped vast deposits of metallic nodules that have precipitated on the bottom. Each of these nodules, called manganese nodules, is made up, on the average, of 24 percent manganese, 14 percent iron, 1 percent nickel, and smaller amounts of cobalt and copper. Investigations have shown that 20 to 50 percent of the floor of the Southwest Pacific Ocean basin is covered with nodules in concentrations of 7,300 metric tons per sq km, valued at 2.35 million dollars per sq km. The total may be more than 100 billion metric tons. The chemical composition of these nodules makes it difficult to extract the manganese. However, this problem will be overcome as necessity demands. The value of copper and nickel in the nodules will motivate the development of the necessary technology. The growth rate of nodules is such that they approach being a renewable resource: They are a perennial source of metal for modern industry.

The recovery of solar energy from the sea is an exciting prospect for the civilization of the future. Plans exist for converting the differential between surface and deep-sea water temperatures to electrical power. Winning the solar energy converted to biological substances by plankton and seaweed appears to be a feasible method of deriving fuel energy in the form of methane as well as food energy in the form of livestock feed. The energy of the tides is already being recovered; sources of energy in the form of waves and of winds at sea are under investigation.

Food resources of the sea are as important as the physical resources. The annual catch of the world marine fisheries exceeds 74 million metric tons which supports an international trade of approximately 20 billion dollars. Of the ocean harvest, over 90 percent is finned fish, with small percentages of shellfish and whale. Geographically, the Pacific Ocean yields 53 percent of the marine harvest; the Atlantic Ocean yields 42 percent; and the Indian Ocean, 5 percent. The low figure for the Indian Ocean indicates a lack of exploitation rather than a poor source.

The marine fisheries' harvest is used for several purposes, depending on the species involved. In the United States the more desirable species are reserved for human consumption, whereas other species are converted to fish meal (as a high-protein supplement for livestock and poultry) and fish oil. The development and production of fish protein concentrate (FPC) has provided a potential market for various less popular fish species. At the same time FPC offers significant relief to protein-deficient countries. FPC is a tasteless, odorless, highly nutritious food supplement. For a cost of only two dollars per year, it satisfies the daily animal protein requirements of a growing child. It is hoped that this supplement will relieve serious problems of protein malnutrition that occur in some areas of the world.

1.5   *The Future of the World Ocean*

Before the nineteenth century, the sea could be exploited in any way without causing significant change in it. Population pressures were low and the lack of technology severely limited exploitation of the sea for food, fossil fuels, and other raw materials. Even dumping waste into the sea did not pose any serious problems, except in certain local situations.

In the nineteenth and twentieth centuries, however, significant changes have occurred. The human population has increased alarmingly, making tremendous demands on all natural resources. Furthermore, the advance in technology has paralleled the population expansion. As a result, materials and food resources are obtainable on such massive scales that the depletion of many resources can be expected in the foreseeable future. Perhaps worst of all, the ocean is still used indiscriminately as a dumping ground for industrial and municipal wastes.

Increased quantities of lead in ocean waters has followed the use of leaded gasolines in ever-increasing numbers of gasoline engines. In some areas in fresh waters and bottom sediments, the mercury content has increased because of the increased use of fungicides and their introduction into the water. Similarly, the residues of DDT have increased too, following its development and continued use since World War II. These examples are among the more obvious observations made by oceanographers. They illustrate the point that technological advances may bring short-term advantages; but, without control, serious damage (i.e., mass destruction of biological species) could occur in only a few decades. This statement does not mean that we should discontinue our search for new products or chemicals or techniques of exploitation that will aid humankind. It suggests, however, that the evaluation of these advances should be thorough and that long-range effects are more important than short-term gains.

Experience has shown that the world ocean is not infinitely large and that it is a perishable resource. For it to continue to be useful for all peoples today and in the future, two things are necessary. First, there must be international cooperation. Serious misuse by one country will eventually affect the world ocean—and hence all countries. This situation is true whether the misuse is extreme overfishing, dumping of radioactive wastes (or any pollutant in significant quantities), or even improper oil drilling techniques that release large quantities of oil onto the sea surface. The old concept of the freedom of the sea is no longer valid. The resources of the world ocean are so valuable that they must be maintained cooperatively for the mutual benefit of all.

Second, oceanographic research must expand and continue. The findings of environmental scientists should be the key to the planned use of the sea. The food chains, paths of energy transfer, and various chemical and physical interactions are so complex that it will require the sustained effort of many scientists to monitor the sea adequately and predict future conditions. This is the challenge facing oceanographers in the immediate future.

reading list

Davis, R. A., Jr., *Principles of Oceanography.* Reading, Mass.: Addison-Wesley, 2nd ed. 1977. 505p.

Dietrich, G., *General Oceanography.* New York: Interscience Publishers, 1963. 588p.

Fairbridge, R. W., ed., *The Encyclopedia of Oceanography.* New York: Reinhold Publishing Corp., 1966. 1021p.

Gross, M. G., *Oceanography, a View of the Earth.* Englewood Cliffs, N.J.: Prentice-Hall, Inc., 1972. 581p.

Hill, M. N., ed., *The Sea*, Vols. I, II, III. New York: Interscience, 1963.

King, C. A. M., *An Introduction to Oceanography.* New York: McGraw-Hill Book Company, 1963. 337p.

Linklater, E., *The Voyage of the Challenger.* Garden City, N.Y.: Doubleday & Company, Inc., 1972. 288p.

Pickard, G. L., *Descriptive Physical Oceanography.* New York: Pergamon Press, 1968. 200p.

SVERDRUP, H. U., M. W. JOHNSON, AND R. H. FLEMING, *The Oceans, Their Physics, Chemistry and General Biology.* Englewood Cliffs, N.J.: Prentice-Hall, Inc., 1942. 1087p.

TUREKIAN, K. K., *Oceans.* Englewood Cliffs, N.J.: Prentice-Hall, Inc., 1968. 120p.

VETTER, R. C., *Oceanography Information Sources.* Washington, D.C.: National Academy of Sciences-National Research Council, 1970. 51p.

WEYL, P., *Oceanography.* New York: John Wiley & Sons, Inc., 1970. 535p.

WILLIAMS, J., *Oceanography, An Introduction to the Marine Sciences.* Boston: Little, Brown & Company, 1962. 242p.

general features of the earth and the world ocean

2

To begin the study of oceanography, the student should understand the structure and the topographic features of the earth, especially the sea floor. Initially, oceanographers conceived of the floor of the sea as a vast, undistorted plain covered with fine sediment. As sampling equipment became more sophisticated and soundings were made, this concept changed. We now know that the floor of the sea is quite diverse in its structure and topography.

2.1 The Shape and Size of the Earth

Our concept of the earth's shape has changed over the years. The idea that the earth is a sphere was modified when scientists realized that the earth is flattened slightly at the poles, i.e., it has nearly the shape of an oblate spheroid. This shape is the one assumed by a rotating body with equilibrium between gravitational and rotational (centrifugal) forces. The flattening causes the polar radius to be 22 km shorter than the equatorial radius.

With the advent of space exploration, scientists were able to examine the earth's shape from a distance. Their observations of the gravitational effects on orbiting satellites led to the conclusion that the shape of the earth is really that of an irregular, fat pear. As refined observations disclose more irregularities, it becomes obvious that the earth has a unique shape unlike any regular geometric solid. Indeed, we might say that the earth is "earth-shaped" much as we say an egg is "egg-shaped."

Table 2–1   Table of Earth's Dimensions

Dimension	Magnitude	Units
Mass	6×10^{27}	kg
Volume	1.1×10^{12}	km³
Circumference	40×10^3	km
Polar radius	6,356	km
Equatorial radius	6,378	km
Total surface area	510×10^6	km²
Land surface area	149×10^6	km²
Ocean surface area	361×10^6	km²
Ocean volume	$1,370 \times 10^6$	km³
Ocean mass	1.4×10^{21}	kg
Ocean average depth	3,795	m
Ocean mean temperature	3.90	°C
Seawater mean density	1.03	g/cm³
Atmosphere height* (troposphere plus stratosphere)	32	km
Atmosphere volume*	1.6×10^{10}	km³
Atmosphere mass*	5×10^{24}	kg
Air density (dry, near sea level)	1.3×10^{-3}	g/cm³

* These values are arbitrary estimates inasmuch as the atmosphere grades into outer space.

These small departures from the oblate spheroid shape are of some interest to oceanographers, but it is geodesists* and cartographers who are most concerned with such refinements. For our purposes, it is sufficient to regard the earth as an oblate spheroid or a sphere, whichever is appropriate.

The size of the earth has been known for a long time. As early as 200 B.C., the scholar Eratosthenes calculated the earth's radius to be about 7,370 km, within 16 percent of the accepted value. Table 2-1 gives some estimates of the earth's dimensions.

2.2   *The Gross Aspects of the World Ocean*

When a student examines the world map shown inside the front and back covers, he or she should note the following:

1. *Most of the earth's surface is covered by water.* The surface of the earth is 510 million sq km. Of this area, 361 million sq km, or 70.8 percent, is covered by water; 149 million sq km, or 29.2 percent, is land area. These percentages are not constant, because there have been variations in sea

---

*Geodesists are specialists in the determination of the size and shape of the earth.

level during the earth's past.* For example, during the last Ice Age in the Pleistocene epoch (2,000,000 to 11,000 years ago), enough water accumulated (as ice) on the continents to lower the sea level about 150 m. When the sea level went down, vast areas of the continental margins were exposed, and the relative proportion of land increased as much as 6 percent. Glaciation comparable to that in the Pleistocene occurred in the late Paleozoic era and also in the late Precambrian era. The extensive proportion of water on the earth's surface determines the manner in which the ocean and the atmosphere respond to the gradient of temperature that exists between the poles and the equator. The global climate is in fact controlled by this effect.

2. *Land is not distributed evenly over the globe.* Seventy percent of all land is located in the northern hemisphere. There is still more water than land in both hemispheres. In the northern hemisphere, however, the ratio of water to land is 1.5 to 1; in the southern hemisphere, the ratio is 4 to 1. This leads to important differences in the circulation of seawater in the north and south hemispheres and determines local climates.

3. *Continents are separated by ocean basins connected to form a single body of water.* The earth's six continents, Eurasia, Africa, North America, South America, Australia, and Antarctica, are surrounded by the depressions of the Pacific Ocean basin, Atlantic Ocean basin (including the Arctic Ocean basin), and the Indian Ocean basin. Each ocean basin extends northward from the ocean surrounding the Antarctic continent. Because all the basins are contiguous, the system of ocean basins is called the *world ocean.*

The boundaries of the Indian, Pacific, and Atlantic ocean basins are shown on the world map (inside the front and back covers). By convention, the Atlantic Ocean basin is separated from the Indian Ocean basin along the 20°E meridian between the Cape of Good Hope and the Antarctic continent. Likewise, the Pacific Ocean basin is separated from the Indian Ocean basin along the 147°E meridian between Tasmania and the Antarctic continent. In contrast to these arbitrary boundaries, the boundary between the Atlantic and Pacific ocean basins is a narrow, curved shoal, called a *sill*, that connects Cape Horn with Antarctica's Palmer Peninsula. This sill delineates the Scotia Sea as a tongue of the Pacific Ocean basin extending quite far east of the southern tip of South America.

Each of the three major ocean basins has a different appearance. The Atlantic Ocean basin is the longest. It is relatively narrow and extends northward in an irregular, twisting shape. It is marked by few oceanic islands and by isolated, adjoining seas, such as the Baltic Sea, North Sea, Hudson Bay, Mediterranean Sea, and Caribbean Sea. The Arctic Ocean basin is considered another sea adjacent to the Atlantic Ocean basin.

---

*A chart of geologic time is given in Table A-3 in the Appendix.

The Pacific Ocean occupies the largest ocean basin; its east-west dimension is equal to about one-half the circumference of the earth. It has a roughly symmetrical shape and contains many oceanic islands and *island arcs:* for example, the Aleutian Islands, the islands of Japan, and the Philippine Islands. The Gulf of California and the Scotia Sea are the only adjacent seas in the eastern part of the Pacific Ocean. The western or Asiatic side of the Pacific basin, however, contains many adjacent seas, such as the South China Sea, the East China Sea, the Sea of Japan, the Sea of Okhotsk, and the Bering Sea. The world ocean is deepest in the Pacific Ocean basin. These depths are found in great trenches just seaward of the island arcs; the deepest (11,034 m) occurs in the Mariana Trench east of the Mariana island arc.

The Indian Ocean is also roughly symmetrical, but contains few islands, and is about as wide as the Atlantic Ocean basin. It lies at latitudes mostly below the Tropic of Cancer (23°N latitude). The Andaman Sea, Persian Gulf, and Red Sea, for example, are marginal to the Indian Ocean, and the Java Trench lies along its eastern edge.

The areas of these ocean basins differ significantly. The Indian Ocean basin, the smallest, occupies 75 million sq km. The Atlantic Ocean basin occupies 106 million sq km, and the Pacific Ocean basin, the largest, 180 million sq km. The area occupied by the Pacific Ocean basin is about equal to that occupied by the combined Atlantic and Indian ocean basins. Furthermore, all of the land area of the earth's surface could fit within the borders of the Pacific Ocean basin.

In studying the world map, we must remember that some terms used to describe geographic bodies of water have imprecise meanings. "Seas" such as the Mediterranean Sea, Sargasso Sea, Caspian Sea, and Arabian Sea are geographically quite dissimilar bodies of water. The Mediterranean Sea is virtually landlocked. The Sargasso Sea lies in the middle of the Atlantic Ocean and has only hydrographic boundaries. The Caspian Sea is a saline lake, and the Arabian Sea is merely the body of water lying on the west side of India. The term "sea" obviously has no unique connotation and should be used with caution. The term "bay" is, likewise, ambiguous. The Bay of Bengal is the body of water occupying the east side of India. The Bay of Biscay is only an irregularity in the French coast. Portage Bay is a freshwater lake in the state of Washington and is quite small in comparison with Hudson Bay, which is saline and quite large. Another of these imprecise terms is "gulf." The Gulf of

Table 2–2   Average Depth of the Ocean Basins

Ocean basin	With adjoining seas	Without adjoining seas
Pacific	4,028 m	4,282 m
Atlantic	3,332	3,926
Indian	3,897	3,963
World ocean	3,795	4,117

California is a long arm of the sea. The Gulf of St. Lawrence is really a river mouth, or estuary. The Gulf of Mexico is a semienclosed sea.

Nevertheless, these terms are established geographic conventions that are not likely to be changed. Despite the variety of usage, they designate areas that are but parts of a single entity, the world ocean.

2.3   *The Depth of the Oceans*

The average depths of the ocean basins are given in Table 2-2. It is noteworthy that the ocean basins exclusive of adjoining seas have average depths within 180 m (5 percent) of the average for the world ocean. This fact provides the first inkling that the bottom of the ocean represents a uniform global feature. This idea is verified by the statistical distribution of depth in the world ocean and elevations on continents displayed by a hypsographic curve (Fig. 2-1). A curve of this type answers the question: What percentage of the earth's surface lies above a particular level? It is not to be construed as a profile of the earth's

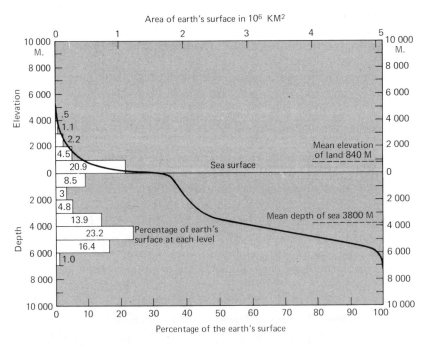

Figure 2-1 The hypsographic curve showing the percentage of the earth's surface above a given level. The solid bars represent the percentage of the earth's surface within each particular 1,000-m interval. (After Sverdrup, Johnson, and Fleming, by permission of Prentice-Hall, Inc.)

surface. Observe from the bar graph that most of the earth's solid surface lies at two dominant levels: One lies between sea level and 1 km and represents 21 percent of the earth's surface, and the second is the average ocean depth level lying between 3 km and 6 km. Over half the earth's surface is at elevations or depths lying between these levels. Only about 10 .percent of the earth's surface lies at the extremes of elevation and depth.

The existence of the dominant levels is significant. These are planetary features that must be considered in determining the origin and structure of the earth. Their existence is one piece of observational evidence to be included in forming hypotheses of the earth's origin and in constructing a conceptual model of its structure.

2.4 *The Structure of the Earth*

The structure of the surface of the earth to a depth of 10 or 20 km has been observed directly using drill holes and mine workings. Much has been deduced from geological and geophysical maps of the earth's surface, but an understanding of the structure of the earth's deep interior is acquired only by applying indirect evidence to a theoretical model of the earth's structure. Scientists have had to use evidence gained from volcanology, from studies of the chemical and physical properties of surface rocks and meteorites, gravity, geomagnetism, thermal properties of surface rocks, and seismology. Indeed, even studies of the geology of the moon and planets bear indirect evidence of the structure of the earth. The study of seismology is one of the more important lines of research that provides evidence of the earth's structure. The earth continually undergoes deformation due to internal stresses. Some of this stress is relieved by sudden releases of energy that cause earthquakes. Earthquake energy associated with rock fracturing is transmitted as seismic waves that propagate through the earth radially from the center of disturbance.

Seismic waves are of several kinds. *Surface waves*, for example, propagate only in the uppermost regions or boundaries of the earth. *Body waves*, on the other hand, pass through the interior of the earth. Two kinds of body waves are generated, *P-waves* and *S-waves*. P-waves are transmitted by a "push-pull" or longitudinal deformation of the rocks through which they travel, similar to sound waves. S-waves are transmitted by a shear, or transverse deformation, analogous to light waves (Fig. 2-2).

The velocity of propagation of seismic waves is dependent on the elastic properties and density of the materials through which they pass. S-waves cannot be transmitted through a liquid because a liquid is not rigid, i.e., it has no shear strength. These particular properties of seismic waves are critical for determining the interior structure of the earth.

When an earthquake occurs, the earth is set into vibration, and various seismic waves propagate outward from the disturbance. The waves reflect off

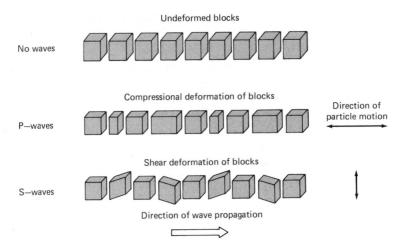

Figure 2-2 Deformation produced by the passage of P-waves and S-waves. Blocks represent discrete regions within a continuous solid material such as rocks. Note that S-waves do not propagate through a fluid. (After S.P. Clark, *Structure of the Earth*, 1971, by permission of Prentice-Hall, Inc.)

distinct boundaries between rock layers, refract through rock layers depending on their rigidity and density, and may be absorbed in any regions that have the properties of a liquid. A representation of the paths of seismic waves passing through the earth gives an idea how P- and S-waves may be used to interpret the earth's structure (Fig. 2-3). Such data can be reduced to a velocity-depth curve for P- and S-waves as shown in Fig. 2-4.

Seismic studies reveal that the earth's interior consists of concentric layers, some of which may be in a liquid phase. The earth model has three main layers: (1) the *core*, which has the properties of an iron-nickel mixture divided into an outer liquid region and an inner core that has the properties of a solid; (2) the *mantle*, which has the properties of iron magnesium silicate rock rich in olivine and pyroxene (see Fig. A-8); and (3) the *crust*, a thin outer layer composed of aluminum and magnesium silicates having a high feldspar content (see Fig. A-8). The geometry of these layers is based on seismic velocity evidence. Some physical properties of these layers are given in Table 2-3. The layered structure probably was formed during the formation of the earth or soon after.

Either of two hypotheses of the earth's origin is compatible with the three-layer earth model. According to the *tidal disruption hypothesis*, the earth originally was molten and became layered by differentiation of the earth materials as the heavier metals migrated toward the center and the lighter silicate minerals moved toward the crust and solidified. This view of the origin of the earth is not widely held.

According to the *condensation hypothesis*, however, the earth began in a relatively cool state. Differentiation of earth materials into core, mantle, and crust occurred because much heat was generated by the collision of particles and compression and by the spontaneous decay of radioactive substances.

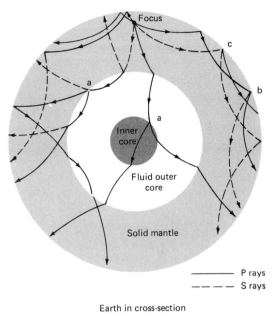

Earth in cross-section

P rays
––––– S rays

Figure 2-3 Representative seismic rays through the earth. Rays are curved because the density of the earth increases toward its center. Note that a P-wave can produce both a P-wave and an S-wave when it encounters an interface with a solid as at (a) (refraction) and at (b) (reflection). An S-wave can produce both a P-wave and an S-wave as at (c) (reflection). Note absence of S-wave in fluid outer core. (After Bullen, 1954)

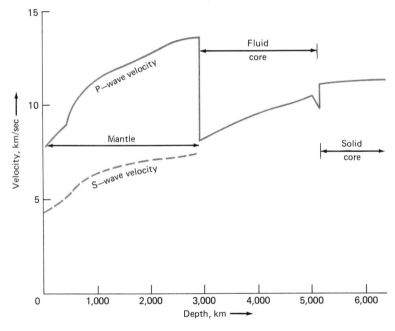

Figure 2-4 Seismic velocities of P- and S-waves as a function of depth. Note the discontinuities at the boundaries of the fluid core. For comparison, P-wave velocities are 1.5 km/sec in seawater, 2.0 km/sec in marine sediments, and 5.0 km/sec in oceanic crust. (After F. Birch, *Journal of Geophysical Research* Vol. 57, p. 227, 1952 copyright by the American Geophysical Union)

Table 2–3   Some Physical Properties of the Earth's Structure

Layer	Composition	Depth range (km)	Approximate average density (gm/cm³)	Estimated average temperature (°C)	Relative mass (%)
Crust	Silicates of magnesium and aluminum	0–65	2.9	500	0.4
Mantle	Silicates of iron and magnesium	10–2,900	4.5	2,500	68.1
Core					
Outer	Liquid iron and nickel	2,900–5,100	11.5	5,000	31.5
Inner	Solid iron and nickel	5,100–6,370	13.0	6,000	
Total earth			5.5		100.0

Once the temperature increased to the melting point of iron, differentiation of the core began. As the temperature increased, the silicate minerals migrated to the surface and formed the structure depicted in Fig. 2-5. The "hot origin" idea means differentiation occurred concurrently with the earth's formation; with the "cold origin" idea, differentiation covered perhaps a period of 2 billion years.

2.5   *The Crust of the Earth*

Let us examine the outer shell of low-density silicate rocks that form the crust of the earth. The boundary between the crust and the mantle is 10 to 55 km deep (Fig. 2-6) and is defined by an abrupt increase (from 6.7 to 8.1 km/sec) in the velocity of propagation of seismic waves. This boundary is named the *Mohorovicic discontinuity* (or Moho) in honor of the Yugoslav seismologist who discovered the feature in 1909. It is generally supposed that the Mohorovicic discontinuity represents a chemical boundary separating olivine-pyroxene-rich materials of the mantle from the overlying crustal rocks that are rich in feldspar.

Above the Moho, the earth's crust was shown by early investigations to be divided into two layers. The crust just above the Moho (approximately 5 km thick) has properties resembling basalt (a common volcanic rock found on the earth's surface), which is composed of silicates of calcium, magnesium, and iron. The average density of this material is 3.0 gm/cm³.

The upper layer has properties similar to those of granite, a common igneous

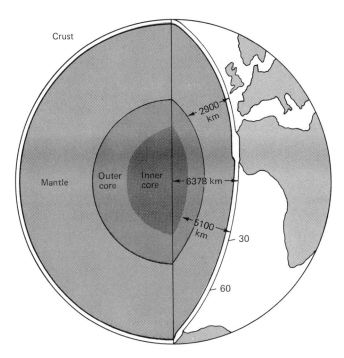

Figure 2-5 Structure of the earth's interior. The crustal thickness has been exaggerated so that it can be shown at this scale.

rock, composed mainly of silicates of aluminum and potassium. The average density of this layer is 2.8 gm/cm^3. A more complete description of the mineral compositions of these two common rock types is given in the Appendix. The arrangement of layers in the crust is shown in Fig. 2-6. The basaltic layer might extend over the entire earth but the granitic layer does not; it exists as massive continental blocks "floating" on a layer of basalt. The granitic rocks are referred to as *continental crust;* the *oceanic crust* refers to the basaltic-type rocks exposed on the sea floor. The dominant levels in the hypsographic curve (Fig. 2-1) represent the mean elevation of the tops of the continental crust blocks and the mean depth of the oceanic crust surface.

Furthermore, the dominant levels express how density differences between these two types of crust affect the configuration of the ocean basins and continents. The densities of the continental and oceanic crusts are almost the same (2.8 versus 3.0 gm/cm^3); therefore, about 93 percent of a continental block is submerged in underlying material the same way that 92 percent of an iceberg is submerged in water. If a continent is composed of several blocks of various sizes, all in "floating" equilibrium, the Moho must assume a shape that reflects the surface of the continent, but with a relief nine times greater. Continental "flotation," or *isostasy* (Fig. 2-7), requires that the bottom of a continental block must rise as material is removed from the continental surface in order to keep the exposed-submerged ratio constant. This movement maintains isostatic equilibrium and is called *isostatic adjustment.*

In areas of the world that were covered by great masses of ice during parts of the Pleistocene glacial epoch, the added weight of ice caused the crustal mass to sink deeper into the mantle. When the ice melted about 11,000 years ago this weight was removed and the crust started to rebound toward its former isostatic equilibrium position. The crust is still rebounding in many places. On the Scandinavian peninsula, for example, the present rate of rebound is as much as 1 cm per year; but as equilibrium is approached, the rate will decrease and eventually rebound will cease. In North America, rebound is tilting the Great Lakes basins down to the south; the lakes will drain into the Mississippi River eventually.

2.6   *The Morphology of the Ocean Basins*

Many of the features comprising the sea floor are very large in scale (thousands of kilometers) and occur repeatedly at certain positions within the ocean basins, thus indicating that their origin must be associated with dynamic processes active within the earth or with worldwide oceanic processes. Other features are of a smaller scale and appear to be related to local oceanic conditions. In Chap. 3 we attempt to relate the configuration of the ocean basins to the earth's structure and to oceanic processes. First, however, we must describe systematically the topography of the ocean floor.

If we were to construct a series of cross-sectional profiles across the ocean basins, such as seen in Fig. 2-8, we would find some features common to all profiles. Our first observation would be the very steep nature of the slope that separates shallow from deep water at the periphery of all ocean basins. The abruptness of this slope is accentuated by the vertical exaggeration in the figure; however, it is still many times greater than most other areas of the world ocean. This slope serves as a boundary dividing the ocean basins into two major divisions called the *continental margin* and the *deep sea.* These divisions serve as a focal point for our catalog of sea-floor features.

Continental Margins

The continental margin, the zone where the continents merge into the ocean basins, is characterized by several prominent and distinct topographic features. These features are illustrated in Fig. 2-9. Surrounding the continents of the world is a relatively flat platform called the *continental shelf.* Offshore, the inclination of this shelf increases abruptly to form the *shelf break* or *shelf edge.* Beyond the shelf edge, the *continental slope* extends downward to the deep-sea

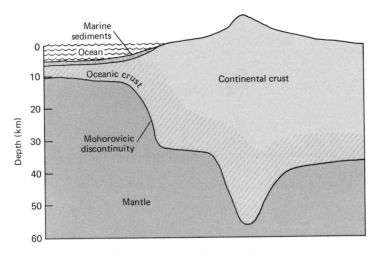

Figure 2-6 Idealized profile of the earth's crust.

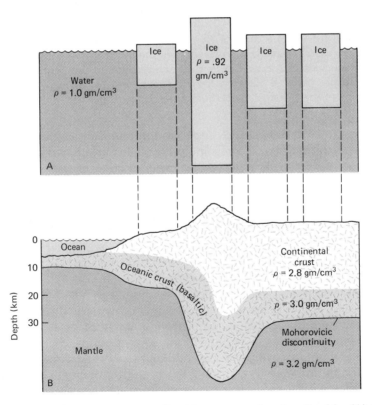

Figure 2-7 The principle of isostasy can be visualized by (A) flotation of ice blocks in water, or (B) flotation of land masses in "fluid substratum."

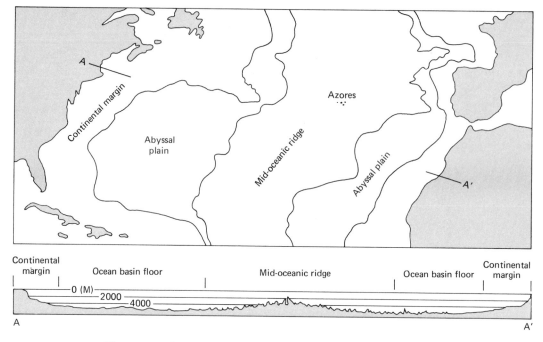

Figure 2-8 Outline map of the major division of the North Atlantic Ocean basin. Below is a representative profile from New England to the Sahara coast of Africa. The vertical exaggeration of this profile is about 40 times. (After B. C. Heezen, M. Tharp, and M. Ewing, 1959, "The Floors of the Oceans," Geol. Soc. Amer. Spec. Paper 65)

floor. Sometimes the shelf and slope are lumped as a single feature and are called the *continental terrace*. In some places, such as along the margins of the Atlantic Ocean, the inclination of the lower portion of the continental slope decreases to form what is called the *continental rise*.

Continental shelves. Continental shelves can extend as far as 1,500 km in width and 20 to 550 m in depth. On the average, the continental shelf is 78 km wide and 133 m deep at the outer edge. The average inclination of the continental shelf is 7' of arc or a drop of 1.8 m per km (11 ft per mile). This inclination is too small to detect by eye.

The dimensions and shape of continental shelves reflect the nature of the adjacent coast and local oceanic conditions, both past and present. Table 2-4 shows how continental shelves differ from place to place. If the coastal plain is rough and narrow, as in regions of young mountains, the continental shelf is narrow and deep or even missing. Adjacent to a broad, smooth coastal plain, such as occurs in the eastern United States, the continental shelf is broad and smooth. Where strong ocean currents impinge on the continent, the shelf is narrow, deep, and is composed of coarse sediment. At the Blake Plateau off Florida, the Gulf Stream affects the shelf in this manner. Wide, shallow shelves

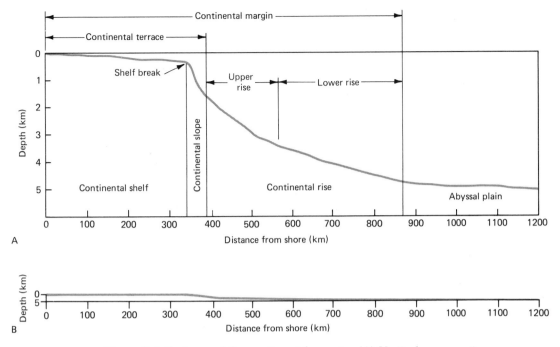

Figure 2-9 Features of the continental margin: (A) Vertical exaggeration 150:1; (B) No vertical exaggeration.

Table 2–4   Characteristics of Continental Shelves

Nature of the coastal zone	Nature of associated continental shelf				
Shelves	Width		Depth		
	Narrow	Wide	Deep	Shallow	
Bordering glaciated land masses		X	X		Very rough topographically
Off broad coastal plains but not glaciated		X		X	Very smooth platform
Associated with strong currents	X		X		Coarse sediment types
Bordering large river deltas		X		X	Muddy sediment
In clear tropical seas		X		X	Coral reefs
Off new mountain ranges	X		X		Distinct shelf may be lacking, coarse sediment

23

exist off large river deltas or behind coral and algal reefs, because sediments and biological growth are extending the continental margin seaward in these areas. Wide, deep shelves with rough topography occur in areas of the world that were covered by great masses of ice during the Pleistocene glacial epoch.

Continental slope.   The continental slope is one of the major topographic features of the earth's surface. The average inclination of the continental slope is about 4° of arc or about 66 m per km (400 ft per mile), but inclinations between 1° and 25° of arc exist. As with continental shelves, the inclination of a continental slope can be related to effects of both geological and oceanic phenomena. The slope adjacent to young mountain areas is generally steeper than average, ranging from 5° to as much as 25°. Adjacent to large rivers that introduce great quantities of sediment, the average slope is slightly greater than 1°. Several types of continental slopes are described in Table 2-5.

Table 2–5   Types of Continental Slopes

Type	Nature of slope	Examples
Structural deformation	Steep	California
		West coast of South America
Continental rift scar	Steep	Gulf of California
Extended coastal plain and shelf	Moderate	East coast of United States
Sedimentation beyond shelf	Gentle	Gulf coast of United States
Carbonate reef	Very steep	West coast of Florida
		Yucatan, Mexico

(After R. S. Dietz, "Origin of Continental Slopes," *American Scientist*, LII, No. 1 (1964), 50–69.)

Continental rise.   Where observed, the continental rise is a thick prism of sediment that has been carried from the continents and deposited at the base of the continental slope. The continental rise can be as wide as 600 km, has slopes between 0.5 and 25 m per km, and lies at depths of between 1,400 and 5,100 m. Sometimes the rise occurs in two distinct sections, which are labeled the upper and lower rises in Fig. 2-9.

The development of these features appears to be related to the abundance of sediment introduced from the continents. At present, the Atlantic and Indian ocean basins receive the majority of the sediment eroded from the continents, and so continental rises are developed better in these basins.

Submarine canyon.   Most of the continental shelves in the world ocean are transected by *submarine canyons* that cut the continental terrace and empty onto the deep-sea floor. A submarine canyon is similar in shape and size to a large canyon on land (Fig. 2-10). It is characterized by a V-shaped cross section sometimes with a flat floor, an axis sloping seaward, and a sinuous course with accordant tributaries (tributaries that enter the main channel at the elevation of the main channel). Canyons cut through both unconsolidated marine sediments and hard rocks. Often they are seaward extensions of rivers that exist now or existed when the sea level was lowered during the Pleistocene epoch.

The origin of submarine canyons has been debated for many years. It appears that rivers cut these canyons through the continental terrace when the shelf emerged during the Pleistocene. The canyons were excavated further by the action of *turbidity currents:* flows of sediment-laden water moving over the bottom of the sea. Turbidity currents have been observed directly in freshwater lakes, but their existence in the marine environment is only inferred. A series of submarine cables, cut in sequence following the Grand Banks earthquake of 1929, gave the first direct evidence that turbidity currents have erosive

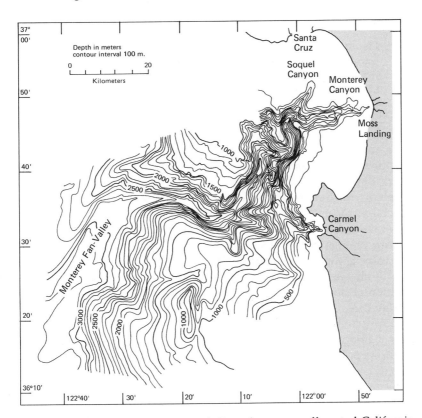

Figure 2-10A Monterey and Carmel canyons off central California. (From soundings of Coast and Geodetic Survey and surveys by F. P. Shepard)

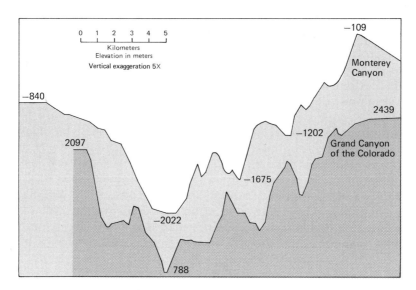

Figure 2-10B Comparative profiles of Monterey Canyon and the Grand Canyon using the same number of points and same scales. The resemblance is striking. (From F. P. Shepard, *Submarine Geology*, 2nd edition, Harper and Row, New York, 1963)

capabilities. Marine geologists have discovered the remains of shallow-water fauna and flora, anomalously coarse sediments, and certain sedimentary flow structures far seaward of the continental margins. These discoveries leave little doubt that turbidity currents are important mechanisms for transporting sediment from shore areas to the deep sea and that they account for wide dispersion of sediments over a large portion of the deep-sea floor.

Vast submarine *alluvial fans* or sediment aprons are built where submarine canyons emerge onto the sea floor. Where fans from several canyons coalesce, they form a continuous continental rise parallel to the continental periphery (Fig. 2-11). Additional material is added to the continental rise from the continental slope by submarine landslides or slumps of sediment triggered by earthquakes.

Reefs. Continental margins in tropical regions are covered with massive platforms of limestone containing the calcareous skeletal remains of plants and animals, called *coral reefs*. Since coral remains comprise only a small percentage of the total material in a reef, a better term for this feature is *carbonate reef*. Because of the life requirements for these carbonate-secreting organisms, most carbonate reefs occur in the western tropical regions of ocean basins (Fig. 2-12).

A classification of carbonate reefs proposed by Charles Darwin in 1842 and

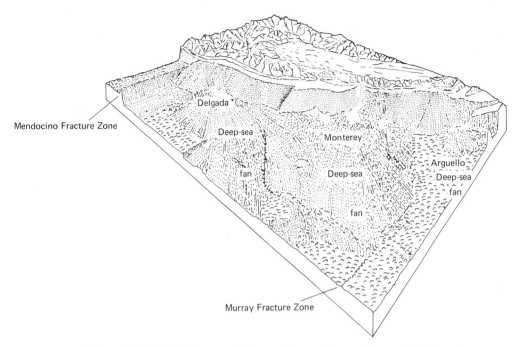

Figure 2-11 Block diagram of the sea floor and coast of central California. Deep-sea fans spread out from the mouths of Delgada, Monterey, and Arguello canyons. The first two fans are confined in a broad trough between the Mendocino and Murray fracture zones. (After H. W. Menard, Geological Society of America Bulletin, 1960)

still in use defines reefs according to their proximity to shore. A reef that has been built close to shore, so that it fringes the shoreline, is called a *fringing reef* (Fig. 2-13A). The width of a fringing reef may be several hundred meters or more, but it is generally less than 30 m.

If there is a lagoon between the inner edge of the reef and the shoreline, the structure is classed as a *barrier reef* (Fig. 2-13B). Barrier reefs are generally much larger than fringing reefs. The Great Barrier Reef of Australia is a good example. It is 40 to 320 km wide and parallels the northeastern coast of Australia for a distance of 2,000 km. The lagoon depth varies from 1 m to greater than 30 m, but much of it is quite shallow.

A third type of reef, the *atoll* (Fig. 2-13C), is associated with the deep sea (page 37).

Deep-Sea Floor

The deep-sea floor is described in terms of the individual major features comprising it. These are abyssal plains, oceanic ridges, sea-floor fractures, deep-sea trenches, islands, and seamounts.

Abyssal plains. Abyssal plains are broad, featureless areas of the sea floor

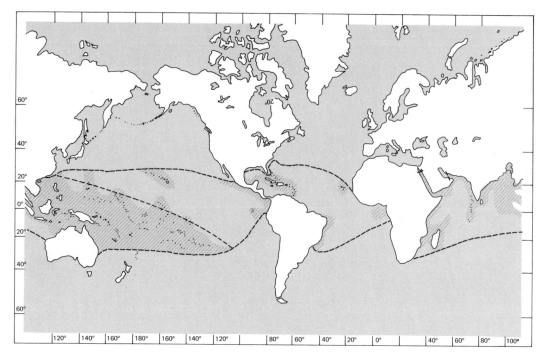

Figure 2-12 Distribution of coral reefs and atolls in the world ocean. The dashed lines represent the approximate cold limit for reef coral (20°C). The diagonal lines cover the major reef areas. The long dashed line is the northern limit of atolls. (Data from Putnam et al., 1960)

between 3,000 and 6,000 m deep that slope less than 1 m per km (6 ft per mile). Abyssal plains usually lie adjacent to the continental margins rather than in the centers of the ocean basins. This feature is evident particularly in the Atlantic and Indian Oceans (see map on inside front and back covers). Approximately 42 percent of the world ocean floor consists of abyssal plains. Seismic evidence indicates that abyssal plains are formed by deposition of sediment over the original sea floor. Whatever roughness existed on the sea floor when it formed has been covered or greatly smoothed. Although abyssal plains exist in the Pacific Ocean, most of the Pacific basin floor has a "hilly" topography of 200 to 400 m in relief. This hilly terrain exists in parts of all ocean basins; it is, however, covered by sedimentary layers in most areas. Since relatively few large rivers drain into the Pacific Ocean, the amount of sediment introduced since its formation has not been adequate to bury these topographic irregularities.

Deep-sea drilling in the abyssal hills of the Northeast Pacific has revealed that the hills are basalt mounds covered by sediments.

Oceanic ridges and rises.   These are mountain ranges on the sea floor that rival the size of those on the continents. The Mid-Atlantic Ridge, shown in profile

28

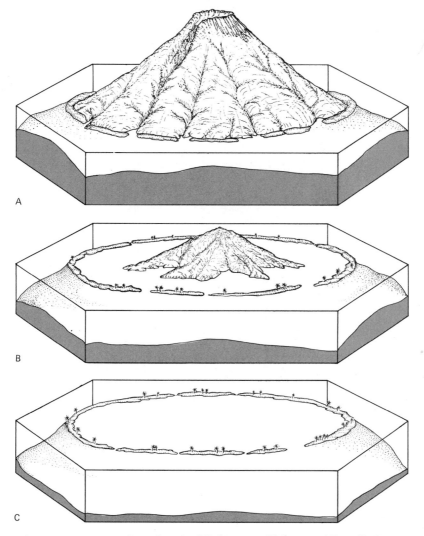

Figure 2-13 Types of coral reefs: (A) fringing (B) barrier (C) atoll. (From F. P. Shepard, *Submarine Geology*, 2nd edition, Harper & Row, New York, 1963)

in Fig. 2-14, is approximately 1,000 km wide and has rugged topography in its center and gentle foothills at its margins. Compare the profile of the Mid-Atlantic Ridge with the profile of the Rocky Mountains of North America, included in Fig. 2-14, and notice their gross similarities. In places, individual "peaks" rise to break the surface of the ocean and form islands. Peaks of the Mid-Atlantic Ridge form Iceland, the Azores, Ascension Island, and the island of Tristan de Cunha. In some regions, such as the southeastern Pacific basin (Fig. 2-15), the submarine mountain range is rather wide, low, and has gentle slopes on its flanks. This kind of feature is referred to as a *rise*, such as the East Pacific Rise.

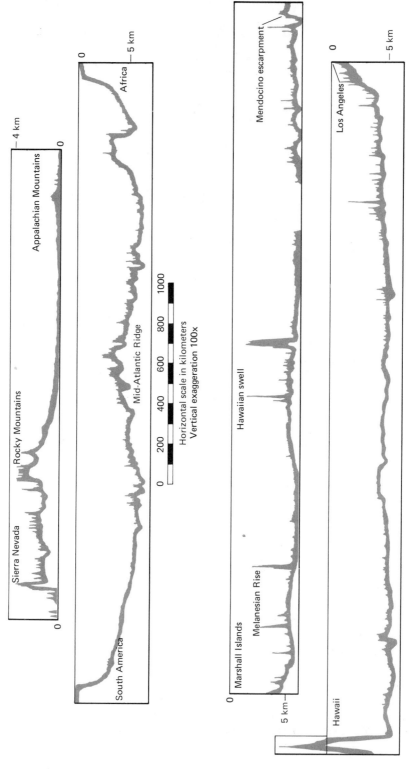

Figure 2-14 Comparison between a profile across the United States and profiles across the Atlantic and Pacific Oceans showing the general similarity that exists between oceanic and continental topography. Vertical exaggeration times 100 for all profiles. (After F. P. Shepard, *Submarine Geology*, 2nd edition, Harper & Row, New York, 1963)

Horizontal scale in kilometers
Vertical exaggeration 100x

30

Oceanic ridges or rises have been discovered in all ocean basins. In the North Indian Ocean and eastern Pacific basins, the ridges are extensions of surface cracks, or *fractures*, in the continental land mass. Elsewhere they form a continuous mountain chain between the continents (Fig. 2-15), so that the abyssal plains are enclosed between the oceanic ridge system and the continental rise. In almost every area where detailed bathymetric surveys have been conducted, a narrow, deep *rift valley* has been discovered in the central part of oceanic ridges. The rift valley is about 25 to 50 km wide and lies as much as 2,000 m below the adjacent peaks (Fig. 2-14). Rift valleys do not occur on the East Pacific Rise.

Sea-floor fracture zones.   The floor of the sea is cut by large fracture zones, 1 to 100 km wide, that are characterized by linear escarpments or mountainous bands, some over 3,500 km long. Fracture zones are developed prominently in the eastern Pacific Ocean basin (Fig. 2-15) where they form a series of long east-west scarps with relief exceeding 1,500 m. The scarps face both northward

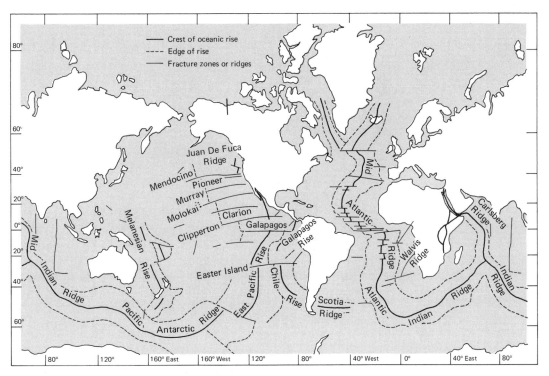

Figure 2-15 The worldwide system of rises and ridges with related features. (After H. W. Menard from *A Symposium on Continental Drift*, 1965, by permission of the Royal Society)

and southward; sometimes both kinds of scarps occur in a single fracture zone. Elsewhere, as in the Atlantic Ocean basin, shorter (but still major) east-west faults offset the Mid-Atlantic Ridge along most of its trend. The Carlsberg Ridge in the Indian Ocean and the East Pacific Rise also are cut and offset by many fractures. These *transform faults,* as they are called, are usual rather than exceptional features on the sea floor. The transform fault zones transect rises and ridges at right angles (or nearly so) and they trace segments of circular arcs on the surface of the earth.

Sea-floor fracture zones abut the continents as do oceanic ridges. The Mendocino Fracture Zone displaces the continental shelf break near northern California and the Murray Fracture Zone continues landward as the transverse mountain ranges of southern California. There is little doubt that the major topographic features of the ocean and continents are related and form a single global system of ranges, rifts, ridges, and volcano chains.

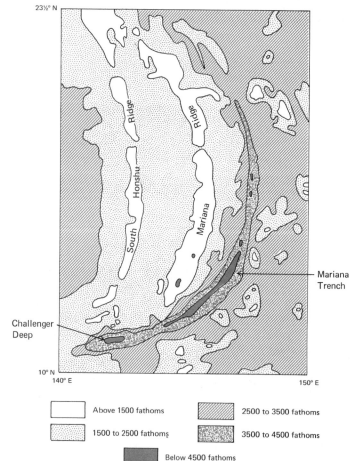

Figure 2-16 Detailed bathymetric chart of the Mariana Trench area of central western Pacific Ocean. (Based on U.S. Navy Oceanographic office chart)

Deep-sea trenches and troughs.   Trenches are observed along the margins of all ocean basins and are most extensive in the Pacific basin (see inside front and back covers). Most of them occur seaward of continental mountain ranges or volcanic island arcs. Examples are the Peru–Chile Trench adjacent to the Andes Mountains off South America and the Japan Trench seaward of the Japanese archipelago. Trenches and troughs are either rectilinear or arcuate elongate depressions in the sea floor and range from 7 to 10 km deep. Their sides slope from approximately 4° (troughs) to as much as 45° (trenches) at the bottom and are often asymmetric in profile. A bathymetric chart of the Mariana Trench is shown in Fig. 2-16. This trench is approximately 70 km wide and its length is over 2,550 km. The Challenger Deep, located in the southwest corner of the Mariana Trench, is the deepest place known in the world ocean. In 1960, the bathyscaphe *Trieste* descended 11,034 m to this point. The dimensions of some Pacific trenches are given in Table 2-6.

Table 2–6   Dimensions of Some Pacific Trenches

Trench	Depth	Approximate width	Approximate length
	m	km	km
Aleutian	8,100	70	2,300
Kurile	10,542	120	2,200
Japan	9,810	100	900
Mariana	11,034	70	2,550
Mindanao	10,497	60	1,400
Tonga	10,882	55	1,400
Peru-Chile	8,055	70	5,900

Data from U.S. Naval Oceanographic Office, Washington, D.C. and from R. L. Fisher and H. H. Hess, in *The Sea*, Vol. III, ed. M.N. Hill. New York: Interscience, 1963.

Trenches and troughs also occur in seas between island arcs and the continents. The Manila Trough, the New Britain Trench, New Hebrides Trench, Crete Trough, and Amirante Trench are examples.

Some trenches or troughs occur in parallel pairs associated with double island arcs. The Bali Trough and Java Trench off Java form such a pair. The island arc between the two depressions is nonvolcanic, whereas the inner arc is a volcanic zone. The inner trough is more shallow and less steep than the outer trench.

Another type of trench cuts oceanic ridges in oblique, transverse, or echelon patterns. These trenches are not associated with island arcs; instead, they are related to large faults on the ocean floor. They have rectilinear trends and have symmetric profiles. The Romanche Trench in the southern Mid-Atlantic is an example of this type.

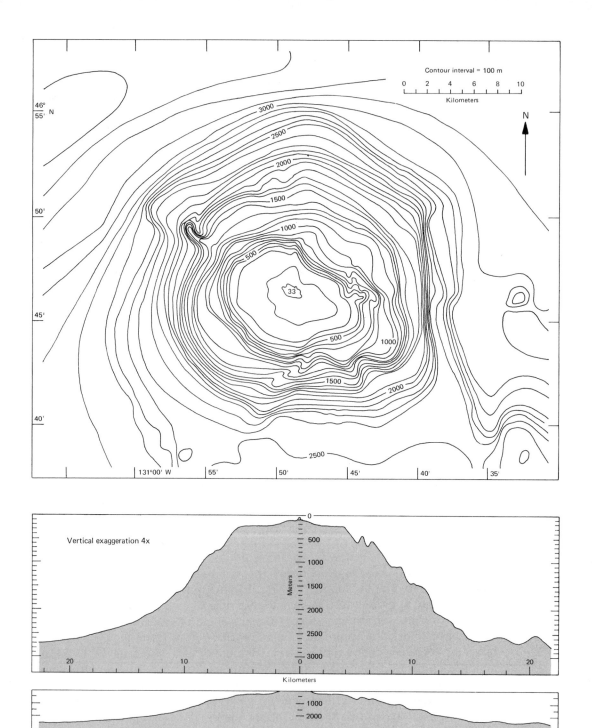

Figure 2-17 Plan and profile view (with and without vertical exaggeration) of Cobb Seamount.

Seamounts and islands. Throughout the world ocean, irregularities rise from the sea floor. Small volcanic extrusions that rise less than 1,000 m from the sea floor are called *abyssal hills* or *knolls*. Larger volcanic extrusions that rise more than 1,000 m from the sea floor are called *seamounts*. They become *islands* if the summit broaches the sea surface. An example of a seamount that comes very close to being an island is Cobb Seamount. This volcanic cone, located approximately 325 km (180 miles) off the Washington coast of the United States (Fig. 2-17), rises from a depth of 3,000 m to within 35 m of the sea surface. This great undersea volcano is about 1.5 million years old and is part of a seamount chain extending over 1,600 km toward the Gulf of Alaska (Fig. 2-18). Frequently, seamounts occur in groups called *seamount provinces*. Some prov-

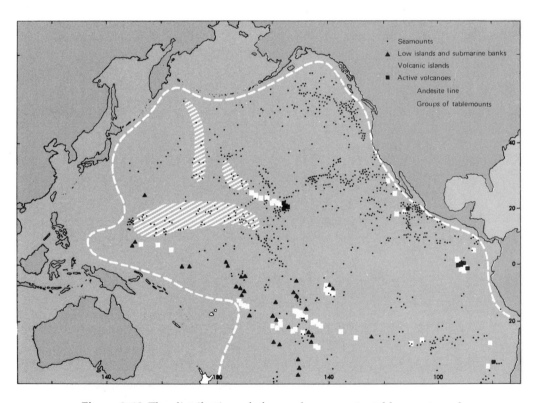

Figure 2-18 The distribution of observed seamounts, tablemounts, volcanic islands and low islands (e.g., atolls), and submarine banks in the Pacific Ocean. To date more than 2,000 such isolated features, with elevations of one kilometer or greater above the sea floor, have been discovered. There are probably at least ten times that number. (After H. W. Menard, *Marine Geology of the Pacific*, 1964, by permission of McGraw-Hill Book Company)

inces, such as in the Northeast Pacific basin, contain no islands. Other seamounts are shown on the world map (inside the front and back covers).

The composition of seamounts and islands is closely related to their proximity to the continental masses. In the central part of the Pacific Ocean, the islands are composed of the basaltic-type rocks characteristic of the oceanic crust, whereas in the marginal areas, islands are composed of the granitic-type rocks that are found on the continents. An imaginary line, called the Andesite Line, divides these two regions (Fig. 2-18).

Seamounts that have flat tops are called *guyots*, or *tablemounts*. They occur at all depths, and many rise to within a kilometer of the sea surface. Tablemounts are usually found in groups or provinces; the Marshall Islands in the equatorial West Pacific is an example (Fig. 2-18). The origin of most tablemounts is volcanic; nevertheless, the flat top is difficult to explain. The top might be a wave-cut platform. But, if so, why are the tops of some tablemounts several kilometers below the sea surface and why do they appear to occur in groups?

Figure 2-19 Oblique aerial photo of an atoll in the western Pacific Ocean.

Several possibilities exist: Either the sea level rose after the waves truncated an island or group of islands, or the newly formed tablemounts sank. Possibly the tablemount never reached the surface and was always shaped that way. A flat-topped volcano in eastern Ethiopia, which appears to have formed underwater, shows no sign of wave-truncation. Instead, its shape is attributed to formation by explosions attending a submarine volcanic eruption.

In tropical areas, tablemounts and seamounts often support carbonate reefs in the form of *atolls*. An atoll is generally circular in plan and consists of a central lagoon up to 40 km in diameter and 75 m deep surrounded by a narrow carbonate reef dotted with islands (Fig. 2-19). Apparently an atoll forms as an island sinks, so that the rate of upward growth of the reef matches the sinking of the island or the rise of the sea level. Charles Darwin proposed this idea in 1842. According to his theory, a slowly sinking island first develops a fringing reef, then a barrier reef, and finally becomes an atoll when the original surface of the island is submerged (see Fig. 2-13). Drilling on atolls in the West Pacific has revealed that the structure of an atoll conforms to his theory.

The features of the earth and the world ocean all have significance. In the following chapters we shall see how these features provide evidence of their origin and evolution and how they influence the chemistry, physics, and biology of the water that the basins contain.

reading list

DARWIN, C. R., *The Structure and Distribution of Coral Reefs*. Berkeley, Calif.: University of California Press, 1962. 214p.

DIETZ, R. S., "The Pacific Floor," *Scientific American*, CLXXXVI, No. 4 (April 1952), 19–23.

FISHER, R. L., AND R. REVELLE, "The Trenches of the Pacific," *Scientific American*, CXCIII, No. 5 (November 1955), 36–41.

GUILCHER, ANDRÉ, *Coastal and Submarine Morphology*. New York: John Wiley & Sons, Inc., 1958. 274p.

HEEZEN, B. C., *The Floors of the Oceans*, Vol. I, *The North Atlantic*, Geological Society of America Special Paper No. 65. New York, 1959. 122p.

KING, C. A. M., *Ocean Geography for Oceanographers*. New York: St. Martin's Press, Inc., 1963. 336p.

KUENEN, P., *Marine Geology*. New York: John Wiley & Sons, Inc., 1950. 568p.

MENARD, H. W., "The East Pacific Rise," *Scientific American*, CCV, No. 6 (December 1961), 52–61.

———, "Fractures in the Pacific Floor," *Scientific American*, CXCIII, No. 1 (July 1961), 36–41.

———, "Sea Floor Spreading Topography and the Second Layer," *Trans. Amer. Geophys. Union*, XLVIII, No. 1 (March 1967), 217.

MORGAN, W. J., "Trenches, Great Faults, and Crustal Blocks," *Jour. Geophys. Res.*, LXXIII, No. 6 (March 15, 1968), 1959–82.

"The Ocean," *Scientific American*, CCXXI, No. 3 (September 1969), 288p.

RINGWOOD, A. E., *Composition and Petrology of the Earth's Mantle*. New York: McGraw-Hill, Inc., 1975. 618p.

ROBERTSON, E. C., *The Interior of the Earth, An Elementary Description*, U.S. Geological Survey Circular 532. Washington, D.C.: Government Printing Office, 1966, 10p.

SHEPARD, F. P., *The Earth beneath the Sea*. Baltimore: The Johns Hopkins Press, 1959. 275p.

STRAHLER, A. N., *The Earth Sciences* (2nd ed.). New York: Harper & Row, Publishers, 1971. 824p.

origin and history
of the continents,
ocean basins,
and continental margins

3

So far we have considered only a description of the structure and surface topography of the earth. Now let us consider the following: (1) what caused the continents and ocean basins to assume their present shapes and locations; (2) when the shape and location originated; and (3) whether their shape and location have been the same throughout geologic time or whether they have evolved slowly.

3.1 Sea-Floor Spreading and Plate Tectonics

Only recently have scientists been able to provide a coherent explanation of the origin and history of the earth's crustal configuration by relating many diverse observations and measurements of the earth's features in a viable theory. The theory is called *plate tectonics* and it states that the surface of the earth consists of at least six large, almost rigid plates (Fig. 3-1) in lateral motion, on a viscous, plastic substrate. The plates form an outer shell of the earth called the *lithosphere;* the underlying region is called the *asthenosphere*.

The lithosphere is approximately 70 to 100 km thick and includes the crust and part of the upper mantle. It moves as a rigid material and maintains its integrity over geologic time because of its strength. The lithosphere includes either oceanic crust or both continental and oceanic crustal material. No exclusively continental plates are known to exist. The asthenosphere consists of lower mantle material that is able to flow because it is near its melting point.

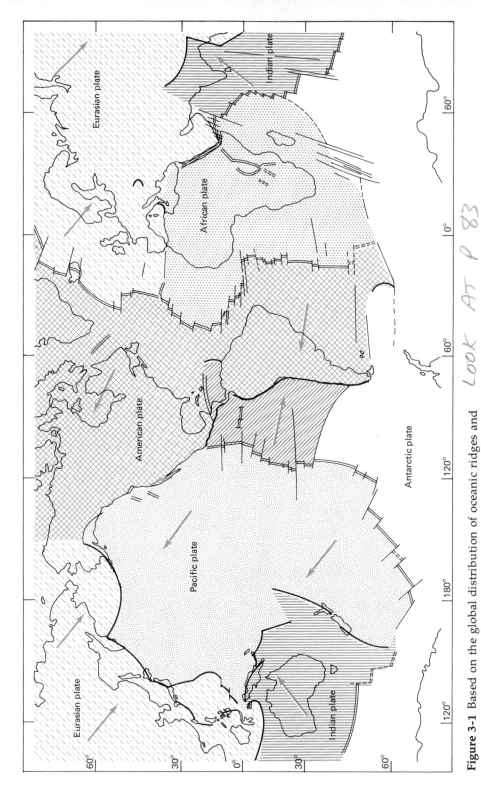

Figure 3-1 Based on the global distribution of oceanic ridges and trenches it is possible to divide the crust into relatively few major plates. Arrows show relative plate motion. (After Isacks et al., by permission of the American Geophysical Union)

LOOK AT P 83

SOME DIFFERENCES

40

The plates of the lithosphere are bounded by ridges (or rises), faults, and trenches or mountain chains. The plates form at the ridges where molten material from the asthenosphere is brought to the sea floor to solidify and replace the material moved away during *sea-floor spreading*. Observations of the rift valley in the Mid-Atlantic Ridge made from submersibles during the 1974 French–American Mid Ocean Underseas Study (FAMOUS) revealed many open fractures and fissures verifying that tensional forces are pulling the ridge apart. The fissures are sites of irregular effusions of molten rock which in turn become fractured and pulled apart along cracks in the ridge. New sea floor forms from molten intrusions because the sea floor is spreading; the intrusions are not, however, the cause of sea-floor spreading. Studies of the rocks extruded from the chain of volcanic centers along the ridge suggest that the molten rock lies within 2 km of the sea floor. The fissures near the axis of the ridge are quite narrow; the width of fractures lying progressively farther from the axis ultimately increases to 30 m. This indicates that the ridge is being pulled apart gradually and continuously. On the other hand, the replacement of sea floor by volcanism is sporadic.

According to the sea-floor spreading hypothesis, the sea floor acts as a large conveyor belt moving new oceanic crust from the ocean ridges toward the trenches and carrying seamounts, oceanic islands, tablemounts, and even continents with it. This is shown in Fig. 3-13. Plates are destroyed at boundaries where one plate sinks below another at a plate collision. A trench forms in such a case. The intense stress and deformation in trench areas often give rise to mountain ranges which can be regarded as a later stage in the development of a plate boundary where the sea floor is being subducted, consumed, and regenerated as continental material. The entire process of sea-floor spreading, generation, and *subduction* and the resulting plate boundaries is shown in the diagram in Fig. 3-2.

A plate can sink at a continental border for tens of millions of years. However, if the sinking plate carries a continental block, a collision of continents will occur. The process of sinking must then stop or shift direction, because it is impossible for a continental block to sink into a region of significantly higher density. Throughout geologic time, continents and ocean basins have split, collided, rejoined, and drifted over the earth's surface several times. This can explain the formation and position of the world's mountain ranges. These processes might have begun with the formation of the earth, with continents and ocean basins forming and reforming a number of times. The sequence of events is described in detail later in this chapter (page 69).

The sea-floor spreading and plate tectonics hypotheses seem to be the best ones devised so far for answering many questions regarding the history and development of the ocean basins. They relate more diverse geological information than any other hypotheses and are the most in accord with the results of deep-sea drilling into the floor of the world ocean. We shall now consider

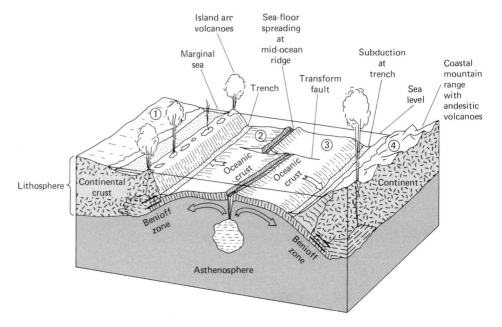

Figure 3-2 Diagram showing the processes of the formation of new crustal plates at spreading centers, sea-floor spreading, and destruction of plates by subduction at trenches. Each different plate is numbered. The motion of sea-floor spreading is shown by the broad arrows.

these important theories in more detail, noting the evidence obtained from studies of glacial geology, biological evolutionary patterns, the shape and topography of the sea floor, petrology of the oceanic crust, crustal heat flow, gravity, seismic activity, and geomagnetism.

The theories of plate tectonics and sea-floor spreading arose from former speculations regarding the configuration of continents and oceans. It is instructive to digress momentarily and review one particularly important piece of such inquiry and then trace the development of the theories via two major pieces of innovative work by earth scientists.

3.2 *Historical Review*

Alfred Wegener, a German meteorologist, published in 1915 the hypothesis that the position of the continents and the shapes of the ocean basins have not been unchanged since the origin of the earth but that the continents have been in continual motion during the past 150 million years. At that time, his idea seemed rather bizarre.

The first line of evidence for his hypothesis is the shape of the continents.

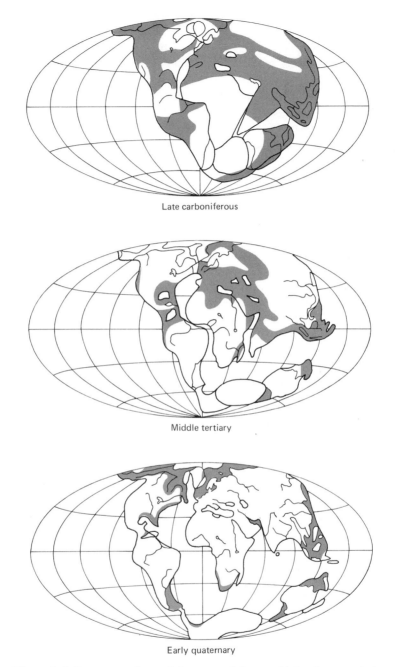

Late carboniferous

Middle tertiary

Early quaternary

Figure 3-3 Reconstructions of the map of the world for three periods according to Wegener's theory of continental drift. Dotted areas represent shallow seas. (From Alfred Wegener, *The Origin of Continents and Oceans,* Dover Publications, Inc., New York, 1966. Reprinted through permission of the publisher)

Alfred Wegener observed, as do most students of elementary geography, that the east coasts of North and South America fit the west coast of Africa and Europe like pieces of a jigsaw puzzle. If the continents are attached, moreover, it is found that mountain ranges that had formed prior to the Cretaceous period appear to fit together, whereas younger strata and mountain ranges do not bear such resemblance. Possibly, therefore, some sort of physical separation occurred about 150 million years ago.

When paleontological evidence is studied, fossils indicate that the evolutionary trends of many animal groups began to diverge during the Early Cretaceous period. Prior to this divergence, the evolutionary development of many species of animals now preserved as fossils on different continents suggests that they formed continuous, interbreeding populations. During the past 150 million years, however, related species of animals on different continents evolved differently and produced markedly different sequences of fossils. This evidence suggests that before 150 million years ago the continental regions of the world were somehow connected, allowing free migration of animals throughout the world. After that time, a physical separation isolated different continental regions and caused independent evolution within the isolated areas.

These observations led Alfred Wegener to propose the *theory of drifting continents*. According to this hypothesis, there was originally one large continent, which he called Pangaea, that resulted from the formation of the earth's crust (Fig. 3-3). About 150 million years ago, this continent began to break into individual blocks and drift apart in a nonuniform fashion. North and South America drifted to create the Atlantic Ocean basin between the Americas and the Europe–Africa continental masses. Australia moved south and east from its initial position in what is now the Indian Ocean basin.

Although continental drift did account for the evidence as presented by Wegener, many scientists disputed his interpretations. Furthermore, the continental drift theory failed to explain the mechanism that moves continents, so it remained in dispute until the late 1950's. However, with the advent of sophisticated geophysical measuring techniques and data on earth magnetism, seismicity, heat flow, and sea-floor topography, we have obtained substantial evidence that tends to support his theory, or a similar one. Deep-sea drilling, begun in the late 1960's, has provided samples of marine sediments and underlying basement rock that has virtually confirmed the idea of moving continents although the original idea of Wegener has been highly modified. The mechanism causing these effects, however, is still a matter of controversy.

The first major advance in our concept of the origin of the ocean and continents came in 1962 when H. H. Hess published his work on the history of ocean basins. Hess marshalled geologic and geophysical information and concluded, in part, that the earth's mantle is convecting at a rate of 1 cm per year. The convection brings mantle material upward at mid-ocean ridges and rises and causes higher heat flow there. The relatively high temperatures at the ridges account for their being elevated above the sea floor. The oceanic crust and the continents are carried on the laterally convecting mantle until eventually mantle convection turns downward. Oceanic crust, volcanic sea-mounts, and marine sediments are drawn downward with the mantle but the continental crust, being lighter, remains at the surface and experiences peripheral deformation and volcanism. The transit of the oceanic crust on the laterally convecting mantle takes 300 to 400 million years, so sediments older than this cannot be expected to occur in the ocean (a daring prediction!).

Hess's ideas later were named sea-floor spreading and they formed the nucleus around which present concepts of the history of the ocean basins and plate tectonic mechanisms are built. Most of his ideas survive, little changed, to the present day.

The second major work that led to the development of our understanding of the history of oceans and continents was the concept of plate motion and its associated geometry. The concept appears to have originated simultaneously among scientists working in the United States and England in 1964. The realization that convective motion of the mantle moved segments of the earth's crust as discrete plates containing continents, ocean floor, and in some cases both, unified the notions of continental drift and sea-floor spreading into a single cohesive body of theory that fits many of the facts of earth science. The appreciation of the geometry of motion of plates on a sphere and the implication of such geometry provided the necessary intellectual tools for interpreting those facts to construct a history of the ocean basins and an explanation of the configuration of the oceans and continents that we see today.

Let us now proceed to examine the details of sea-floor spreading and plate tectonics to gain an understanding of how the surface of the earth came to be as we described it in Chap. 2. We will consider pertinent evidence and observations from which the principles of sea-floor spreading and plate tectonics are derived.

3.3 *Elements of Plate Tectonics Theory*

Seismology

The seismic activity of the earth affords us an overview of the pattern of sea-floor spreading. The distribution of *epicenters* (points on the earth's surface directly above the *focus* where stress is released during an earthquake) is shown on Fig. 3-4. These are calculated from seismic records of each earthquake collected at a worldwide network of seismographs. The first seismograph was used in 1889. Since then, and especially in more recent decades, considerable data have been collected on the epicenters and relative magnitudes of earth tremors occurring throughout the world. The earthquakes occur in zones as shown in Table 3-1.

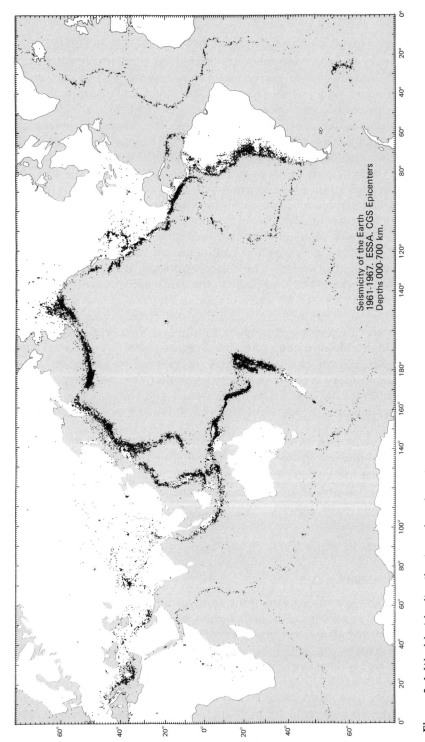

Seismicity of the Earth
1961-1967. ESSA. CGS Epicenters
Depths 000-700 km.

Figure 3-4 Worldwide distribution of earthquake epicenters, oceanic trenches, and ridges. Note the association of earthquake activity with trenches and ridges.

Table 3–1   Types of Earthquake Zones and Features Associated with Them

Only shallow-focus earthquakes (less than 70 km deep)	*All kinds of earthquakes: shallow, intermediate (70 to 300 km), and deep (300 to 700 km) focus*
1. Along major faults having mainly lateral displacement. No volcanic activity. *Example:* San Andreas rift in California	3. Along trenches. Associated with volcanic island arcs. *Example:* Japan Trench
2. Along mid-ocean ridges and rises. High heat flow. Volcanic activity producing basaltic lava. *Example:* Mid-Atlantic Ridge	4. Along high mountain ranges on continents. Deformation of rocks in mountains was by intense compression. Mainly shallow focus earthquakes; intermediate focus earthquakes in some areas; deep-focus earthquakes are rare. *Example:* Himalaya Mountains

The pattern of epicenters plotted on Fig. 3-4 shows that many earthquake activities are associated with oceanic ridges and trenches. The pattern is most evident in the deep trenches of the Circum-Pacific region and the Mid-Atlantic Ridge, but an obvious correlation occurs throughout the world ocean. The earthquakes are caused by the release of stresses caused by the formation of oceanic crust at ridges and rises and its consumption at trenches.

The configuration of earthquake foci at trenches describes a dipping planar zone, called a *Benioff zone* after the man who made an exhaustive study of deep-focus earthquakes. Benioff zones dip 30° to 60° away from spreading centers and extend over 600 km deep, as shown in Fig. 3-5.

Less seismic activity is observed at ridges and rises. Earthquakes at the ridges occur in swarms typical of those associated with volcanic eruptions. The epicenters located on transforms occur only between ridges and not along the entire length of those faults. Shallow-focus earthquakes occur under volcanic island arcs more frequently than do deeper-focus earthquakes. The number of earthquakes decreases by 1/10 for every 100 km of depth. Such seismic activity results from the volcanic generation of new sea-floor crust at ridges and rises, differential motion of the sea floor along transform fault segments, subduction of oceanic crust along Benioff zones, and island arc volcanic activity associated with subduction at trenches.

The nature of impulsive first motion associated with earthquakes indicates the directions and types of movement involved in sea-floor spreading. The first motion of a seismic wave arriving at a seismograph is either compressional or dilational, depending on the location of the seismograph with respect to the

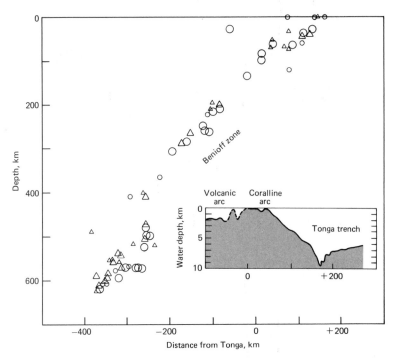

Figure 3-5 Vertical section oriented perpendicular to the Tonga arc. Circles represent earthquakes projected from within 0 to 150 km north of the section; triangles correspond to events projected from within 0 to 150 km south of the section. All shocks occurred in 1965. (After Isacks et al., by permission of the American Geophysical Union)

focus of the earthquake. When the nature of the first motion reaching the seismograph stations is plotted for several widespread seismograph stations, a pattern of quadrants, such as in Fig. 3-6, is revealed. The orientation of the quadrants permits us to deduce the dip of the fault plane along which sudden movement has occurred and the direction (called the *slip vector*) of the movement. All that is necessary is to know the orientation (*strike*) of the trace of the fault plane on the sea floor. First motion studies have established the following: (1) movement of the sea floor is tensional at ridges and rises (the sea floor is being pulled apart there); (2) movement along transform fault segments lying between ridges is lateral slipping parallel to the fault; and (3) movement at trenches consists of thrusting of the sea floor under the crust lying above the Benioff zone. These movements are depicted on Fig. 3-2. A map of slip vectors derived from earthquake studies is presented in Fig. 3-7.

Heat Flow

Tensional movement at ridges and rises permits deep-seated mantle material to liquify and rise to the sea floor as volcanic effusions that form new oceanic crust. Heat is transported toward the surface at ridges and rises by this process. Conversely, subduction of trenches carries cool oceanic crust downward and

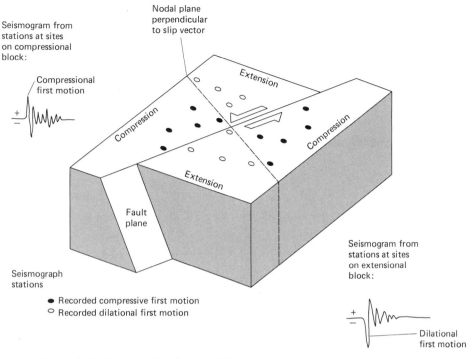

Figure 3-6 Diagram of a faulted block, showing the distribution of the types of first motion recorded at seismographs at various locations. The pattern defines the direction of the slippage that produced the earthquake if the location of the fault plane is known.

heat transfer upward is inhibited. Between ridges and trenches heat is transferred from the earth's interior to the ocean by conduction alone. Measurements of heat flow at the ocean floor reflect these mechanisms.

Precise measurements of the temperature gradient in the upper few meters of the marine sediments and knowledge of the thermal conductivity of the sediments allow an oceanographer to calculate the rate at which heat is being transferred through the sea floor. Measurements over the past two decades have shown that a worldwide average for terrestrial heat flow is about 1.5×10^{-6} cal per sq cm per sec or 30 to 40 cal per sq cm per year. This magnitude of heat loss is about equivalent to the heat generated within the crust by the decay of radioactive elements. Variations in terrestrial heat flow follow the pattern shown in Fig. 3-8. Heat flow is higher than average at *heat sources* on oceanic ridges, island arcs, and continental margins and lower than average at *heat sinks* in the vicinity of oceanic trenches (Table 3-2).

The distribution of heat in the rocks of the oceanic crust and mantle is reflected in the topography of the sea floor. Rocks at ridges and rises, being hot, are less dense than rocks lying under most of the sea floor. As a consequence, isostasy causes them to ride higher than adjacent, cooler rocks. Measurements of gravity over such areas verify this concept, inasmuch as no excess (isostatically uncompensated) mass is indicated at ridges or rises.

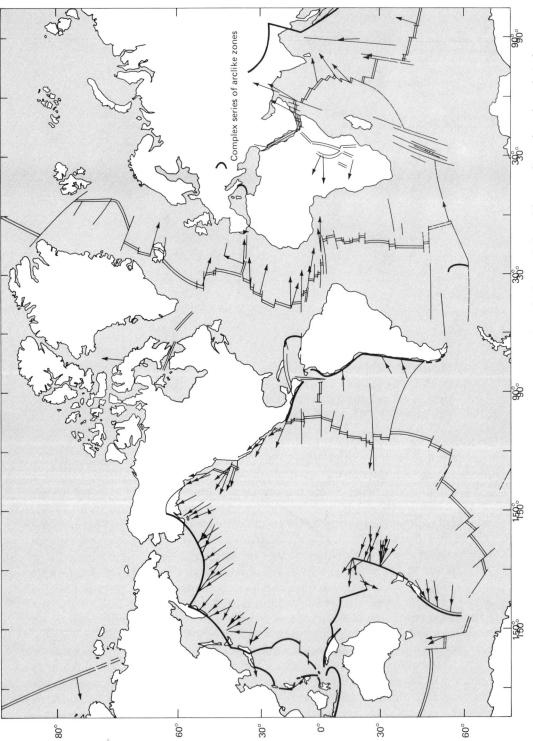

Figure 3-7 A map of the world ocean showing the direction of slippage along faults as deduced by studies of earthquake's first motions. Spreading centers are shown as double lines, trenches as heavy lines, and transform faults as light lines. (From B. Isacks and Jack Oliver, *Journal of Geophysical Research* Vol. 73, No. 18, September 15, 1968 copyrighted by the American Geophysical Union)

Complex series of arclike zones

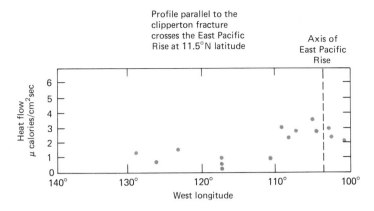

Figure 3-8 The pattern of heat flow on the sea floor and in the vicinity of a spreading center. Note the anomalously low heat flow at the ridge. The average heat flow for the entire Pacific Ocean basin is about 1 μ cal per sq cm per sec. (From J. G. Sclater, R. N. Anderson, and M. L. Bell, *Journal of Geophysical Research* Vol. 76, No. 32, November 10, 1971, copyrighted by the American Geophysical Union)

Table 3–2   Heat Flow Values for Various Tectonic Regions*

Tectonic region	Mean value: 10^{-6} cal/cm²/s
Nontectonic continental areas	1.49
Ocean basins	1.27
Mid-ocean ridges	1.90
Ocean trenches	1.16
Continental margins	1.80

* After J. A. Jacobs, *A Textbook on Geonomy*, New York: John Wiley and Sons, 1974.

3.4   *The Direction of Plate Movement*

Transform Faults

A powerful indicator of the direction of sea-floor movement is the orientation of transform faults. Because oceanic crust is neither created nor destroyed at a transform fault, lateral motion of the sea floor near such faults must be parallel to the fault trend. This is a consequence of the geometry of the motion of rigid plates on the surface of a sphere. If two adjacent plates travel at different rates, their *relative* motion (the apparent motion of one plate viewed by an observer riding on the other plate) must occur along a transform. Figs. 3-9 and 3-10 show several examples of how transform motion can occur on a

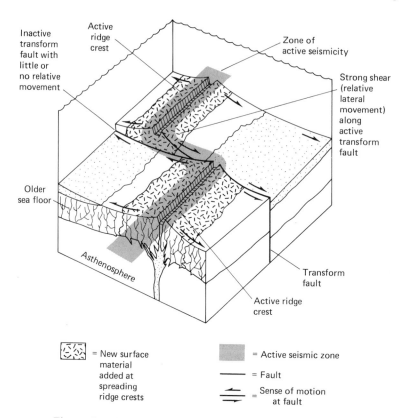

Figure 3-9 A ridge-to-ridge transform fault. The active part of the transform is restricted to the part between the ridge segments.

spreading sea floor. The transform faults describe circular arcs (Fig. 3-11) because the rigid plates on either side of the transform must move past one another along a line of relative motion defined by a circle of rotation about an axis that passes through the center of the earth (here taken to be a sphere). Otherwise the moving plates would move together or move apart and a spreading center, subduction, or plate deformation would occur, not a transform. Deformation does not occur within plates, according to geophysical reflection profiles showing marine sediments on the sea floor in undisturbed, virtually horizontal beds.

Volcanic Island and Seamount Chains

The direction of the sea-floor movement between ridges and trenches is traced by chains of volcanoes (Hawaiian chain) and guyots (Marshall and Caroline Islands). Sometimes a source of rising molten material, called a *hot spot*, has remained active at various points in the world ocean long enough to

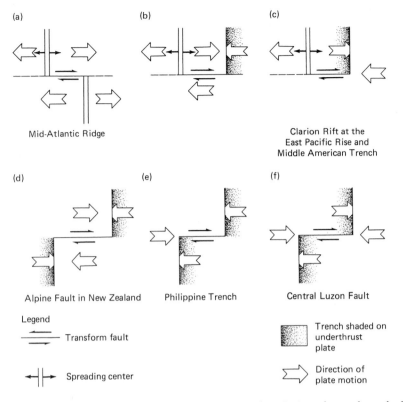

(a) Mid-Atlantic Ridge

(b)

(c) Clarion Rift at the East Pacific Rise and Middle American Trench

(d) Alpine Fault in New Zealand

(e) Philippine Trench

(f) Central Luzon Fault

Legend

——— Transform fault

——|+— Spreading center

▨ Trench shaded on underthrust plate

⇨ Direction of plate motion

Figure 3-10 The diagrams show several varieties of transform faults that can occur in the world ocean. Some examples are given. Type A is a ridge-to-ridge transform. Types B and C are ridge-to-trench transforms, and Types D, E, and F are trench-to-trench transforms. (After J. Tuzo Wilson, *Nature* Vol. 207, 1965)

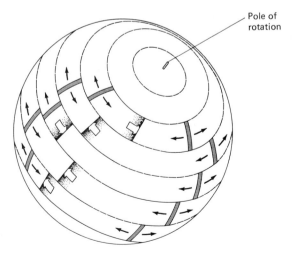

Pole of rotation

Figure 3-11 This diagram illustrates that transform faults are circular arcs. In this hypothetical example, the transform faults follow latitudinal arcs about a common pole of rotation.

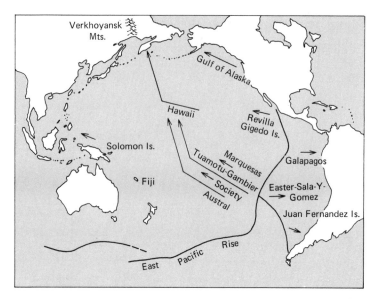

Figure 3-12 The arrows show linear chains of islands or seamounts which get older in the direction of the arrows. (From J. Tuzo Wilson, 1965, by permission of the Royal Society)

create *nemataths,* or linear trends of volcanoes on the sea floor as it moved. Several hot spots and associated trends are shown in Fig. 3-12. Compare the directions of implied sea-floor movement with those shown in Fig. 3-7. Note that the volcanoes trailing the Pacific hot spots mark a change in trend of the direction of movement of the sea floor. Several hot spots lie on or near present ridges or rises. They are thought to represent sources different from those supplying the volcanism of the ridges, because the hot spot volcanoes produce more lava than is extruded at ridges. (Hot spot volcanoes usually form islands.) Also, hot spot lava is of a different kind. Hot spot lavas are basalt, but contain more alkali metals (Na, K, Li) than do ridge basalts. The lavas originate deeper than do ridge basalts that come from about 2 km deep.

3.5 *Rate of Plate Movement*

The rate of movement of the lithospheric plates during sea-floor spreading must be known before we can reconstruct the geologic history of the ocean basins. An indication of the rate of sea-floor spreading is obtained by comparing the ages of volcanic rocks on the islands and seamounts shown in Fig. 3-12.

Volcanic Island Chains

The Hawaiian Islands are progressively older toward the northwest. A similar trend is noted in the Tuamotu Islands, and the Austral Islands. The distance between the islands in each group and their respective ages indicate a rate of spreading of about 8 cm per year in each direction away from the East Pacific Rise (Fig. 3-13). This rate is called a *half-rate* because the separation between points on opposite sides of the spreading center proceeds at twice this half-rate.

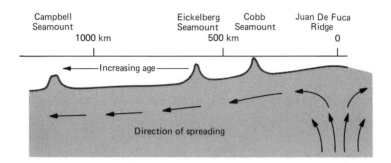

Figure 3-13 Schematic drawing showing several seamounts in the Northeast Pacific Basin. According to the sea-floor spreading hypothesis, the seamounts form on the ridge and move with the crust in the direction of spreading.

Islands close to the Mid-Atlantic Ridge are relatively young (Fig. 3-14). For example, the Azores are 15 million years old, and Iceland is 13 million years old. With increased distance from the ridge, the islands are increasingly older. Bermuda is 35 million years old; the Faroe Islands, 25 million years old; and the Cape Verde Islands, 150 million years old. Calculations based on the age and horizontal displacement of these islands indicate that the rate of crustal movement is 1 to 8 cm per year.

Some of the volcanic island chains in the Atlantic (the Walvis-Rio Grande Ridge) suggest that they formed at hot spots situated on the Mid-Atlantic Ridge. Other chains formed from mid-plate hot spots.

Hot spots appear to move over the earth's surface, but at rates much slower than those of the sea floor. The hot spots in the Pacific appear to have been nearly stationary with respect to each other for at least 80 million years.

Marine Sediment Ages

The rate of sea-floor spreading is derived also from the ages of sediments lying on volcanic oceanic crust at successive distances from a spreading center. The validity of such rate calculation was verified dramatically when the cores recovered by the *Glomar Challenger* during the Deep Sea Drilling Project were analyzed. Fossils in the cored sediments showed that the initial sediments (those lying directly over crustal rocks) near the Mid-Atlantic Ridge and East Pacific Rise are younger than the initial sediments at a site farther away (Fig. 3-15). The lavas that these sediments rest upon are likewise youngest near the

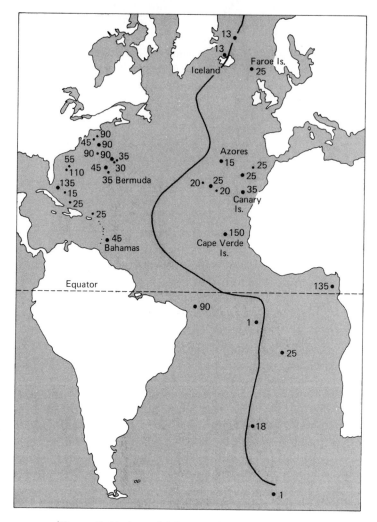

Figure 3-14 Age of Atlantic islands, as indicated by the age of the oldest rocks found in them. The numbers associated with the islands and seamounts (●) and of cores (•) give ages in millions of years. (After J. Tuzo Wilson, 1965, by permission of the Royal Society)

ridge or rise and are older farther away. Furthermore, the total thickness of sediments deposited on the bottom increases with distance from the Mid-Atlantic Ridge and from the East Pacific Rise.

Depth of the Sea Floor

Yet another feature indicating the rate of sea-floor spreading is the depth of the sea. As new oceanic crust moves from the spreading center, it cools and becomes more dense. The denser crust sinks deeper into the crust than does the lighter, hot crust at the spreading center because of isostasy. Consequently the sea floor is progressively deeper with distance from the ridges and rises

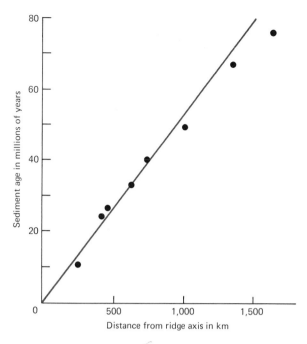

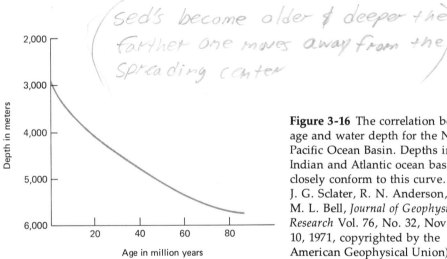

Figure 3-15 Age of the oldest sediments from the southern Atlantic and their distance from the ridge axis. The diagonal line indicates a spreading rate of 2 cm per year. (After Maxwell et al., 1970, Initial Reports of the Deep Sea Drilling Project Vol. III, Washington, D.C.)

sed's become older & deeper the farther one moves away from the spreading center

Figure 3-16 The correlation between age and water depth for the North Pacific Ocean Basin. Depths in Indian and Atlantic ocean basins closely conform to this curve. (From J. G. Sclater, R. N. Anderson, and M. L. Bell, *Journal of Geophysical Research* Vol. 76, No. 32, November 10, 1971, copyrighted by the American Geophysical Union)

(Fig. 2-15). The sea floor is also older with distance from the ridges and rises, so a correlation exists between age and depth of the sea floor (Fig. 3-16). The variation of depth with distance from a ridge or rise is an index of the spreading rate. Where spreading is rapid, hot crust extends farther from the spreading center than it does where spreading is slow, so at a rapidly spreading center, the sea floor forms a broad shoal, whereas a slowly spreading center forms a narrow one. In fact, broad rises such as the East Pacific Rise are indeed spreading rapidly compared to ridges such as the Mid-Atlantic Ridge. This is illustrated in Fig. 3-17.

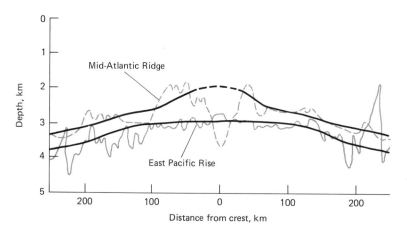

Figure 3-17 A comparison of the bathymetric profiles of the slowly spreading Mid-Atlantic Ridge (1 cm per year) and the rapidly spreading East Pacific Rise (4.4 cm per year). Solid lines are generalized profiles, broken lines are actual profiles.

Volcanic islands resting on the sea floor became progressively submerged as the oceanic crust supporting them spread to the northwest, and cooled and settled isostatically (to depths of 1 to 2 km). Ancient volcanic islands leveled flat by waves became guyots in this manner and the present depth of their upper surfaces correlates with their ages. The guyots in the tropical zone developed carbonate reefs that grew upward as the islands sank. The sinking of tropical guyots while they were carried away from the spreading center provides the mechanism for the formation of atolls that Darwin proposed (see Chap. 2). It has been possible to locate the former northern limit of the tropics in the western Pacific using this principle because the guyots south of a line (shown on Fig. 2-13) are crowned by atolls or submerged carbonate reefs, but those to the north are not.

Geomagnetism

The most comprehensive measure of sea-floor spreading is derived from the rate at which new crust forms at spreading centers. The rate at which oceanic crust is created at ridges and rises provides a measure of plate movement because the new crust is preserved on the sea floor at least until it is consumed by subduction in a trench. The new crust is volcanic rock (basalt) that is intruded as molten material at about 1,100°C. It fills cracks formed when the sea floor is pulled apart at spreading centers (ridges and rises). Upon reaching the sea floor, the basalt solidifies and cools to the temperature of seawater. In so doing, the rock acquires a magnetic property that permits determining its date of formation. The particular property is *thermoremanent magnetism* or TRM. When a rock containing the ferromagnetic mineral magnetite cools below 580°C (the *Curie temperature* for magnetite) in the presence of the earth's magnetic field, it becomes magnetized in such a way that its polarity has the

58

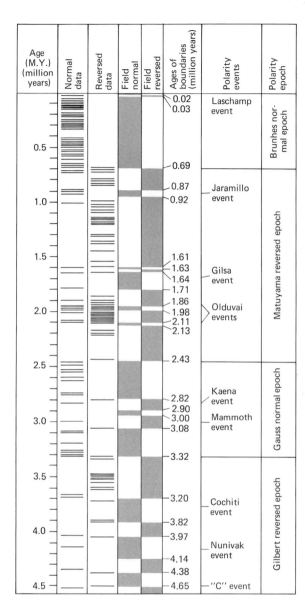

Figure 3-18A Time scale for geomagnetic reversals. Normal and reversed polarity intervals are placed in chronological order based on radiometric dating of samples. (After Cox, from *Science* Vol. 163, 1969, by permission of the American Association for the Advancement of Science, modified after N. D. Opdyke)

same orientation as the geomagnetic field. Furthermore, the intensity and orientation of the rock magnetism is permanent, so it indicates the magnetic field that prevailed when the lava solidified.

Paleomagnetic studies on land have shown reversals in the magnetic polarity of volcanic rock in sequences of layered flows. This suggests that the north and south magnetic poles have reversed many times in the past. The exact reasons for these reversals are unknown. Nevertheless, because the reversal pattern records a series of global events that permit worldwide correlation of the age of volcanic rocks, it has become an important tool.

Fig. 3-18A illustrates the magnetic orientation of volcanic formations in both

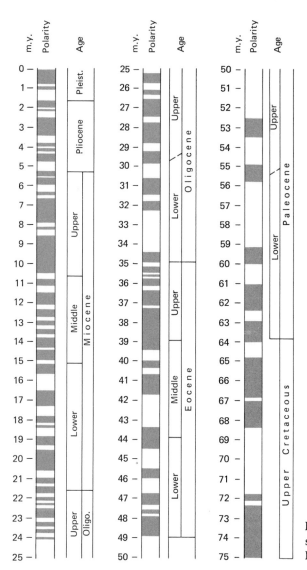

Figure 3-18B Cenozoic polarity time scale. (After D. H. Tarling and J. G. Mitchell, *Geology* Vol. 4, No. 3, 1976)

hemispheres. Two worldwide reversals in the magnetic field are indicated, occurring over the past 4½ million years. So far, approximately 170 reversals of the earth's magnetic field are known. The reversals extend far beyond the date of 4½ million years shown in Fig. 3-18A; estimates suggest that they date back as far as 76 million years (Fig. 3-18B). Methods for dating rocks and sediments are described in Chap. 15.

The orientation of magnetic mineral particles in marine sediments also preserves a record of magnetic field reversals. As a magnetite particle settles through the water column and comes to rest on the bottom, it tends to orient in alignment with the earth's magnetic field. When these particles are incorporated into layers of marine sediments, they preserve their magnetic align-

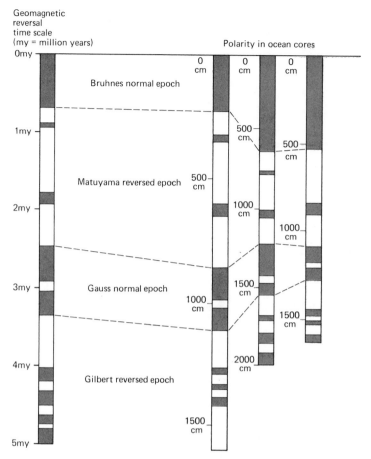

Figure 3-19 The geomagnetic reversal time scale is also observed in the deep-sea sediment record. These cores were collected from the Antarctic. The gray portions represent normal polarity, the white portions represent reversed polarity. (After Heirtzler et al., by permission of the American Geophysical Union)

ment. Sedimentary layers on the sea floor contain a record of the same magnetic epochs that are recorded in volcanic rocks. An example is shown in Fig. 3-19.

Geomagnetic investigations at sea reveal that the magnetic intensity of oceanic crustal material near oceanic ridges follows a definite pattern. Bands of equal magnetic intensity lie parallel to the axis of the oceanic ridge system and strips of equal magnetism are arranged symmetrically on either side of the ridge axis (Fig. 3-20). The sequence of bands of equal magnetic intensity on one side of the ridge is duplicated in a mirror image on the other side. These bands are called *magnetic anomalies* because they represent local zones of magnetic intensity different from that expected if the earth were homogeneous (with respect to the distribution of magnetic minerals) and had a uniform field such as shown in Fig. 3-21. Positive anomalies represent intensities higher than expected and negative anomalies lower than expected.

61

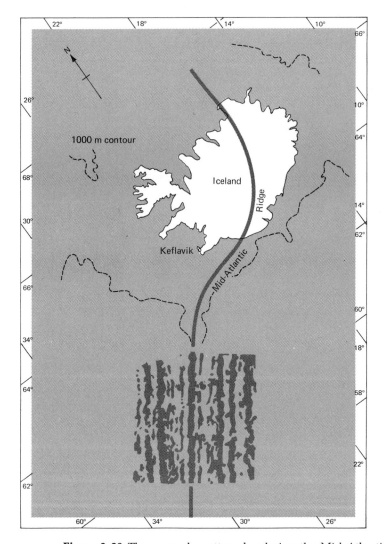

Figure 3-20 The anomaly pattern bordering the Mid-Atlantic Ridge in the area south of Iceland is strikingly symmetrical. The parallel bands in which the earth's field is stronger (stippled) or weaker (white) than the regional average are oriented along the ridge's axis. The magnetic bands are presumably produced by bands of rock with normal and reversed magnetism. (After Heirtzler et al.)

A magnetic anomaly in the earth's magnetic field is produced when the magnetic field of a mass of magnetic rock and the earth's field interact as shown in Fig. 3-22. The earth's field has a polarity following the convention that the north magnetic pole is in the direction of the earth's geographic pole. Notice that the inclination of the earth's magnetic field varies from vertical at the poles to horizontal over the magnetic equator. The mass of magnetic rock

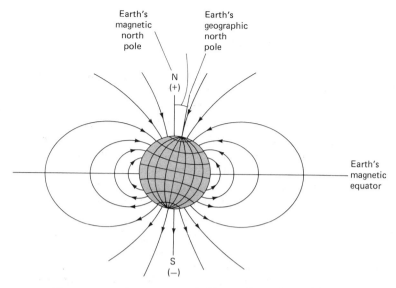

Figure 3-21 The magnetic field on a hypothetical homogeneous earth. The light lines represent lines of magnetic force. Note that the field is oriented vertically at the magnetic poles and horizontally at the magnetic equator.

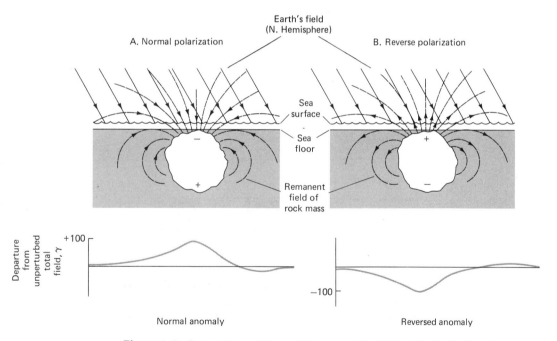

Figure 3-22 Interaction of the earth's magnetic field with the induced and remanent field of two masses of magnetic rock. The rock mass in (A) has normal polarity and the rock mass at (B) is of reverse polarity. The resultant magnetic signature of each, registered by a magnetometer, is shown below.

itself has a field that consists of two components: (1) an induced field arising from its presence in the earth's field; and (2) a remanent magnetic field. The polarity of the induced field is oriented with the earth's present field and its intensity depends upon the amount of magnetite in the rock. The remanent field has its polarity oriented with the field present at the time of its cooling past the Curie temperature. The intensity of the remanent field in a volcanic rock is about ten times that of its induced field. The fields of the rock mass and the earth combine additively if the remanent magnetism formed in a field oriented like today's *normal field,* but they combine subtractively if it formed in a field of *reversed polarity.* The anomaly patterns registered by a magnetometer towed over both kinds of anomaly are shown in Fig. 3-22.

Comparisons of magnetic intensity patterns near ridge crests and magnetic reversal chronology over the past 4 million years (determined from studies of land geology) show a correlation between the positive and negative magnetic anomalies observed at sea and normal and reversed polarity of the earth's magnetic field (Fig. 3-23). The crustal rocks appear to grow older away from the ridge and have a particular magnetic pattern that is similar on *either* side

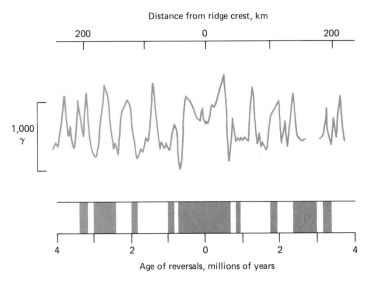

Figure 3-23 Magnetic anomaly curve from the East Pacific rise (top) and the chronology of magnetic reversals (bottom). At the bottom, periods of reversed polarity are shown in white, and normal polarity in black. The anomalies are measured in units of gamma (γ) $= 10^{-5}$ Oersted, a measure of the intensity of the earth's magnetic field. The age of the anomalies and their distance from the ridge crest indicate a spreading half-rate of about 100 km in 2.3 million years or 4.3 cm per year. (After S. P. Clark, *Structure of the Earth*, 1971, by permission of Prentice-Hall, Inc.)

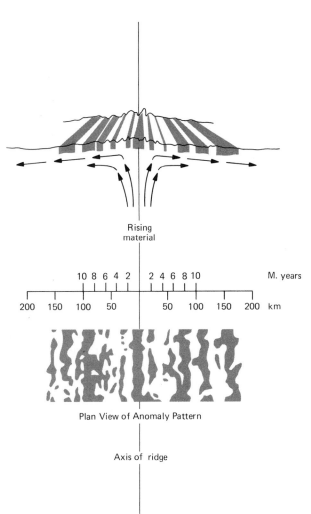

Rising
material

10 8 6 4 2   2 4 6 8 10   M. years

200   150   100   50   50   100   150   200   km

Plan View of Anomaly Pattern

Axis of ridge

Figure 3-24 The pattern of magnetic anomaly bands observed at a location on the Mid-Atlantic Ridge. The dark tone represents normal polarity. The ages of the anomalies and their distances from the axis of the ridge indicate a spreading half-rate of 100 km in 10 million years, or 1 cm per year. The method of formation of the anomalies by the combined effect of sea-floor spreading and alternating magnetic field reversal is depicted in the upper drawing. (After J. J. Vine, 1966)

of the ridge (Fig. 3-24). The age of the anomalies and their distance from the spreading center permit calculating the rate of spreading of the sea floor in the directions indicated by earthquake slip vectors and the trends of transform faults. The rate of spreading at a location on the East Pacific Rise is calculated in Fig. 3-23. A similar determination for a Mid-Atlantic Ridge location is shown in Fig. 3-24.

Before proceeding to discuss the geologic history of the ocean basins and the origin of continental margins, we should conclude our examination of plate tectonics theory by addressing the question of what ponderous forces cause the tectonic plate to pull apart and move toward subduction at trenches or toward plate collisions.

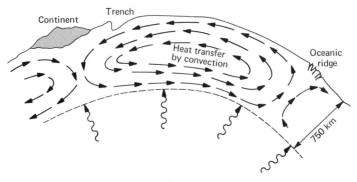

Figure 3-25 Conceptual drawing of one of the thermal convection cells thought to cause sea-floor spreading.

3.6   *The Mechanism of Sea-Floor Spreading*

The search for a suitable mechanism for driving plate motions is still a matter of intense interest for earth scientists. Forces arising from the earth's rotation and rock tides caused by lunar attraction have been considered but rejected in favor of a mechanism of large thermal convection cells in the asthenosphere (Fig. 3-25).

The convection cells are believed to extend approximately 750 km into the mantle, the maximum depth of earthquake foci. Above this depth, heat transfer by conduction is not sufficient to remove heat (generated by radioactive decay) from the earth. The temperature gradient maintained between the upper mantle and the earth's surface is large enough to produce thermal convection of the upper mantle. The rising current of mantle material reaches the base of the lithosphere, spreads laterally, cools, and finally sinks (Fig. 3-25). This process is analogous to a pan of water in which the heat energy added to the bottom of the pan is carried rapidly to the surface by the convective motion of the water. In the earth, however, the vertical motion is quite slow—on the order of 0.5 to 1 cm per year.

The ocean-ridge system drawn schematically at (A) in Fig. 3-26 shows the characteristics that would result from a rising convection current: large heat flow, earthquakes, and fracturing of the crust. The region where the convected material flows under the continental block is shown at (B) in Fig. 3-26. Here the crust is bowed down, forming a trench; heat flow from the crust is quite small; and earthquakes are frequent. The convection cell concept fits the theory of sea-floor spreading: it is, however, difficult to determine if these cells are the cause of sea-floor spreading or merely another effect of it. It is thought that rising plumes of hot asthenosphere material, represented at the surface by hot

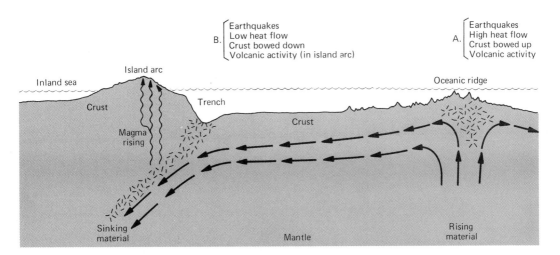

Figure 3-26 Idealized section through the upper mantle and crust showing the hypothesized convective motion and general characteristics of the crust in the regions of rising material (A) and sinking material (B). Regions of seismic activity are depicted by the symbol ($\frac{1}{7}\frac{/}{1}$).

spots, drive plate motions and cause sea-floor spreading. The coincidence of many hot spots and spreading centers (Fig. 3-27) supports such a view.

Yet another mechanism is suggested by observations of the distribution of seismic velocities with depth at various locations in the ocean. The velocity profiles in Fig. 3-28A show that a zone of high velocity occurs in the lithosphere and upper mantle. It lies above the zone of low velocity, deeper in the asthenosphere. The velocity of the seismic waves is proportional to the density of the rocks in those zones, implying that the lithosphere is denser than the material it rests upon (Fig. 3-28B). Accordingly the lithosphere would tend to sink spontaneously into the asthenosphere at trenches and drag the entire oceanic plate behind it. Tensional stress causes rupture only at the spreading center because the oceanic crust is free to slide along the viscous upper surface of the asthenosphere. According to this scheme, molten basaltic lava rises to fill the tensional cracks formed at the spreading center.

First motion studies of earthquakes at trenches indicate that the upper part of a descending lithospheric plate is indeed in tension while the lower part is being compressed, presumably because its motion is retarded by encountering denser material in the lower part of the asthenosphere. On the other hand, such a mechanism predicts that small plates should move faster than large plates, but such is not the case. Also, not all moving plates have a trench at their boundaries.

The actual driving mechanism might be some combination of all the mechanisms described above, and it might involve a mechanism yet to be discovered. Investigation of this matter is a subject of zealous research in the earth sciences.

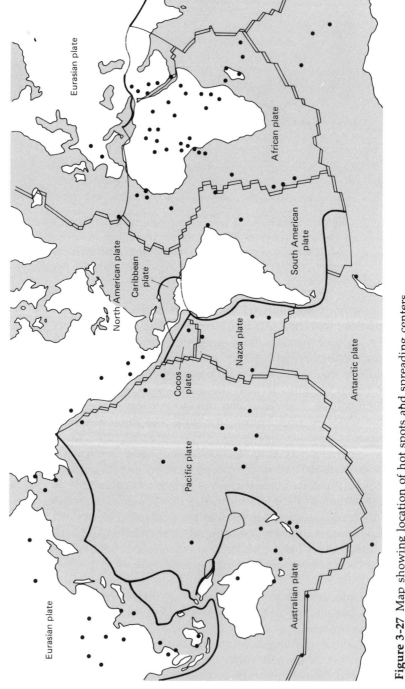

Figure 3-27 Map showing location of hot spots and spreading centers. Note that not all hot spots are located on spreading centers. Several hot spots are found also on the Pacific coast of Antarctica. (From "Hot Spots on the Earth's Surface" by K. C. Burke and J. T. Wilson, copyright © 1976 by Scientific American, Inc., all rights reserved.)

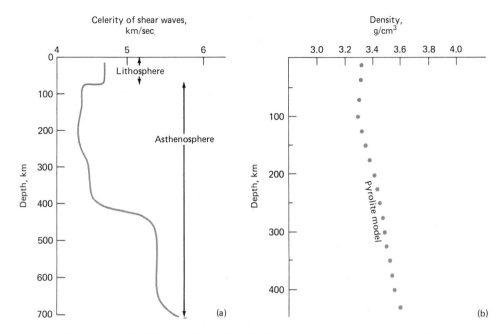

Figure 3-28 (A) The depth profile of seismic shear wave velocities. (B) Density profiles deduced from seismic velocities assuming that the mantle is composed of pyrolite. Pyrolite is a hypothetical rock having the chemical composition of a mixture of 1 part basalt and 3 parts peridotite. Note that the density of the uppermost crust is more dense than the material 100 km deep. (From "Plate Tectonics" by J. F. Dewey, copyright © 1972 by Scientific American, Inc., all rights reserved, and F. Press, "The Suboceanic Mantle," *Science* Vol. 165, 1969, copyright 1969 by the American Association for the Advancement of Science.

3.7 *Geologic History of the Ocean Basins*

Our understanding of the history of the world ocean (Table 3-3) is based upon the principle of *uniformitarianism* which holds that geologic processes active today acted the same way in the past. Plate tectonics principles provide the basis for deducing the history of the world ocean by providing estimates of spreading rates and directions of plate motion since the end of the Permian period (225 million years ago), the age of the oldest rocks and sediments in the ocean today.

The principle of uniformitarianism predicts that sea-floor spreading was active prior to the end of the Permian period as well, but evidence for reconstructing the early history of the world ocean must come from the continents where the oldest rocks are found. Mountain ranges indicate continental borders where subduction caused continents to accrete new crust. The age of the youngest rocks exposed in the mountains indicates the date of the

Table 3–3   Geologic History of the World Ocean

Era	Period (Geologic succession (not to scale))		Epoch	Approximate age in years × 10⁶	Events in the formation of ocean basins and continents
CENOZOIC	Quaternary		Recent		San Andreas Rift forms.
			Pleistocene	3	
	TERTIARY	Neogene	Pliocene		Gulf of Aden and Red Sea form.
			Miocene	22	
		Paleocene	Oligocene		Mediterranean Sea forms.
			Eocene		Australia separates from Antarctica. New Zealand splits off Australia.
			Paleocene		
MESOZOIC	Cretaceous			62	South Atlantic Ocean forms.
	Jurassic			130	India detaches from Gondwana.
	Triassic			180	North Atlantic forms. South Indian Ocean forms.
PALEOZOIC	Permian			230	Separation of Pangaea into Laurasia and Gondwana starts. The world ocean at its largest. Formation of Pangaea.
	CARBON-IFEROUS	Pennsylvanian Mississippian		280 / 325	Larussia and Gondwana fuse. The Tethys Sea starts to take form.
	Devonian			340	The continents start to cluster. The southern ocean shrinks.
	Silurian			400	Laurentia fuses with Baltica. Southern Ocean rings Gondwana. Gondwana moves to south pole.
	Ordovician			450	Baltica moves toward south pole.
	Cambrian			500	
				570	Six continents are located between 60° N and S in a global ocean.
PROTEROZOIC				640	
ARCHEAN					Earliest fossils found in ancient sedimentary rocks.
	No record			3600	World ocean forms. Differentiation of masses of continental crust.

Oldest meteorites and terrestrial lead

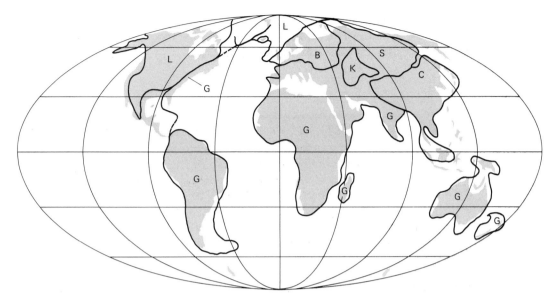

Figure 3-29 Generalized geography of the modern world showing present position of earliest continents. This kind of map projection (called a Mollweide projection) shows the entire globe. It displays areas equally but distorts the shape of the continents around its edge.

G = Gondwana, L = Laurentia, B = Baltica, K = Kazakstania, C = China, S = Siberia

accretion, as does the age of intrusive and volcanic rocks associated with the mountain range. The existence of mountains in the interior of present continents is evidence of the fusion of two preexisting continents after subduction caused them to collide.

The lithology and fossil content of sedimentary rocks of the Paleozoic era (570 to 230 million years ago) bear evidence of the climate, geographic orientation, and latitudinal position of the basins in which they formed. The composition and texture of the rocks allow us to deduce the proximity of eroding highlands (mountains formed by earlier tectonic processes). Collectively this evidence identifies those areas that existed as separate continents (Fig. 3-29). It also indicates the time sequence during which continents formed, accreted new crust, collided, split, or coalesced.

The geographic orientation and latitudinal position of former continents is deduced from the paleoclimate represented by ancient glacial deposits (polar latitudes), coal beds (warm, rainy latitudes), salt beds (hot, dry regions), and deposits rich in organic materials (west coasts in temperate regions). The

position of these deposits (east or west coast) on a former continent is
determined by taking the uniformitarian view that the present climatic controls
of such deposits are the same as in former times.

3.8   *Historical Sequence of Events*

The dim past (4.7 billion to 0.5 billion years ago)   The mode of formation and
time of occurrence of the earliest continents is not known exactly, but it seems
likely that continents formed by differentiation from the material comprising
the earth during or soon after the formation of our planet 4.7 billion years ago.
The evidence indicates that six continental masses, Laurentia, Gondwana,
Baltica, Kazakstania, China, and Siberia (Fig. 3-29), formed by the time the
remains of earliest life were preserved in the rocks of the Pre-Cambrian era
(0.5 to 3.5 billion years ago). The global ocean formed during this time
surrounded the six continents.

550 to 540 million years ago (Late Cambrian period)   The sedimentary and
paleontological record in the rocks of this age indicate that the six continents
were separated and distributed in an equatorial belt lying between 60° N and

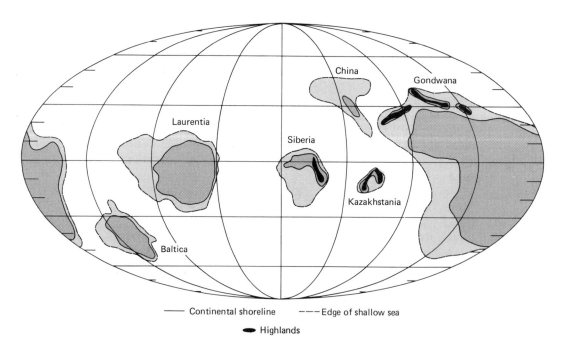

—— Continental shoreline   – – –Edge of shallow sea

◤ Highlands

Figure 3-30 The surface of the earth as it appeared in the Late
Cambrian (550 to 540 million years ago). Four continents were situated
in the equatorial zone and two in the temperate regions. (Reprinted by
permission of *American Scientist*, journal of Sigma Xi, The Scientific
Research Society)

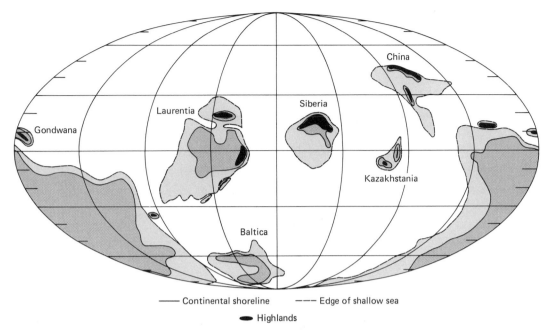

Figure 3-31 The earth during the Middle Ordovician (490 to 475 million years ago). Baltica has moved toward the South Pole. (Reprinted by permission of *American Scientist*, journal of Sigma Xi, The Scientific Research Society)

60° S latitudes as shown in Fig. 3-30. Shallow seas occupied the continental margins of most of China and Siberia and much of the other continents. Highlands supplying sediments to the shallow seas were located in what is now Australia, Antarctica, eastern Siberia, and central Kazakstania. The world ocean consisted of two polar seas connected by passages between the six continents.

490 to 475 million years ago (Middle Ordovician period)   Glacial deposits of this age in the Sahara desert suggest that Gondwana had moved toward a position at the south pole (Fig. 3-31) during this time. Baltica also moved south over the south pole at the same time; possibly Gondwana and Baltica were on the same lithospheric plate. Mountains formed along the eastern margin of Laurentia.

435 to 430 million years ago (Middle Silurian period)   Baltica continued to move past the south pole and headed northward to the equator while Gondwana was centered at the south pole. Siberia moved northward to a north temperate latitude (Fig. 3-32). Baltica and Laurentia converged and mountains formed along the eastern margin of Baltica. Shallow seas were extensive at the periphery of all six continents. The world ocean consisted of a north polar sea that extended southward over half the earth. The region between the continents was occupied by relatively narrow arms of the hemispheric ocean.

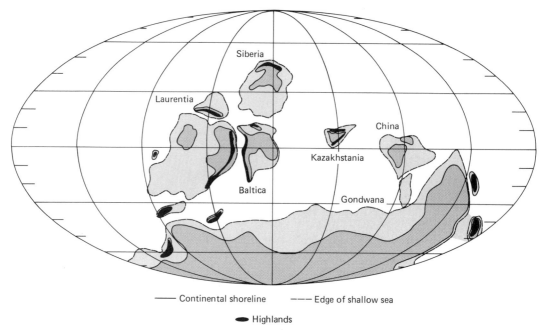

Figure 3-32 The earth during Middle Silurian (435 to 430 million years ago). Gondwana moved to the South Pole and Baltica to the equator. (Reprinted by permission of *American Scientist*, journal of Sigma Xi, The Scientific Research Society)

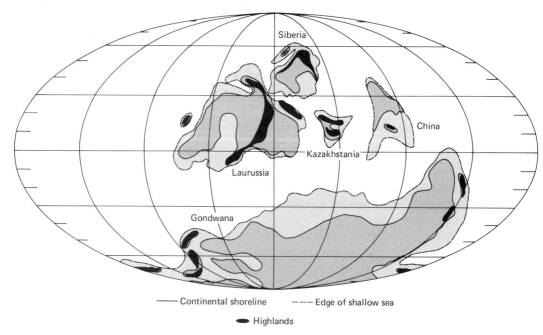

Figure 3-33 The earth during the Late Early Devonian (410 to 405 million years ago). The continents are starting to cluster together to form larger continental masses. The world ocean covers much of the earth's surface and a southern ocean rings Gondwana. (Reprinted by permission of *American Scientist*, journal of Sigma Xi, The Scientific Research Society)

74

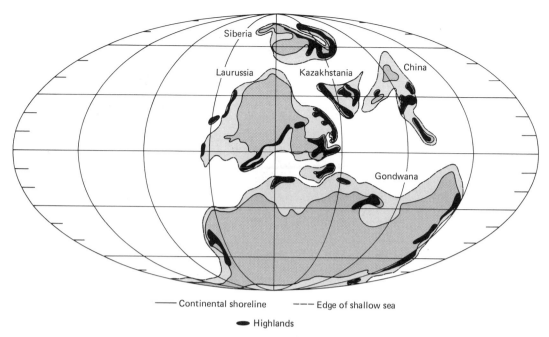

——— Continental shoreline   ——— Edge of shallow sea

●━● Highlands

Figure 3-34 The earth during the Mississippian (360 to 340 million years ago). The outline of the future Tethys Sea is taking form. (Reprinted by permission of *American Scientist*, journal of Sigma Xi, The Scientific Research Society)

410 to 405 million years ago (Late Early Devonian period) By this time Laurentia and Baltica had collided and fused to form the continent Larussia (Fig. 3-33). Gondwana remained at the south pole but the other continents shifted northward to form a continuous ocean basin in the southern hemisphere. Mountain building was extensive on all the continents at this time.

360 to 340 million years ago (Mississippian period) Gondwana moved northward toward Larussia and narrowed the southern hemisphere ocean basin between them (Fig. 3-34). Siberia moved to the north and occupied an arctic position. Kazakstania and China shifted from the equator to a northern temperate latitude and described the outline of the Tethys Sea embayment. All the continents occupied a single hemisphere; over half the earth was covered by the world ocean, which extended from the north pole to the south pole. Shallow seas were prevalent on the northern edge of Gondwana and the margins of the other continents, despite the fact that much of Gondwana was covered with glaciers.

310 to 300 million years ago (Pennsylvanian period) Continued northward migration caused the collision and fusion of Gondwana with Larussia and of Kazakstania with Siberia (Fig. 3-35). The mountains that formed at the suture between Gondwana and Larussia are the present southern Appalachians. Baltica sheared northward relative to Laurentia along the present northern Appalachian Mountains. Subduction between Baltica and Kazakstania began narrowing the ocean between them. Glaciation of Gondwana reached its

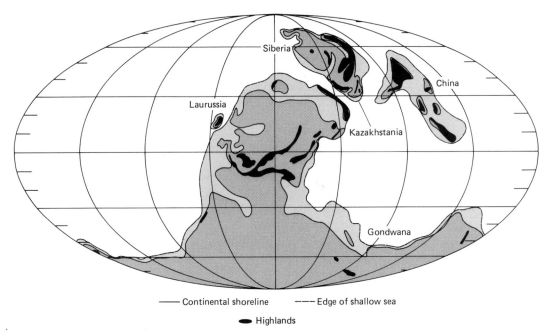

— Continental shoreline ---- Edge of shallow sea

● Highlands

Figure 3-35 The earth during the Pennsylvanian (310 to 300 million years ago). The continents continue to coalesce and form the Tethys Sea as an embayment of the world ocean. (Reprinted by permission of *American Scientist*, journal of Sigma Xi, The Scientific Research Society)

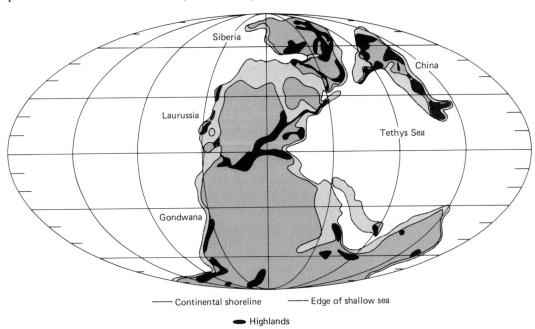

— Continental shoreline ---- Edge of shallow sea

● Highlands

Figure 3-36 The earth during the Early Late Permian (260 to 250 million years ago). The continents have virtually coalesced into the supercontinent, Pangaea. The world ocean is the largest it has ever been. (Reprinted by permission of *American Scientist*, journal of Sigma Xi, The Scientific Research Society)

maximum extent and the Tethys Sea assumed its ultimate configuration during this time.

260 to 250 million years ago (Early Late Permian period)   Siberia and Gondwana collided at what is now the Ural Mountains as subduction closed the sea between them. China moved toward Siberia but did not collide with it and form the supercontinent Pangaea until after the Permian period. Shallow seas were less extensive than previously; only the Tethyan shore of Gondwana, northern and central Larussia, and parts of China bore marginal seas. The world ocean covered 5/6 of the surface of the earth (Fig. 3-36), the largest expanse of ocean ever to occupy our planet.

The Breakup of Pangaea

The evolution of the basins of the world ocean since the formation of Pangaea in the Permian period is reconstructed by projecting plate motions backward in time. The plate motions are deduced by combining spreading rates (Table 3-4) and the directions as motion vectors that describe the magnitude and direction of each plate's movement away from spreading centers at ridges and rises. The pattern of plate motion vectors describing present motions is shown in Fig. 3-37. Projecting these movements backward in time is possible because past changes in the rate and direction are shown by the pattern of geomagnetic anomalies on the sea floor; motion prior to the earliest anomaly is assumed to be constant in speed and direction.

The motion of the plates is relative to spreading centers that are not stationary on the earth's surface, so it is necessary to assume a fixed point of reference in order to describe absolute motion of plates on the earth. The Antarctic continent is chosen to be stationary because it is virtually surrounded by ridges or rises. This configuration implies that the ring of spreading centers

Table 3–4   Rates of Sea-Floor Spreading

	Half-rate*, cm/yr
Atlantic Ocean	
Northern Atlantic Ridge	1.6
Southern Atlantic Ridge	1.5
Pacific Ocean	
East Pacific Rise	8.9
Antarctic Rise	6.4
Juan De Fuca Ridge	4.8
Indian Ocean	
North Indian Ocean	1.9

* The half-rate refers to the rate that a lithospheric plate spreads from a ridge or rise. Points on opposite sides of a spreading center move apart at a whole-rate that is twice the half-rate.

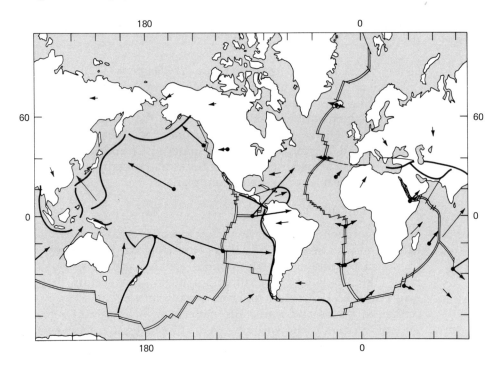

Figure 3-37 A map of the world ocean showing the direction and spread of present plate motion deduced from transform fault trends and plate-spreading rates (light arrows) and from the orientation of nemataths and the age of volcanoes along them (heavy arrows). Hot spots are shown by double lines, trenches by heavy lines, and transform faults by light lines. (After W. Jason Morgan, *Nature* Vol. 230, 1971)

surrounding Antarctica must migrate away from that continent as must all plates lying beyond the spreading centers. There is no certainty that Antarctica is not moving, but at least all other plates bear evidence that they are not stationary.

225 million years ago (Early Triassic period) The supercontinent of Pangaea (Fig. 3-38) existed surrounded by the ancestral Pacific Ocean. The large equatorial embayment of the Tethys Sea extended from the Pacific on the east to the point where Africa and Europe now meet at Gibraltar. The southern part of the Tethys Sea was the northern Indian Ocean basin.

200 million years ago (middle of the Triassic period) Pangaea began to break apart when a subduction zone formed in the Tethys Sea and a spreading center developed along the line of contact between western Laurasia and western Gondwana. The result was the creation of the present North Atlantic Ocean as

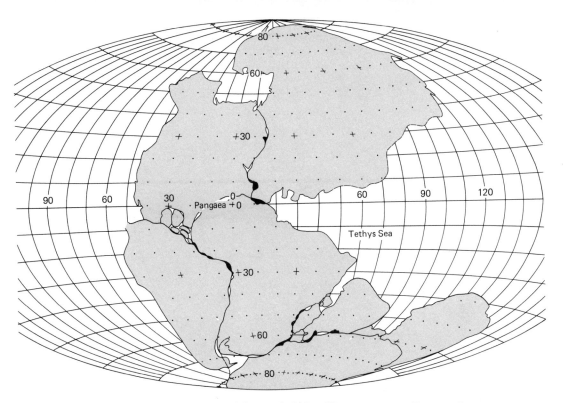

Figure 3-38 A map of the earth 225 million years ago. Pangaea is surrounded by the ancestral Pacific Ocean, and the Tethys Sea is an embayment on the east coast of the supercontinent. (After R. S. Dietz and J. C. Holden, "Reconstruction of Pangaea: Breakup and Dispersion of Continents, Permian to Present," *Journal of Geophysical Research* Vol. 75, No. 26, September 10, 1970, copyrighted by the American Geophysical Union)

an embayment extending from the Pacific on the west to Gibraltar on the east. Also, a forked spreading center formed along central Gondwana and between the Indian subcontinent and east Gondwana. This was the site of the early South Indian Ocean basin.

180 million years ago (end of the Triassic period)   A rift valley similar to the one now in East Africa formed in western Gondwana. It was later to become a spreading center that formed the South Atlantic Ocean basin (Fig. 3-39).

The trench in the Tethys Sea extended from Gibraltar to Indonesia, and the sea narrowed as Laurasia and western Gondwana converged. India was moving northward toward Asia as the southern Indian Ocean basin widened.

135 million years ago (end of the Jurassic period)   The sea flooded the rift valley formed by the spreading center between Africa and South America. The result was the early South Atlantic embayment which opened southward and extended northward to what is now southern Brazil (Fig. 3-40). The sea in the South Atlantic embayment was warm enough for carbonate sediments to accumulate there; it resembled the present Red Sea.

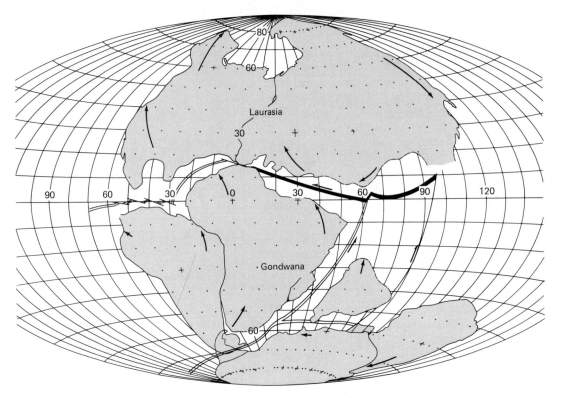

Figure 3-39 The separation of Pangaea 180 million years ago.
Subduction zones are shown as heavy lines and transform faults are
light lines. The open arrows indicate plate motions. (After R. S. Dietz
and J. C. Holden, "Reconstruction of Pangaea: Breakup and Dispersion
of Continents, Permian to Present," *Journal of Geophysical Research* Vol.
75, No. 26, September 10, 1970, copyrighted by the American
Geophysical Union)

At this time the Walvis hot spot formed on the South Atlantic spreading
center and started to produce the nemataths that now chart the course of
former spreading there. India was moving north toward another hot spot that
would form the extensive lavas found in that country today, and would also
form the Laccadive–Chagos nematath.

The North Atlantic widened to about 600 km by the movement of western
Laurasia. It remained connected to the Pacific Ocean. The present eastern coast
of the United States was oriented E–W at about 25° N latitude and corals
flourished in the shallow waters near shore. The North Atlantic spreading
center extended to the northeast as far as the embayment that formed as the
Labrador Sea. The Bay of Biscay formed as the Iberian Peninsula rotated away
from the European part of Laurasia.

The Indian Ocean continued to open, but the Tethys Sea continued narrowing because of the relative motion of eastern Laurasia and western Gondwana
along the Tethys Trench.

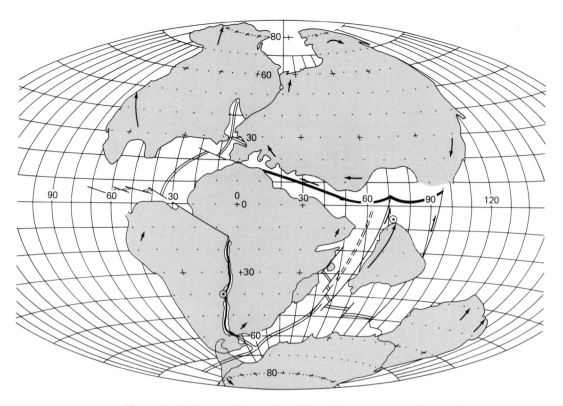

Figure 3-40 The earth's surface 135 million years ago. The circled dots are hot spots that developed at this time. (After R. S. Dietz and J. C. Holden, "Reconstruction of Pangaea: Breakup and Dispersion of Continents, Permian to Present," *Journal of Geophysical Research* Vol. 75, No. 26, September 10, 1970, copyrighted by the American Geophysical Union)

The behavior of the oceanic crust of the Pacific Ocean basin up to this time is not well known because the trenches active in the Pacific today have subducted it back into the asthenosphere. Apparently a trench existed at this time somewhere to the west of North America and South America.

105 million years ago (Early Cretaceous period) The Walvis hot spot formed the Rio Grande and Walvis nemataths and divided the South Atlantic Ocean into two basins. The northern basin was in an arid region and evaporation there led to the formation of salt deposits on the sea floor.

100 million years ago (Mid Cretaceous period) North America moved westward over the Pacific Trench and formed the California Coast Ranges.

86 million years ago (Late Cretaceous period) The North and South Atlantic ocean basins became united along a series of transform faults and spreading center segments. A shallow sea, the Benue Trough, formed on West Africa at the Gulf of Guinea.

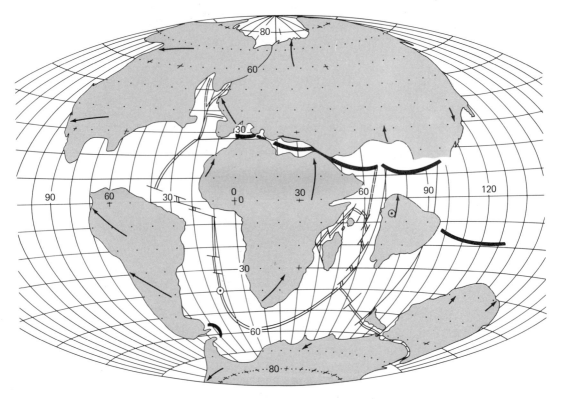

Figure 3-41 The separation of South America 65 million years ago. The nemataths extending from the Walvis hot spot are shown in the South Atlantic Ocean basin. (After R. S. Dietz and J. C. Holden, "Reconstruction of Pangaea: Breakup and Dispersion of Continents, Permian to Present," *Journal of Geophysical Research* Vol. 75, No. 26, September 10, 1970, copyrighted by the American Geophysical Union)

62 million years ago (end of the Cretaceous period)   The South Atlantic continued to spread and became almost 3,000 km wide. India was now nearly 3,000 km north of its starting point (Fig. 3-41). Africa moved about 1,000 km northward and rotated counterclockwise. The Tethys Sea narrowed and sealed to form the ancestral Mediterranean Sea, which looked much as it does today. The northern end of the Mid-Atlantic Ridge changed its location to the east side of what is now Greenland and the spur of the ridge in the Labrador Sea became inactive. Spreading ceased in the Caribbean region. Australia began to separate from Antarctica along a spreading center that extended southeastward from the Mid-Indian Trench. Madagascar split off the African continent along an extinct southern extension of the present Carlsberg Ridge.

South America reached the trench in the eastern Pacific but displaced it westward and formed the Andes Mountains. Nemataths from the Walvis hot spot extended for hundreds of kilometers toward the northeast and northwest, leaving a permanent record of the direction and rate of spreading of the African and South American plates.

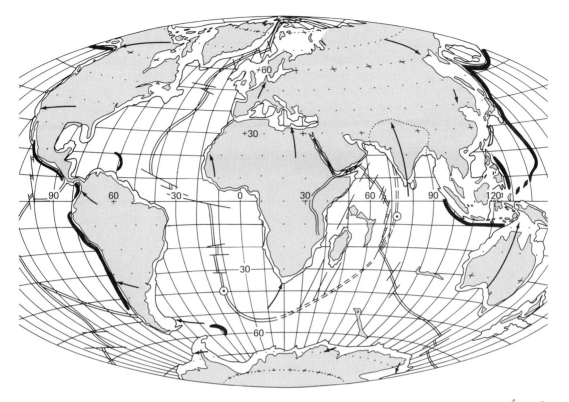

Figure 3-42 The earth's surface today showing present plate motion, spreading centers, and major transform faults. (After R. S. Dietz and J. C. Holden, "Reconstruction of Pangaea: Breakup and Dispersion of Continents, Permian to Present," *Journal of Geophysical Research* Vol. 75, No. 26, September 10, 1970, copyrighted by the American Geophysical Union)

The last 62 million years (Cenozoic era)   During the early Cenozoic era, the world ocean achieved its present shape (Fig. 3-42). The Mid-Atlantic Ridge extended northward into the Arctic region and separated Greenland from Eurasia. North and South America became united by the Panamanian Isthmus, which was formed by crustal arching and volcanism.

The southwestern Indian spreading center became inactive, and about 50 million years ago Australia separated from Antarctica; New Zealand detached from Australia at the same time. Australia moved northward from the Indo-Australian Ridge about 4 cm per year (half-rate), while Antarctica appears to have had only slight westward rotation. India collided with, and thrust under, Asia to form the Himalayan Mountains.

In the late Cenozoic era (about 20 million years ago) a spur of the Carlsberg Ridge split Arabia from Africa to form the Gulf of Aden and the Red Sea. Sea-floor spreading was active in the Pacific Ocean basin, and active subduction

83

occurs at much of the Pacific plate margin today. Apparently the Indian-Australian Ridge extended northeastward to form the East Pacific Rise in the early Cenozoic era, sometime after the American continents reached the trenches in the eastern Pacific Ocean basin.

Later in the Cenozoic era the North American continent moved to and over part of the East Pacific Rise. The spreading center there became inactive and Pacific plate motion shifted. The Pacific plate spread westward 8 to 13 cm per year about 15 million years ago, but since then additional motion toward the Aleutian Trench about half that rate has occurred. The west coast of south and central California became the site of a major transform, the San Andreas fault. South of the San Andreas fault the East Pacific Rise opened the Gulf of California along its axis. The northernmost part of the eastern Pacific spreading center persists today as the Juan de Fuca Ridge off Oregon, Washington, and British Columbia.

The Future of the World Ocean Basins

During the next 50 million years we can expect the Atlantic and Indian ocean basins to expand while the Pacific Ocean basin (which contains most of the plate-consuming trenches) shrinks. The eventual result will be the collision of North and South America with Japan and the Philippine Islands. Australia will hit Eurasia, and East Africa will split from the mainland. Northward movement of Africa will extinguish the Mediterranean Sea and close the Bay of Biscay. The Antarctic plate should remain where it is and continue its slight westward rotation.

New land should emerge in the Caribbean Sea because of crustal compression there. The Baja California Peninsula and the coast of central and southern California should move northward and bring Los Angeles to San Francisco in about 10 million years. Los Angeles will continue to move and disappear into the Aleutian Trench in about 60 million years.

A hot spot thought to exist under the Yellowstone area of northwestern Wyoming may cause the eventual breakup of the North American continent.

In summary, the plate tectonics theory has provided an appreciation of the main points of the earth's recent history. Future investigations should yield the finer details of that history and elucidate the earliest events in the formation of the features of the earth's surface.

3.9   The Origin of the Continental Margins

The continental margins of the world ocean are the zones of transition between the continental masses and the oceanic crust and the sites of the dynamic processes of the earth. Processes such as volcanism, earthquakes, and isostatic adjustments are active at the continental margins. They form and modify the configuration at the surface in a variety of ways. Water motions shift sediments and cause a general filling and smoothing of the sea floor, chemical reactions produce changes in the surface rocks, and biological growth produces massive limestone reefs and skeletal materials, an important component of marine sediments. Therefore, a study of the mode of origin of the continental margins must consider a combination of processes starting with the plate tectonics hypothesis and including a variety of other oceanic processes as well.

Plate Tectonics and Continental Margins

The continental masses are embedded in the rigid plates in the lithosphere (Fig. 3-1). The edges of a continental block might lie at a convergent plate boundary and experience collision or *active* motion relative to an adjacent plate. Conversely, the margin might lie in an interior or *passive* region of a plate rather than at a plate boundary. Examples of active continental margins in the world ocean are the west coast of South America and the east coast of Asia. Examples of passive continental margins are the east coasts of North and South America and the coasts of Africa. The positions of the continents with respect to plate boundaries are shown in Fig. 3-1.

Active Margins

At least three types of active margins can be recognized from bathymetric and geophysical evidence. These are the following: (1) the ocean–continental margin; (2) the island arc–continental margin; and (3) the ocean-faulted continental margin. The genesis of these types is not well understood, although they result in part from the nature of the movement occurring at plate boundaries. Types (1) and (2) occur where one plate is thrust under another, as shown in Fig. 3-2. The characteristic morphology and tectonic framework is a deep-sea trench, much seismicity, deformation of rock masses, remelting of crustal rocks, and volcanism. In some instances, thrust faulting forms an active margin at the continent–ocean boundary (Fig. 3-43A). Examples of this type of active margin are the Gulf of Alaska, Washington, Oregon, and South America. In some of these examples the deep-sea trench has been filled by sedimentary materials.

At many plate boundaries thrust faulting seaward of the continental mass forms an island arc–continental margin configuration (Fig. 3-43B). The geophysical characteristics seaward of the island arc are very similar to the ocean–continental margin system; however, a marginal sea occurs between the island arc and the continental mass. Examples of this type of active margin include Aleutian Arc–Bering Sea; Kuril Arc–Sea of Okhotsk; and Japan Arc–Sea of Japan.

In some regions of the world ocean *strike-slip* (rifting) or parallel plate movement rather than a thrusting movement (one plate riding over another)

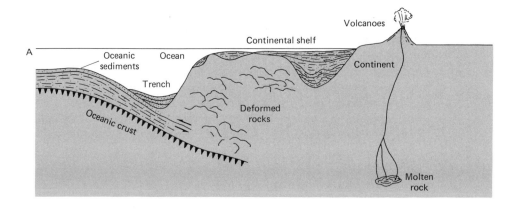

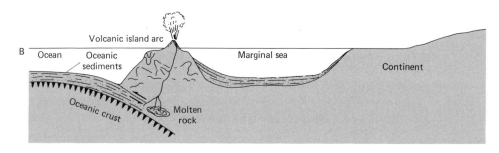

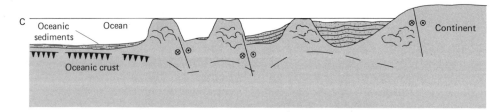

Figure 3-43 Schematic representation of active margin types.
A = Ocean–continent margin with predominantly thrust faulting. *S A*
B = Island arc–continent margin with predominantly thrust faulting. *JAPAN*
C = Ocean–continent margin with predominantly strike-slip faulting. *S CALIF.*
⊙ = Movement out of page; ⊗ = Movement into page.

produces the oceanic-faulted continental margin (Fig. 3-43C). Examples of this type of margin occur in western Canada, central and southern California, and northern Venezuela. Some continental borders lack trenches and seismic activity, because those continental masses move with the plates. Such margins are called *trailing edge* margins. For example, the plate moving westward from the Mid-Atlantic Ridge (Fig. 3-1) includes the South American continent. It rides over the eastern Pacific plate along the Peru–Chile Trench, and no trench has formed along the eastern border of South America.

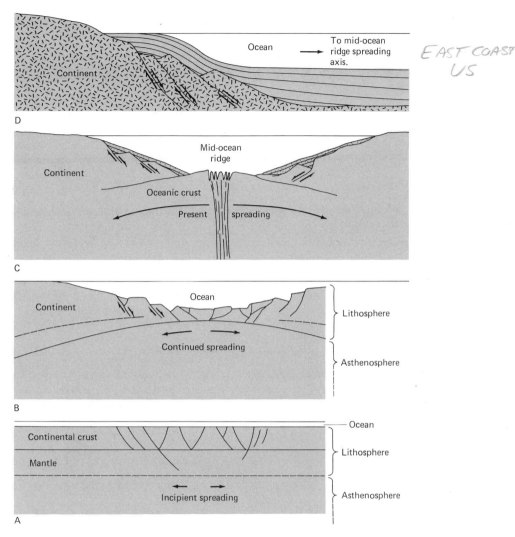

To mid-ocean
ridge spreading
axis.

Ocean

Continent

EAST COAST US

D

Mid-ocean
ridge

Continent

Oceanic crust

Present ||| spreading

C

Continent

Ocean

Lithosphere

Continued spreading

Asthenosphere

B

Ocean

Continental crust

Lithosphere

Mantle

Asthenosphere

Incipient spreading

A

Figure 3-44 Schematic representation of a passive continental margin
(D). The sequence of development of the passive margin follows steps
A → B → C.

Passive Margins

Passive continental margins are generally quite ancient, because their structural evolution begins when the lithosphere originally starts to fracture and
move apart. An example of a passive continental margin is the east coast of
North America. It is shown in Fig. 3-44D and its structural evolution is
depicted in Figs. 3-44A, B, and C. Passive margins are not associated with
converging plate boundaries; hence they are quite stable, have low levels of
seismicity, and have no volcanism.

Table 3–5   Average Rates of Several Major Geologic Processes

Process	Average rate, cm/1,000 yr
Weathering (soil development)	10–30
Denudation of continents	10
Sedimentation	5
Tectonic movements (vertical)	50–100

From K. Zdenek, *Geology of Recent Sediments*, New York: Academic Press, 1971, p. 42.

As in the case of active margins, the deposition of terrigenous sediment plays an important role in filling basins and masking the original shape of the bottom. Nonetheless, the tectonic nature of a margin or basin is often discernible because weathering and denudation of the continental surface and sedimentation tend to proceed at rates that are slower than the rate of tectonic movements (see Table 3-5). Further, the accumulation of sediments in basins produces isostatic loads that foster tectonic adjustments.

Other Types of Continental Margins

Salt domes.   Other processes in the world ocean influence the formation of continental margins. The *diapir* margin is formed by massive intrusions of salt that have been pushed upward from salt deposits deep within the marine

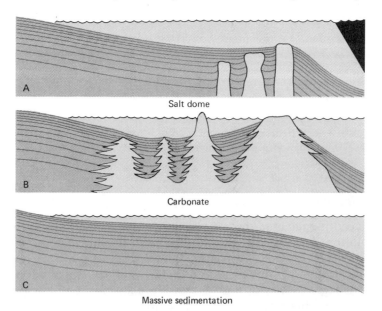

Figure 3-45 Examples of typical shelf cross sections. (After K. O. Emery)

sediments overlying the oceanic crust (Fig. 3-45A). The origin of the salt deposits are related to marine conditions during the original splitting and spreading of the crust as shown in Figs. 3-44B, C, and D. Conditions at that time were the following: (1) restricted water circulation; (2) hot and extremely saline brines filling the bottom of the ocean basin; and (3) an arid climate with excessive evaporation. These conditions led to the deposition of extensive salt deposits that were subsequently covered by marine sedimentary deposits. At some later geologic time the salt layers were deformed by sedimentary overburden pressures and pushed upward in domelike features as shown in Fig. 3-45A. Salt dome structures are observed in the Gulf of Mexico, northeast North America, eastern South America, and western Africa.

Carbonate reefs.   In the areas of the world ocean where conditions are appropriate for carbonate reef development (see Chap. 2 page 26), the continental margins are formed or modified by these massive features. Here the continental margins are wide and irregular and contain a complex combination of reef structures and sedimentation from biogenic remains (Fig. 3-45B). The locations where carbonate reefs influence continental margins are shown in Fig. 2-12.

Massive sedimentation.   Another type of continental margin occurs where sedimentary material supply is excessive and deposition is rapid. The character of the margin is controlled by sedimentary processes. The continental margin is depositional off the mouths of the major rivers of the world, (e.g., Ganges, Indus, Mississippi). The margin consists of sedimentary layers several tens of kilometers thick (Fig. 3-45C).

Depositional margins, or for that matter any kind of margin having a thick sedimentary cover, are of considerable interest because of their potential for bearing petroleum accumulations. It is evident that sedimentation margins, diapir margins, and carbonate reef margins on passive continental margins and thrust fault margins on active continental margins could possess the properties required for the formation of petroleum prospects shown in Table 3-6. Certainly the requirement of sediment thickness is met at sedimentary

Table 3–6   Geological Properties Required for Petroleum Prospects

1.	Rich source of organic matter of the proper kind.
2.	Organic matter must be preserved until buried by sediments.
3.	At least 1,000 m of blanketing sediments to provide temperatures between 50° and 150°C for thermochemical conversion of organic matter to petroleum.
4.	Adjacent porous and permeable sediment layers for migration of newly generated petroleum in response to compaction pressure or other forces.
5.	Structural or stratigraphic traps for accumulating migrating petroleum.
6.	A cover layer of impervious sediments or evaporites to prevent escape of petroleum from traps.
7.	Proper timing, i.e., trap formation must precede petroleum migration.

Figure 3-46 Map of sediment thickness in the Atlantic Ocean Basin. Sediment thickness exceeding 1,000 m is shaded. (After M. Ewing, G. Carpenter, C. Windisch, and J. Ewing, *Bulletin of the Geological Society of America,* Vol. 84, January 1974)

continental margins. This is apparent in Fig. 3-46, a map of the thickness of sediments along the margins of the Atlantic Ocean basin. Organic matter is produced in the waters of the continental shelves, and near large rivers rapid sedimentation rates can be expected. Changes in the nature of sediments supplied to an area and tectonic changes in sediment structures can occur over the time scales considered, so it is likely that some parts of the margins of the Atlantic bear all the geological requirements of petroleum prospects. This could be especially true at the base of the continental slope where particularly thick sediment accumulations exist.

reading list

BAMBACH, R. K., C. R. SCOTESE, AND A. M. ZIEGLER, "Before Pangaea: The Geographics of the Paleozoic World," *American Scientist*, LXVIII, No. 1 (1980), 26–38.

BIRD, J. AND B. ISACKS, EDS., *Plate Tectonics*, Washington, D.C.: American Geophysical Union, 1972. 563p.

COX, A., *Plate Tectonics and Geomagnetic Reversals*. San Francisco: W. H. Freeman and Company, 1973. 702p.

DEWEY, J. F., "Plate Tectonics," *Scientific American*, CCXXVI (May 1972), 56–68.

DIETZ, R. S. AND J. C. HOLDEN, "Reconstruction of Pangaea: Breakup and Dispersion of Continents, Permian to Present," *Jour. Geophys. Res.*, LXXV, No. 26 (1970), 4939–4956.

EMERY, K. O., "The Continental Shelves," *Scientific American*, CCXXI, No. 3 (September 1969), 106–22.

GLEN, W., *Continental Drift and Plate Tectonics*. Columbus, OH: Charles E. Merrill Publishing Company, 1975. 188p.

HESS, H. H., "History of Ocean Basins" in *Petrological Studies: A Volume in Honor of A. F. Buddington*, ed. by A. E. J. ENGEL, H. L. JAMES, and B. F. LEONARD, Geological Society of America, Boulder, Colorado: (1962), 599–620.

ISACKS, B., J. OLIVER, AND L. R. SYKES, "Seismology and the New Global Tectonics," *Journal of Geophysical Research*, LXXIII, No. 18 (September 15, 1968), 5855–99.

KEEN, M. J., *An Introduction to Marine Geology*. New York: Pergamon Press, 1968. 218p.

LE PICHON, X., "Sea Floor Spreading and Continental Drift," *Jour. Geophys. Res.*: LXXIII, No. 12 (June 15, 1968), 3661–97.

MCELHINNY, M. W., *Paleomagnetism and Plate Tectonics*. Earth Science Series, Cambridge University Press (1973). 345p. First paperback edition (1979).

PHINNEY, R. A., ED., *The History of the Earth's Crust*. Princeton, N.J.: Princeton University Press, 1968. 244p.

TAKEUCHI, H., ET AL., *Debate about the Earth*. San Francisco: Freeman and Cooper and Co., 1967. 253p.

WEGENER, A., *The Origin of Continents and Oceans*. New York: Dover Publications, 1966. 246p.

WILSON, T. J., "Continental Drift," *Scientific American*, CCVIII, No. 4 (April 1963), 86–100.

chemical oceanography

4

4.1 Composition of Seawater

Probably every element that occurs on earth is dissolved in seawater, the dilute solution filling the basins of the world ocean. Although the study of seawater is far from complete, we know that it is composed primarily of a dozen or so elements. The remaining elements are present in only small quantities. Water is certainly the most abundant component; it makes up about 96.5 percent of the weight of seawater.

Chemical Properties of Water

Much of the nature of our planet is determined by the properties of water. Elsewhere in this text the influence of water's unique physical properties is demonstrated. In this section the solvent properties of water are of primary interest. The solubility of substances, especially ionic compounds, those compounds yielding ions upon dissociation in solution (see the Appendix), is usually much higher in water than in other solvents. Water is able to dissolve more substances than most known liquids. The remarkable solvent properties of water arise from the atomic structure assumed by liquid H_2O. Each oxygen atom is associated with two hydrogen atoms in an array as shown in Fig. 4-1A. This is the form of water molecules in the gas state. Water vapor consists of individual H_2O molecules. The two tightly bound hydrogen atoms lie on one side of the center of the H_2O group and produce a net concentration of

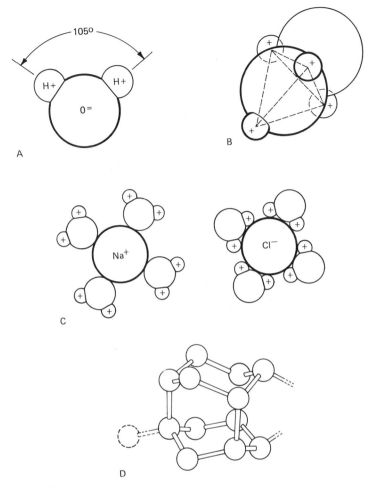

Figure 4-1 Various configurations of the water molecule. (A) The dipole arrangement of the hydrogen atoms in association with the oxygen atom; (B) The interaction of two water molecules showing the tetrahedral array of hydrogen atoms; (C) The hydration of sodium and chloride ions; and (D) The water tetrahedra bonded into hexagonal rings by hydrogen bonds shown as stick-like links. (After R. A. Horne, *Marine Chemistry*, 1969, Courtesy of Wiley Interscience)

positive charge on that side. The side away from the two hydrogen atoms has a net negative charge. The uneven distribution of charge or polarization causes each H_2O group to act as an electric *dipole*.

Because of this dipole configuration water molecules tend to interact strongly with each other as well as with other ions. The interaction between water molecules is such that a tetrahedral array of hydrogen atoms surrounds each oxygen atom (Fig. 4-1B). Two of the hydrogen atoms are bound more loosely to the central oxygen atom but are bonded strongly to an adjacent oxygen atom. This structure is evident in ice where the water molecules are arranged

gas   100°C

liquid   0°C

H_2O

in layers of hexagonal rings (see Fig. 4-1D). The electrical bonding of water molecules causes water to have an especially high latent heat of vaporization— the heat required to separate molecules when converting liquid to gas.

The unusual properties that water exhibits must be explained by the structure of liquid water. Many theories have been postulated to explain the structure and unusual properties of liquid water. The theories attempt to explain the observed properties of water and aqueous solutions; all are successful to a large degree but all have flaws, and our understanding of water is as yet not total. One group of theories holds that liquid water is a mixture of several forms of water such as free molecules, molecules bound in arrangements resembling that in ice or other regular arrangements, and molecules in random arrangements. Another group of theories portrays water as a continuum, in which the arrangement of water molecules changes with temperature and pressure. A major shortcoming of such theories is that they inadequately explain the fluidity of water (water is too fluid) and the difficulty with which water freezes (nuclei for freezing do not appear to exist in liquid water). These shortcomings are overcome in a theory that describes liquid water as a mixture of individual water molecules and clusters of bound water molecules. The clusters exist for 10^{-10} to 10^{-11} seconds before they disaggregate. An individual water molecule spends part of the time as a free molecule bound to other molecules by dipole attraction and by the electrostatic attraction between protons in one molecule and the electrons in another. The rest of the time it is bound in a cluster by rather strong hydrogen bonds. The clusters have an open structure and are less dense than an equal volume of unstructured water molecules. Consequently, an increase in pressure tends to prevent cluster formation, thus increasing the density of water.

The fluidity of water first increases with pressure and then decreases as pressures increase above 300 to 1,000 atmospheres. It appears that initially the destruction of clusters leaves space in which individual water molecules may move more freely; at pressures where clusters can no longer form, an increase in pressure tends to crowd individual water molecules such that they interfere with each other's freedom of movement.

As the temperature increases from 0° to 100°C, a small number of large clusters is replaced by a larger number of smaller clusters; nonetheless, the number of water molecules bound in clusters decreases with a rise in temperature. The existence of a water density maximum at 4°C has been explained as cluster destruction causing increased density from 0° to 4°C. Above 4°C, thermal expansion caused by increased thermal motion of individual water molecules exceeds the decrease caused by cluster destruction. At pressures that exist in the ocean (1 to 1,100 atmospheres), substantial amounts of water molecule clusters persist over the entire liquid range of 0° to 100°C. This is important in considering the effects of dissolved salts in seawater. Ionic compounds dissolve readily in water because water dipoles are attracted to and surround each charged ion with a sheath of oriented water molecules (Fig.

4-1C). This effect, called *hydration,* prevents recombination of dissolved ions and accounts for the large solubility of ionic salts. Nonionic compounds are soluble in water not because they dissociate to form charged ions that can become hydrated, but because the charge distribution in these molecules is irregular and a sheath of water dipoles hydrates and is attracted to sites of high charge.

The electrical charges surrounding chemical species dissolved in water cause the formation of two zones in which the structure of water is altered (Fig. 4-2). Next to the dissolved solute, the water molecules are bound strongly to the extent that they are *electrostricted* by the charge of the solute and are oriented in a configuration in which they are relatively immobile. The water in this zone is considerably more dense and less fluid than ordinary water. Surrounding the electrostricted zone is another zone in which the charge of the solute is insufficient to produce electrostriction or orientation of water molecules but is strong enough to disrupt the formation of clusters of water molecules. The inner zone is one of enhanced water structure and it is thought to exist around all solutes. The outer zone is one of broken structure and increased fluidity. The varied behavior of various solutes in water is thought to be related to their ability to form a broken structure zone.

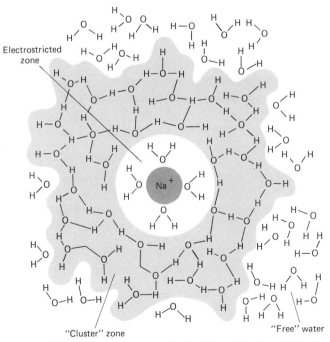

Electrostricted zone

"Cluster" zone

"Free" water

At 1 atmosphere of pressure: density electrostricted water > density clustered water > density free water

Figure 4-2 Two-dimensional representation of the total structure-enhanced hydration atmosphere of the sodium ion. (After R. A. Horne, *Surv. Prog. Chem.,* copyright 1968 by Academic Press, Inc.)

Major Constituents of Seawater

Table 4-1 lists the major constituents dissolved in seawater. They comprise 99.9 percent of the elements dissolved in seawater. These major constituents exist largely as hydrated free ions, but they can exist in other forms. Small amounts of them form *ion pairs* because of electrostatic attraction between highly charged ions even in the presence of water dipoles. The sulfate ion, for example, forms ion pairs with magnesium, calcium, strontium, and other divalent ions; consequently, only 50 percent of it exists as free ions. Some compounds dissociate only slightly. In seawater, undissociated boric acid molecules predominate (90 percent) over borate ions (10 percent). On the other hand, because fluoride and bromide can form *complexes* with metal ions, we can expect that these complexes also exist in seawater. Strontium, however, is chemically much like calcium, so it probably exists largely as hydrated free ions.

dissociation
— breakdown of a
 substance as in

$CaCO_3 \rightarrow CaO + CO_3$

Table 4–1   The Major Constituents of Seawater

Ion	Symbol	% as free ion	% by weight of the total major constituents
Cations			
Sodium	Na^+	99	30.62
Magnesium	Mg^{2+}	87	3.68
Calcium	Ca^{2+}	91	1.18
Potassium	K^+	99	1.10
Strontium	Sr^{2+}	90	0.02
Anions			
Chloride	Cl^-	100	55.07
Sulfate	SO_4^{2-}	50	7.72
Bicarbonate	HCO_3^-	67	0.40
Bromide	Br^-	100*	0.19
Borate	H_2BO_3	10*	0.01
Fluoride	F^-	100*	0.01
			100.00

*Estimated

Trace Elements

The rest of the elements dissolved in seawater are present in concentrations of less than 1 part per million. Table 4-2 lists the trace elements in the order of their abundance in seawater. Some trace elements form free ions and ion pairs, but most of these elements exist as organic complexes and, to a lesser extent, as hydroxide, chloride, and possibly fluoride complexes.

The importance of trace elements in seawater became apparent after early attempts to prepare artificial seawater for marine aquaria failed. Even though the major and nutrient ion concentrations could be adjusted correctly, the trace element impurities in the main ingredients caused an upset in the trace element ion concentrations. This water often would not support life, so it seemed reasonable to assume that some trace element ions are important to the biology of the sea.

Table 4–2   Concentration of Trace Elements in Seawater Exclusive of Nutrients and Dissolved Gases

Element	Symbol	Concentration	Element	Symbol	Concentration
Lithium	Li	170 ppb*	Cerium	Ce	0.005 ppb*
Rubidium	Rb	120	Yttrium	Y	0.3
Iodine	I	60	Silver	Ag	0.04
Barium	Ba	30	Lanthanum	La	0.01
Indium	In	20	Cadmium	Cd	0.1
Zinc	Zn	10	Tungsten	W	0.1
Iron	Fe	10	Germanium	Ge	0.06
Aluminum	Al	10	Chromium	Cr	0.05
Molybdenum	Mo	10	Thorium	Th	0.05
Selenium	Se	0.4	Scandium	Sc	0.04
Tin	Sn	0.8	Lead	Pb	0.03
Copper	Cu	3	Mercury	Hg	0.03
Arsenic	As	3	Gallium	Ga	0.03
Uranium	U	3	Bismuth	Bi	0.02
Nickel	Ni	2	Niobium	Nb	0.01
Vanadium	V	2	Thallium	Tl	<0.01
Manganese	Mn	2	Gold	Au	0.004
Titanium	Ti	1	Protactinium	Pa	2×10^{-6}
Antimony	Sb	0.5	Radium	Ra	1×10^{-7}
Cobalt	Co	0.1	Rare Earths		0.003–0.0005
Cesium	Cs	0.5			

* Parts per billion.
(From E. D. Goldberg, *Chemical Oceanography*, Vol. I. New York: Academic Press Inc., 1963, pp. 164–165.)

Nutrient Elements and Organic Compounds

Nutrient elements exist as nitrate (NO_3^-), phosphate (PO_4^{3-}), and silicate (SiO_3^-) ions. As the name implies, the nutrient ions are the fertilizers of the sea. Although they are present in small quantities, the nutrient ions are important because they are necessary for plant growth. Approximate concentration levels are given in Table 4-3. Their importance will be discussed in Chap. 13, which introduces biological oceanography.

Table 4–3   Average Concentrations of Nutrient Ions Dissolved in Seawater

Dissolved element	Concentration
Nitrogen	500 ppb*
Phosphorus	70
Silicon	3,000
Carbon	Extremely variable 1,000–10,000

*Parts per billion.

Also found in small quantities in seawater are various organic compounds that occur both as dissolved molecules and as *colloids*. These organic substances are carbohydrates, proteins and their decomposition products, lipids (fatty substances), vitamins, auxins (plant hormones), and humic substances formed by complex reactions involving the decomposition products of organisms. Humic substances are complicated compounds that have been isolated from seawater; they are also called "yellow substances." Fatty acids are particularly important because, upon incorporation in bottom sediments, they rapidly form *kerogen*, a relatively unreactive compound that slowly yields the compounds comprising crude petroleum.

4.2   *Sources of Seawater Substances*

Let us now consider how water in the ocean was composed and how its composition is regulated. Broadly speaking, the initial sources of the substances in the ocean must have been the primordial atmosphere, the original rock of the earth, and gases released from the earth's interior (Fig. 4-3). A small amount may have come to the ocean as cosmic dust from extraterrestrial sources.

In all probability, water evolved from vapor released from volcanoes, fumaroles, and hot springs. Water combined with chemicals has been released also during the erosion of primordial rocks. The present rate of discharge of this *juvenile water* from the interior of the earth is about 66×10^{15} g per year. This rate can easily account for all the water on earth—provided that contributions have remained the same throughout geologic time and provided that allowance is made for considerable recycling of water through the ocean, atmosphere, rivers, lakes, and groundwater. If such assumptions are true, the total amount of water in the world ocean has been increasing at a rate of about 0.4×10^{15} g per year throughout its history.

Most of the major cations (positively charged ions) and minor elements were derived from weathered igneous rocks (see Chap. 15, page 398). This fact has

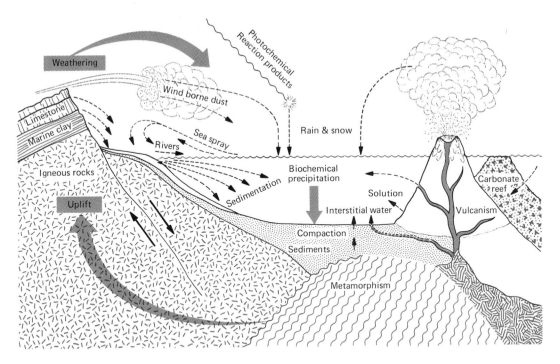

Figure 4-3 Sources of seawater substances and their cycles of transport throughout continents, atmosphere, and ocean.

been deduced by comparing the average compositions of igneous rocks, seawater, and sediments. However, to account for the chloride, sulfate, and bromide anions (negatively charged ions) in seawater, another source is required. These substances are present in volcanic discharges, so it is likely that the major anions in seawater have been added from past emissions of volcanoes.

The most abundant anions in the world ocean—chloride, sulfate, and bicarbonate—are quite soluble in water but are not saturated in seawater. Consequently their proportions in the ocean should reflect the proportions in which they are released from the earth. They are released from the earth in the proportions in which they exist in the earth's interior, which in turn represents the proportions in which they were formed from the solar system event that formed the earth.

Today, the total amount of dissolved material observed in the ocean is about 5×10^{22} g. Rivers carry about 2.5×10^{15} g to the sea annually. If we assume that dissolved substances began accumulating in the ocean about 3 billion years ago and that the rate of transport by rivers rose steadily to the present value, somehow a large excess of dissolved materials has been removed from the sea. Obviously, therefore, the sea does not trap all the ions brought to it by rivers and by other sources. Instead, there must be regulatory processes that maintain the concentrations of dissolved materials at the levels observed today. Other lines of evidence (noted in a later section) indicate that the composition of seawater has not changed much during the last 1.5 billion years. We can infer that the regulatory processes have been active at least that long.

4.3 *Processes Regulating the Composition of Seawater*

Several processes regulate the chemical composition of the world ocean. They are of four general types:

1. Physical regulatory processes, such as temperature effects, evaporation, and freezing
2. Biological regulatory processes
3. Chemical regulatory processes, such as solubility, adsorption of ions on solid surfaces, and involvement of ions in reactions between minerals and seawater
4. Geological and climatological processes.

The concentration of each chemical component dissolved in seawater is regulated by at least one, and often by several, of the above processes. When we compare the solubilities of all the elements dissolved in the ocean to the concentrations that exist, we find that just a few are present in saturation amounts. Of the major cations in the ocean, only calcium is near saturation; saturation is maintained by the dissolution or precipitation of solid calcium carbonate. Nitrogen and the inert, or noble, gases are near saturation; their concentrations are strongly regulated by temperature.

The amount of major anions in the sea is regulated by the formation of salt (NaCl) and gypsum ($CaSO_4$) deposits in hot shallow embayments in arid regions or by the semipermanent removal of water to the continents during glaciation. The regulation of the major anions is mostly geological and climatological in nature; earth movements produce shallow embayments that desiccate and evaporate seawater, and changes in climate over geologic time regulate the amount of the ocean's water trapped on the continents as ice.

Adsorption, an important chemical process in the ocean, occurs when ions or molecules become attached to atoms at the surface of solids by weak electrostatic bonds. The strength of the attachment varies according to the composition of the solid and to the size and charge of the atoms involved. Small multicharged ions are adsorbed more strongly than are larger ions or ions having fewer charges. Ions absorb more strongly than do molecules, particularly those that have a uniform distribution of positive and negative charges (nonpolarized molecules). As a consequence, ions and molecules exhibit an order of preference of adsorption on a surface, and strongly adsorbable ions or molecules can displace more weakly adsorbable ones from a surface. The process is called *ion exchange*.

The concentrations of sodium, potassium, magnesium, rubidium, cesium, and, to some extent, calcium are controlled by *cation exchange* on clay minerals brought to the oceans by rivers. In river water and in the ocean, the order of preference of adsorption on clays is magnesium, potassium, and then sodium. The removal of these elements from seawater solution should be in that order, and the concentrations of these elements in the ocean should increase in the reverse order. However, potassium is most readily extracted from seawater by clay minerals because clay minerals (especially illite) incorporate potassium in their crystal structures. Consequently, the potassium ion is less concentrated in seawater than magnesium.

Magnesium concentrations in the interstitial water of marine sediments diminish with depth below the sediment–water interface more quickly than do the concentrations of potassium. Apparently, magnesium and, to a lesser extent, potassium are removed by adsorption on clays even after their burial in sediments.

The minor elements manganese, nickel, cobalt, zinc, and copper are greatly undersaturated because they are adsorbed on ferromanganese minerals in nodules on the ocean floor. In addition, apatite (the calcium phosphate mineral in fish-bone debris) adsorbs thorium, barium, strontium, and the rare earth elements, because, like the ferromanganese minerals, it presents active surfaces for adsorption. By these processes, trace elements are removed from seawater and concentrated in sediments and in nodules on the sea floor.

A subsidiary regulatory process is *anion exchange*. Little is known about anion exchange reactions in the ocean except that clay minerals can adsorb anions. Perhaps anion exchange accounts for the relative enrichment of bromine in sediments and to an extent is responsible for the uptake of phosphate in marine sediments.

Adsorption reactions are important in maintaining *electroneutrality* in seawater. The principle of electroneutrality applied to the world ocean means that the total of positive charges on dissolved cations must balance the total negative charges on the dissolved anions. Rivers introduce a surplus of positive charges to the sea in the form of the major cations Na^+, K^+, Ca^{2+}, and Mg^{2+} produced by weathering of rocks on the continents. Adsorption removes the surplus from solution and maintains electroneutrality.

Chemical processes other than adsorption regulate the concentrations of the major ions in the ocean. For example, sodium and magnesium ions are incorporated in the minerals formed by the hydrothermal alteration of basalt rocks exposed at the sea floor. The removal of these ions disturbs electroneutrality and this imbalance is countered by adsorption reactions. Other reac-

Table 4–4   Chemical Elements in Life Processes

Necessary elements
H, B, C, N, O, F, Na, Mg, Si, P, S, Cl, K, Ca, V, Mn, Fe, Co, Ni, Cu, Zn, Br, I
Probably necessary elements
Al, Ti, As, Sn, Pb

(After R. A. Horne, *Marine Chemistry,* New York: Wiley Interscience, 1969, p. 244.)

tions, such as precipitation, form crystalline minerals. Even though the formation of these crystals changes the concentration of major ions in seawater, electroneutrality persists because the crystals are electrically neutral.

Biological activity regulates the concentration of those elements involved in life processes. These are shown in Table 4-4. The elements regulated most by biological activity are oxygen, carbon dioxide, phosphate, nitrate, nitrite, ammonia, silicate, and calcium. Possibly vitamins and trace metals dissolved in seawater are regulated more than it seems inasmuch as these substances are all involved in the metabolism of organisms. Calcium is used by organisms to form carbonate shells; its concentration in the sea is regulated by the influence of biological activity on the carbonate equilibrium of the sea (to be discussed presently).

The molecular ratios of several of the biologically important elements in water of the deep ocean are the following:

P	N	C	Ca	Si
1	16	800	3,200	66

That is, for every molecule of phosphate there are 16 molecules of nitrate, and so on. When deep water wells up into the photic zone, plants extract materials to form their tissue and shells. They require the materials in the ratios:

P	N	C	Ca	Si	
1	16	106	0	0	for tissue
0	0	53	53	66	for shells

When plants are grazed by animals, the elemental uptake is in the same proportions. Plants will extract all the available nitrate and phsophate and proportional amounts of the other elements, leaving the surface water with the ratios:

P	N	C	Ca	Si
0	0	641	3,147	0

Eventually, the plant and animal materials fall to the sea floor as particles of dead tissue, shells, or excrement. Most of this material is attacked by bacteria and becomes redissolved in deep water. A small fraction becomes incorporated in bottom sediments where bacterial action continues, eventually consuming

Table 4–5   Enrichment of Chemical Elements by Marine Organisms

Element	Enrichment factor relative to seawater	Type of organism
Biochemical elements		
C	15,800	Fish
N	1,276,000	Fish
P	2,560,000	Fish
Ca	69	Sea slug
Si	110,000	Diatom
Major ions in seawater		
Sr	82	Sea slug
F	6,900	Sea slug
Cl	1.1	Copepod
Na	1.0	Copepod
K	105	Fish
S	31	Fish
Mg	12.9	Sea slug
Trace elements		
Fe	291,500	Scallop
V	280,000	Ascidian
Zn	110,300	Oyster
Sn	2,700	Snail
Pb	5,300	Scallop
Cd	2,260,000	Scallop
Mo	6,000	Anemone
Co	21,000	Jellyfish
Ag	22,000	Fish
Cu	13,700	Oyster
Mn	55,500	Scallop
Cr	320,000	Mussel

(After R. A. Horne, *Marine Chemistry*. New York: Wiley-Interscience, 1969, pp. 283–286.)

all the oxygen available (Table 4-5). Bacterial action is continued by sulfate-reducing bacteria that regulate the amount of sulfate and sulfide in the sediments and in other oxygen-deficient parts of the ocean. Because they break down organic debris, bacteria are instrumental in regulating the amount and composition of substances involved in biochemical processes in the ocean.

The organic particles formed from excreta and from the disintegration of oceanic organisms present adsorption surfaces that allow them to exert a regulating influence on the concentrations of trace elements and other cations. Proteinaceous decay products, for example, associate with zinc, tin, lead, titanium, copper, silver, magnesium, aluminum, chromium, and nickel. Some organisms have the ability to concentrate trace elements by factors as high as 1 million, so significant amounts of these elements may exist in live organisms as well. Table 4-5 presents a list of enrichment factors for the biochemical elements, for some major ions in seawater, and for trace elements.

Physical processes in the ocean tend to regulate the amount of water in seawater rather than the amount of dissolved substances. The formation and melting of ice, evaporation, and precipitation of rain or snow change the absolute concentrations of dissolved substances by dilution or removal of water, but the amounts of dissolved materials remain in the same proportions. Mixing of water from the surface layer of the ocean with deeper water can influence the vertical distribution of elements involved in biochemical processes. The lateral distribution of biochemical elements is regulated by horizontal water movement, such as the major circulation in oceanic gyres and the mixing motion of water masses.

The net behavior of all processes controlling the concentration of an element dissolved in the ocean can be summarized by comparing the element's concentration to the rate at which it is added or removed from the ocean. The quotient of these is the *residence time* of the element in the ocean. Elements with short residence times (Al, Ti, Fe, Cr) are reactive and form insoluble solids before reaching the ocean or soon after arriving in the ocean. In the latter case, they form ferromanganese nodules and minerals, such as zeolite and glauconite. Elements with long residence times (Na, K, Ca, Mg) are characterized by high solubility. Divalent cations have shorter residence times than their monovalent counterparts because they are adsorbed more easily by clay minerals.

Chemical History of the Ocean

As conditions on the earth changed during the course of geologic time, there must have been corresponding changes in the chemical composition of the ocean. These chemical adjustments would have stemmed from the regulatory processes that we have just discussed. Much indirect evidence has been obtained by studying ancient sedimentary rock strata on the continents. These continental rocks have weathered under the attack of water containing dissolved atmospheric gases. As a result, most of the major cations have found their way to the ocean. Calcium reached saturation quite early, judging from ancient calcium carbonate and calcium sulfate deposits existing on land today. Potassium accumulated in appreciable quantities as early as 1.2 billion years ago because sediments of that age contain glauconite, a potassium-rich claylike mineral. An abundance of magnesium caused the formation of strata of dolomite, a calcium magnesium carbonate mineral. The earliest water-laid sediments appear to be about 3 billion years old.

The first form of life must have been anaerobic, but eventually an organism capable of *photosynthesis* evolved. Photosynthesizing organisms produced an excess of oxygen that gradually escaped to the atmosphere. The amount of carbon dioxide in the atmosphere and dissolved in the sea decreased by being incorporated into organic matter. The hydrogen ion concentration (acidity) of seawater was established and held constant by the *buffering* action of the dissolved silica–clay mineral system and the dissolved carbon dioxide–solid carbonate system (see Sec. 4.5). As oxygen accumulated, the ocean and terrestrial portions of the earth changed from the primordial reducing condition to an oxidizing one. Only in locations removed from contact with air or oxygenated water do reducing conditions persist today. One such location is in the sediments on the ocean floor. Not only are the bulk of bottom sediments isolated from contact with oxygenated seawater, but organic matter incorporated in these sediments decomposes and consumes whatever oxygen may have become trapped in interstitial water when the sediment settled to the bottom. The oxidizing state at the interface of sediment and water has led to the formation of ferromanganese precipitates. These and organic detritus must have begun adsorbing trace metals soon after an excess of oxygen accumulated in the ocean and atmosphere.

Considerable geological evidence leads us to conclude that the volume of seawater in the ocean has been increasing throughout the earth's history. The chemical composition of the world ocean, however, became very nearly what it is at present shortly after the advent of photosynthesizing organisms—that is, about 1.5 billion years ago. There have been small-scale changes associated with the evolution of carbonate-secreting organisms and with temperature fluctuations in the Tertiary and Quaternary periods. Increases in the temperature, for instance, would have caused a decreased solubility of gases and a concomitant decrease in biological activity. Under such conditions, nutrient concentrations would have increased and carbonates would have precipitated. Nevertheless, except for the possible appearance of some new substance capable of ion exchange or chemisorption, the effects on regulatory processes in the world ocean today are limited to changes in the rates of inorganic and biochemical reactions.

4.4 *Quantity of Material Dissolved in the World Ocean*

If we assume that the amount of dissolved material in the ocean remains unchanged even today, we must also assume that the amount of dissolved material entering the sea each year is equivalent to the amount lost in sediment. Actually, the assumption cannot be validated, because scientists have measured the composition of the oceans for only a few decades. If no ions were removed from the sea, the ions added by rivers in 100 years would increase the concentrations of substances dissolved in the world ocean by only 0.0005 percent. Rivers transport approximately 2.5×10^{15} g of dissolved material to the world ocean every year. This amount is minor compared to the amount of dissolved material (5×10^{22} g) already present in the world ocean (this is 20,000,000 times the amount added every year). In any case, the rate of change is so small that the assumption of a steady state is reasonable.

Every kilogram of seawater in the open ocean contains about 35 g of ions. In oceanography, this concentration is expressed as parts per thousand and can be written 35 ‰. The measure of the concentration of total ions in seawater is called the salinity. A *salinity* of 35 parts per thousand is an average value for water in the open ocean; ocean salinities range from about 33 to 37 parts per thousand.

In nearshore coastal regions, bays, and especially in river estuaries, salinity is highly variable. Near river mouths the salinity of surface water may vary from nearly zero to 34 parts per thousand, but low values generally prevail. These variations are also seasonal and depend on river conditions. During summer months when rivers carry less water, nearshore salinities may be close to 34 parts per thousand. During the winter rainy season or spring thaw, the seawater in the nearshore region frequently becomes diluted by floodwater.

Exactly the opposite conditions prevail in hot, dry regions of the world where excess evaporation causes salinities to be higher than average. Salinity values as high as 40 parts per thousand may be found in places like the Mediterranean and Red seas.

The Rule of Constant Proportions

Despite the range in salinity in seawater, the relative proportions of the major ions in the open ocean vary by only negligible amounts. This observation was reported as early as 1819. In 1865, Forchammer noted that the proportions held true in hundreds of samples of surface waters. Later, Dittmar analyzed 77 samples of water collected from various depths in most of the oceans during the Challenger Expedition (1872–1876). His findings verified the theory that has come to be called the *rule of constant proportions:*

> *Regardless of how the salinity may vary from place to place, the ratios between the amount of the major ions in the water of the open ocean are constant.*

This rule applies not only to lateral variations within the open ocean, but also to variations with depth.

The rule of constant proportions illustrates two important points. First, the basins of the world ocean are interconnected, and water is exchanged between one basin and another. Thus, the sea is mixed well enough to eliminate differences in composition caused by substances brought to the sea by rivers. Apparently, this happens within the thousand or so years that it takes to mix the ocean completely. Second, the rule illustrates that the salinity of the water in the open ocean changes by adding or subtracting water, not dissolved substances. If ions were added or removed, we would expect their relative proportions to change. The only processes that can maintain constant proportions of ions are evaporation, precipitation, and freezing or thawing of seawater in the open ocean. It is true that along the coastlines ions are added in abundance, and so it is also true that the rule of constant proportions does not hold in these regions.

Nor does this rule hold for the nutrient ions or trace elements. Because nutrients are utilized by plants, nutrient concentration varies tremendously according to the seasonal life activity of the plants. This activity uses nutrient ions near the surface where the plants grow. When organisms die, they sink, decompose, and release nutrients to deeper water. Similarly, the concentrations of trace elements do not follow the rule of constant proportions because their distribution is governed largely by organic activity.

Nevertheless, the rule of constant proportions makes it possible to calculate the salinity of seawater without resorting to determining concentrations of each of the major ions in seawater, which is a time-consuming and tedious task. If one of the major ions is determined, the concentrations of the other seven can be calculated by use of the rule of constant proportions. Scientists usually determine the chloride ion concentration, because it is the easiest to measure chemically.

The usual chemical method of determining the chloride ion concentration also measures the concentration of bromide, iodide, and several trace anions, so a property called the *chlorinity* is used in lieu of the chloride ion concentration. Chlorinity is defined by the amount of silver required to remove all halogens from 0.3285 kg of a seawater sample.

The salinity or total weight of solids dissolved in seawater can be calculated once the chlorinity is determined.* The salinity of seawater equals the concentration of major ions, trace-element ions, and nutrient ions. The concentration of major ions in a seawater sample is defined as the chlorinity divided by 0.55, or about 1.8 times the chlorinity. Hence S ‰ = 1.8 Cl ‰. This relationship holds fairly true over the entire open ocean.

4.5 *Dissolved Gases in the Ocean*

The most abundant gases in the ocean are oxygen (O_2), nitrogen (N_2), and carbon dioxide (CO_2). These gases are dissolved in seawater and are not in chemical combination with any of the materials composing seawater. Likewise, hydrogen and oxygen combined chemically as water molecules are not to be considered gases dissolved in seawater. The distinction between combined

---

*In this case, the assumption is made that bromide is replaced by an equivalent amount of chloride, that carbonate is converted to an oxide, and that all organic matter is destroyed.

gas and dissolved gas can be made biologically; that is, fish use dissolved oxygen to breathe but cannot utilize oxygen from water molecules.

Gases are dissolved from the atmosphere by exchange across the sea surface. Air of the atmosphere is composed of a mixture of 78 percent nitrogen, 21 percent oxygen, 0.9 percent argon, 0.03 percent carbon dioxide, water vapor in variable quantities, and small amounts of the noble gases (neon, krypton, helium, radon, argon, and xenon). The gases dissolved at the sea surface are distributed throughout the world ocean by mixing, or *advection*, and diffusion. Concentrations are modified further by biological activity, particularly by plants and certain bacteria.

In nature, gases dissolve in water until saturation is reached, given sufficient time and mixing. The volume of gas that saturates a given volume of seawater is different for each gas and depends upon temperature, pressure, and salinity. An increase in pressure, or a decrease in salinity, or a decrease in temperature causes an increase in gas solubility.

There are small additions of dissolved gases from sources other than the atmosphere. Some nitrogen, for instance, is formed near the bottom of the ocean by bacterial action on dissolved nitrate ions. Certain argon isotopes are a product of the radioactive decay of potassium; radon and helium are products of the radioactive decay of uranium and related elements.

Oxygen

Perhaps the most important dissolved gas in seawater is oxygen. Animals require oxygen for respiration. Plants release oxygen as a byproduct of photosynthesis and use it during respiration. The decomposition of organic material in the ocean is dependent upon oxygen concentration. Consequently, the amount of oxygen dissolved in seawater depends not only on mixing but also upon the type and degree of biological activity.

The amount of oxygen dissolved in the sea varies from zero to a maximum of about 9 milliliters per liter of seawater. At the surface of the sea the water is nearly saturated with oxygen because of exchange across the surface and plant activity. In fact, when photosynthesis is at a maximum, it can cause *supersaturation* of seawater. Values of oxygen concentration in the sea often are expressed as percentages of saturation to reflect how nearly the theoretical saturation value has been attained. Oxygen in water found at depth is expressed at *apparent oxygen utilization* (AOU). These values indicate the difference between the observed concentration and the theoretical saturation concentration; they also reflect the amount of change in oxygen content since the water sample had last been at the sea surface.

The vertical distribution of dissolved oxygen is illustrated in Fig. 4-4. At the sea surface, the oxygen content is maintained by mixing surface water with air bubbles and by photosynthetic production. Mixing is effective to a depth of several tens of meters. Below this depth, however, animal respiration and

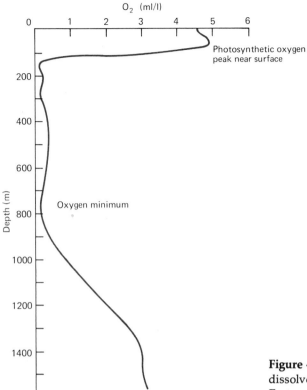

O_2 (ml/l)

Photosynthetic oxygen peak near surface

Oxygen minimum

Depth (m)

Figure 4-4 Typical profile of dissolved oxygen in the sea. (From Eastern Tropical Pacific Ocean)

organic decomposition remove oxygen. Dissolved oxygen decreases with depth to a minimum value between 700 and 1,000 m. Then oxygen values increase slightly with depth, because bottom water, having been at the surface more recently than water at intermediate depth, still contains appreciable dissolved oxygen. The oxygen-minimum zone is usually absent in areas of major convergences where surface water is introduced into intermediate depths. (See the chart of ocean currents in Fig. 7-1.)

In places where vertical mixing is restricted by unique hydrographic and geographic conditions, animal respiration and especially organic decomposition remove all the dissolved oxygen from the bottom water. When these conditions occur, organisms called sulphate-reducing bacteria thrive. These bacteria convert sulphate ions (SO_4^{2-}) to hydrogen sulphide (H_2S), a foul-smelling and poisonous gas.* An example of this situation occurs in the Black Sea and is illustrated in Fig. 4-5. The Black Sea is characterized by a restricted entrance to the ocean, a very large freshwater inflow, and little vertical mixing. Because the deep water cannot be replenished, dissolved oxygen is depleted, hydrogen sulphide is present, and no life except sulphate-reducing bacteria exists below a depth of about 200 m.

---

*Toxic limit for humans is 0.07 percent for 2 minutes.

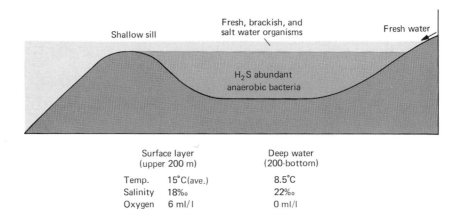

Figure 4-5 Schematic representation of the Black Sea. This is a famous example of a stagnant basin with a shallow layer of oxygenated surface water overlying a great volume of oxygen deficient water.

Oxygen Isotopes

The *stable isotope* of oxygen, O-18, has a larger mass and is more sluggish in its movement than the more common isotope O-16. Therefore, it is *fractionated* during biochemical reactions, so organic matter has a O-18/O-16 ratio that is lower than that in seawater. At elevated temperatures, the heavier isotope is less sluggish, so O-18/O-16 ratios tend to increase with temperature. This effect has been used to ascertain the former temperature of the sea by examining the O-18/O-16 ratio in the remains of ancient marine organisms. Heavy isotopes of other elements in seawater behave similarly, but most of them are not studied because they are either less abundant or do not enter into biochemical reactions.

Nitrogen

Nitrogen is a relatively inert (nonreactive) gas that dissolves in the ocean in concentrations of between 8 and 15 ml per liter. These are the concentrations expected in seawater saturated with nitrogen from the atmosphere. The distribution of dissolved nitrogen in the ocean is governed by its solubility (and hence, temperature), by salinity, and by the mixing of currents. The elaborate cycle of nitrogen through the sea and its organisms is shown in Fig. 4-6. Certain algae living in tropical and subtropical water are capable of incorporating (*fixing*) dissolved atmospheric nitrogen as protoplasm. Where oxygen is present in extremely low concentrations (below 0.15 ml per liter), bacteria convert nitrate ions to molecular nitrogen in a process called *denitrification* (see Chap. 14). Fixation and denitrification probably do not change the quantity of nitrogen dissolved in the nitrogen-saturated ocean. However,

ATMOSPHERE

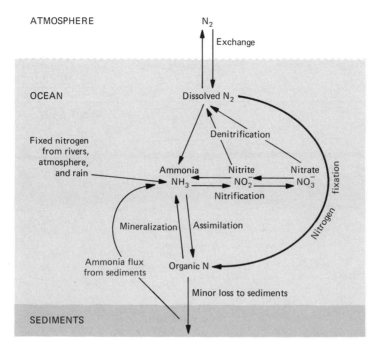

Figure 4-6 The nitrogen cycle in the sea.

denitrification in the ocean must be appreciable. If the amount of fixed nitrogen (nitrate ions and organic debris) lost to sediments were not somehow returned to the atmosphere (presumably via denitrification), molecular nitrogen would have been removed from the atmosphere about 4×10^8 years after the start of life in the ocean.

Denitrification generates nitrous oxide (N_2O), a gas also produced by the combustion of fossil fuels and by biological processes in terrestrial soil. Although this gas is a minor constituent of seawater, it is important in the atmosphere where it is destroyed in a process controlling the ozone layer in the stratosphere.

Carbon Dioxide

Dissolved carbon dioxide is exceedingly important in biological processes in the ocean. Plants and animals release carbon dioxide during respiration, and plants use it in photosynthesis. In seawater, a sensitive equilibrium exists between dissolved carbon dioxide, hydrogen ions, carbonate ions, bicarbonate ions, and solid calcium carbonate in bottom sediments. Biological activity causes no significant change in the amount of carbon dioxide dissolved in seawater. If an excess is produced, calcium carbonate dissolves; if a deficiency exists, calcium carbonate will precipitate. These reactions—called the carbonate buffer system—cause the concentration of dissolved carbon dioxide to remain almost constant between 45 and 54 ml per liter.

The chemical species of carbon in the world ocean are involved in an

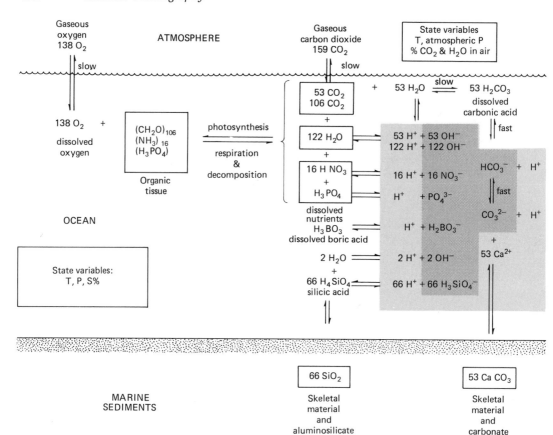

Figure 4-7 Diagrammatic representation of reactions involved in the carbon dioxide, carbonate, and organic carbon species equilibrium. The dark gray area indicates the pool of potentially acid-forming anions influenced by carbonate equilibria. The light gray area represents the pool of potential base-forming cations. Ions important in contributing to sea water alkalinity are underlined. Numerical values in equations are based upon molecular ratios in organisms and the production of 1/2 unit of $CaCO_3$ and 5/4 units of SiO_2 for every unit of organic tissue.

elaborate equilibrium that is influenced by physical, chemical, and biological processes. This equilibrium is shown diagrammatically in Fig. 4-7. Note that this complex equilibrium can be shifted by an exchange of CO_2 across the sea surface, by phytoplankton photosynthesis, and by changes in the values of the state variables (temperature, salinity, and pressure), all of which affect the solubility of CO_2 in seawater. Let us examine the effects of adjustments in the carbonate equilibria in order to gain an understanding of the important role that carbon dioxide plays in the world ocean.

The exchange of CO_2 across the sea surface is controlled by the following:

1. The partial pressure of CO_2 gas in the atmosphere. This depends upon:
   a. The air temperature
   b. The total (barometric) pressure of the atmosphere which varies with the water vapor content and temperature of the atmosphere.
   c. The proportion of CO_2 gas in the atmosphere. This is affected by photosynthesis of plants, exhalations during volcanism, weathering, and the burning of fossil fuels.
2. The solubility of CO_2 gas in seawater as governed by:
   a. Seawater temperature
   b. Salinity of seawater
   c. Hydrostatic pressure (affects solubility at depth).
3. Concentration of CO_2 dissolved in seawater.

The dissolved CO_2 concentration is controlled by two major reactions in the sea (Fig. 4-7):

1. CO_2 reacts with water to form carbonic acid. Carbonic acid concentrations in seawater are quite small because the acid dissociates rapidly to form bicarbonate ions and hydrogen ions.
2. CO_2 is consumed by plants during photosynthesis and is produced during plant respiration and the decomposition of organic debris. Actually, plants use either dissolved CO_2 or the bicarbonate ion in photosynthesis. Carbonate ion is not used and, in fact, is toxic to plants at high concentrations.

The relative amounts of carbonate ions and bicarbonate ions at equilibrium represent an adjustment to maintain electroneutrality in seawater. The amount by which positive charge on base-forming cations in seawater exceeds negative charge on acid-forming ions is compensated by the excess double negative charge on the carbonate ion relative to the single negative charge on the bicarbonate ion. Let us elaborate this important effect. Each cation in seawater is capable of uniting with OH ions to form a base according to the reaction

$$\text{Cation}^{n+} + n(\text{OH}^-) = \text{Cation (OH)}_n, \text{ a base}$$

where n is the number of positive charges on the cation. The total positive charge in seawater is contributed mainly by the major cations and is equal to the sum of the concentrations of each of the cations multiplied by their corresponding positive charge.

Anions in seawater are capable of forming acids according to the reaction

$$m \, \text{H}^+ + \text{Anion}^{m-} = \text{H}_m \text{ Anion, an acid}$$

Table 4-6   Inventory of Ionic Charges in the Ocean and Their Importance in Controlling the Alkalinity of Seawater
(Cl = 19‰, T = 20°C, pH = 8.3, S‰ = 34.295)

	Concentration		Total Charge
Ion	*mg at l**	*No. of charges/ion*	*(milliequivalents l)*
Major cations, potential base formers			
Na^+	470.15	1	470.15
Mg^{2+}	53.57	2	107.14
Ca^{2+}	10.24	2	20.48
K^+	9.96	1	9.96
Sr^{2+}	0.15	2	0.30
H^+	0.5×10^{-5}	1	0.5×10^{-5}
Total equivalent base			608.03
Major anions, potential acid formers			
Cl^-	548.30	1	548.30
SO_4^{2-}	28.24	2	56.48
HCO_3^-	1.61	1	1.61
Br^-	0.83	1	0.83
$H_2BO_3^-$	0.11	1	0.11
F^-	0.07	1	0.07
CO_3^{2-}	0.31	2	0.62
OH^-	0.002	1	0.002
All other minor anions, e.g., NO_3^-, PO_4^{3-}, $H_2AsO_3^-$ and organic acids			0.008 (estimated)
Total equivalent acid			608.03

The ions NH_3^+, S^{2-}, and HS^- may be important in anoxic water.

*mg at/l = milligram atoms per liter.

The total negative charge in seawater is found in a manner similar to that for positive charge. The total of positive charges would not equal the total of the negative charges in the ocean were it not for bicarbonate, carbonate, and borate ions which are able to change their relative concentrations to balance the net positive charge in the ocean. The net positive charge indicates that not all the bases represented by the major cations would be neutralized by the acid represented by the major anions, i.e., seawater has a net base-forming capability. The base-forming capability is termed *alkalinity*. The excess positive charge represented by the alkalinity is balanced by negative charge obtained by forming CO_3^{2-} at the expense of HCO_3^- and to a lesser extent by the dissociation of boric acid and of water.

The relative importance of each negatively charged ion contributing to the alkalinity and its typical concentrations are listed in Table 4-6. The table shows that the bicarbonate ion is the most important, and that borate and especially the hydroxide–hydrogen difference are virtually negligible. The table also

Table 4–7   Measurement of the State of the Carbonate Equilibrium in the Ocean

Parameters	Description
Total alkalinity	Measured by titrating seawater with strong acid
Alkalinity	Alkalinity caused by only carbonate and bicarbonate ions
pH	Hydrogen ion concentration (activity) $= 10^{-pH}$
$[CO_2]$	Dissolved carbon dioxide concentration
$[CO_3^{2-}]$	Carbonate ion concentration
$[HCO_3^-]$	Bicarbonate ion concentration
pCO_2	Partial pressure of CO_2 in inert gas at equilibrium with seawater containing dissolved CO_2
Constants	
α_s	Solubility of CO_2 gas in seawater: $[CO_2] = \alpha_s\, pCO_2$
α_0	Solubility of CO_2 gas in pure water
K_1', K_2'	First and second dissociation constants of carbonic acid
K'_B	Dissociation constant of boric acid
a_{H_2O}	Activity of water in seawater
State variables	
$T°$	Temperature of seawater
$Cl‰$	Chlorinity of seawater

shows that the major anions neutralize all except 0.33 percent of the charge of the major anions.

Just as each of the major ions in seawater is in a fixed ratio to the chloride in concentration (called the *chlorinity ratio* of the major ions of seawater), the total concentrations of the species contributing to seawater alkalinity are in a virtually fixed ratio to chlorinity:

$$\frac{\text{Alkalinity}}{\text{Chlorinity}} = 123 \times 10^{-6}$$

The state of the equilibria of inorganic carbon species dissolved in the ocean is determined by measuring three quantities as shown in Table 4-7. The hydrogen ion concentration in seawater is measured routinely. It is an indicator of the state of the carbonate equilibrium. It is expressed as pH which is defined by

$$[H^+] = \frac{1}{10^{pH}}$$

It measures the amount of H^+ ion in seawater upon the establishment of the equilibrium between all species that consume or liberate H^+ in adjusting the change in seawater to electroneutrality. The pH of seawater ranges from 7.4 to 8.5; the usual value of pH is 8.1.

The concentrations of dissolved CO_2, HCO_3^-, and CO_3^{2-} are determined by water temperature, pressure, alkalinity, and pH. The ratio of concentrations of bicarbonate ion to carbonate ion in seawater is found to be

$$\frac{[HCO_3^-]}{[CO_3^{2-}]} = \frac{1}{K\ 10^{pH}}$$

where K is a constant that depends upon temperature and salinity. The equilibrium of these species is also affected by the precipitation of $CaCO_3$ because the Ca^{2+} ion, a base former, is removed from solution. Likewise, where carbonate-secreting organisms flourish, the extraction of Ca^{2+} ion affects the alkalinity of seawater: the concentrations of HCO_3^-, CO_3^{2-}, and CO_2 shift and the pH adjusts to reflect the change. In anoxic water, conversion of SO_4^{2-} to HS^- changes the charge balance of seawater locally. The alkalinity and the carbonate equilibrium shifts and the pH adjusts accordingly. The production of NH_3^+ ion in anoxic waters has a similar effect. We can see that if Ca^{2+} ion is removed from solution by precipitation of $CaCO_3$, or if the hydrogen ion concentration (pH) is changed, the balance of ionic charge is disrupted and the proportions of carbonate, bicarbonate, borate, and hydroxide must change to maintain electroneutrality. Measurement of any three parameters permits the determination of all others, provided $T°$ and $Cl‰$ are known. The constants are all dependent upon $T°$ and $Cl‰$ except a_{H_2O} which is a function of $Cl‰$ only.

In summary, we see that CO_2 added to seawater behaves chemically like an acid; it causes solid $CaCO_3$ to dissolve. Conversely, when CO_2 is expelled from seawater, a chemical precipitate of $CaCO_3$ forms. Biological productivity extracts CO_2 from solution and precipitates $CaCO_3$ as shell material. Upon decomposition of the organic material, CO_2 is released into solution and $CaCO_3$ tends to dissolve. The effect of pressure at depth causes $CaCO_3$ to dissolve. This subject will be discussed further in the chapter on marine sediments.

Atmospheric carbon dioxide dissolves in ocean water according to its solubility as determined by temperature and salinity. Since the ocean contains vast amounts of dissolved CO_2, carbonate ion, protoplasm, and solid carbonate, it tends to regulate the amount of carbon dioxide in the atmosphere. In turn, carbon dioxide helps to regulate the temperature of the ocean, because carbon dioxide in the atmosphere passes solar radiation energy but absorbs much of the thermal (infrared) energy emitted by the earth. Much of the heat trapped by atmospheric carbon dioxide becomes stored in the world ocean. Over time an equilibrium involving carbon dioxide in the ocean and atmosphere and the mean temperature has been established. The equilibrium also regulates the amount of water vapor in the atmosphere, and hence evaporation and precipitation. It appears that this equilibrium has been upset in the past, and the resulting temperature shift has been linked with the glaciation in the Pleistocene epoch.

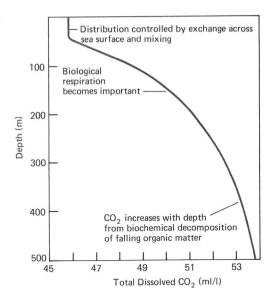

Figure 4-8 Generalized profile of the distribution of dissolved CO_2 in the sea off southern California.

Like any other dissolved substance, carbon dioxide is distributed in the ocean by advection and diffusion. However, its distribution is also affected by its exchange across the ocean surface and bottom and by its involvement in biochemical reactions (Fig. 4-8).

Noble Gases

Noble gases are those gases that are inactive, especially toward oxygen. The noble gases helium, neon, argon, krypton, xenon, and radon dissolve in seawater from the atmosphere just as do the major atmospheric gases; once dissolved, however, they become mixed away from the sea surface. They are distributed only by diffusion and advection, because—being relatively inert—they do not enter into biochemical reactions. Their concentrations in seawater reflect the temperature and salinity possessed by that water when they were dissolved at the sea surface.

4.6 Analytical Techniques of Chemical Oceanography

In order for a chemical determination to be useful to a chemical oceanographer, it must fulfill several requirements. First, it must measure accurately the concentration of a particular substance even though it is present in minute quantities. Secondly, the mechanics of the determination must be rugged enough to go to sea. All of the equipment must be able to function in a salt–air environment on board a ship that is rolling and pitching under severe weather conditions. Finally, the determination should be rapid. The chemist should be able to keep up with the samples as they are being taken.

Seawater is analyzed for trace-element ions with specialized microchemical techniques adapted from biochemistry and clinical chemistry. Many of these determinations cannot be adopted as standard procedure, because they cannot meet the last two requirements just listed. Automated and rapid chemical analyzers, however, have been developed for use at sea.

The concentrations of nutrient ions in seawater are determined by standard chemical techniques for use at sea. These determinations are made at the time the samples are recovered, or the water is frozen for shipment to a laboratory ashore.

The concentrations of the major elements in seawater are usually calculated from the measured concentrations of the halide ions (chlorinity) by invoking the rule of constant proportions. This rule permits one to derive fixed ratios between each major ion and the chlorinity of seawater. The classic method of measuring the halide ion concentration is by titration with a silver salt. In practice a measured volume of seawater is titrated, and the chlorinity is calculated by referring to tables that convert the weight of silver ions to chlorinity values.

The chemical method of determining chlorinity, and hence salinity, has been largely supplanted by electrical methods. The conductometric method derives from the fact that seawater conducts electricity in proportion to the amount of ions contained (provided temperature is held constant). An instrument called a *salinity bridge* is used to measure the electrical conductivity of a sample of seawater under controlled temperature (see Chap. 16, page 446). From the conductivity, the total of the major ions (salinity) is calculated. A device called a *salinometer* exploits the relationship between magnetic susceptibility of seawater and its salinity. A sample of seawater is introduced into the center of a coil, and the measured change in inductance is converted to values of salinity.

The alkalinity of seawater is measured by titrating a sample of known volume with a strong acid until a neutral pH is reached. The required acid is a measure of the excess base represented by the alkalinity. Accurate and durable pH meters are used to measure the hydrogen ion concentration of seawater.

reading list

BROECKER, W. S., *Chemical Oceanography*. New York: Harcourt Brace Jovanovich, Inc., 1974. 214p.

GOLDBERG, E. D., ET AL., EDS., *The Sea, Ideas and Observations on Progress in the Study of the Seas*, Vol. VI. New York: John Wiley, 1977. Chaps. 17, 18 and 19.

HARVEY, H. W., *The Chemistry and Fertility of Sea Water.* Cambridge: Cambridge University Press, 1955. 224p.

HORNE, R. A., *Marine Chemistry.* New York: Wiley Interscience, 1969. 568p.

RILEY, J. P., AND G. SKIRROW, *Chemical Oceanography,* Vols. I, II. New York: Academic Press, 1965. 712p.

WOODWELL, G. M., "The Carbon Dioxide Question," *Scientific American,* CCXXXVIII, No. 1 (January 1978), 34–43.

chemical transport 5

Many of the chemical properties of the world ocean are the result of the transport of dissolved and suspended materials from one region to another laterally and vertically. We can understand the distribution of chemical properties in the ocean if we know how the distribution is accomplished. Conversely, a mapping of the distribution of chemical properties elucidates transport mechanisms operating in the ocean. In this chapter we shall examine this relationship between chemical distributions and chemical transport mechanisms.

The chemistry of the ocean is characterized by mixing processes that cause materials introduced into the ocean from several sources to be distributed uniformly. On the other hand, regulatory processes tend to segregate materials and prevent ultimate homogenization of seawater. The interaction of these processes is quite complex, but we can gain an understanding of the chemistry of the ocean by systematically applying the concepts of chemical transport. Before we do, several definitions are necessary.

5.1 Definitions

The chemicals of the sea exist as distinct *species*, each having characteristic chemical properties. Ionic species of the major elements in seawater have been discussed; a list of the chemical speciation of other elements is presented in Table 5-1. It is common for an element to exist in several species. Chemical species are distributed among the aqueous, solid, and gaseous *phases* of the

Table 5–1 Abundance and Speciation of Elements in Seawater

Element	Abundance mg/l	Principal species
H	108,000	H_2O
He	0.000005	He (g)
Li	0.17	Li^+
Be	0.0000006	—
B	4.6	$B(OH)_3$; $B(OH)_2O^-$
C	28	HCO_3^-; H_2CO_3; CO_3^{2-}; organic compounds
N	0.5	NO_3^-; NO_2^-; NH_4^+; N_2 (g) organic compounds
O	857,000	H_2O; $O_2(g)$; SO_4^{2-} and other anions
F	1.3	F^-
Ne	0.0001	Ne (g)
Na	10,500	Na^+
Mg	1350	Mg^{2+}; $MgSO_4$
Al	0.01	—
Si	3	$Si(OH)_4$; $Si(OH)_3O^-$
P	0.07	HPO_4^{2-}; $H_2PO_4^-$; PO_4^{3-}; H_3PO_4
S	885	SO_4^{2-}
Cl	19,000	Cl^-
A	0.6	A (g)
K	380	K^+
Ca	400	Ca^{2+}; $CaSO_4$
Sc	0.00004	—
Ti	0.001	—
V	0.002	$VO_2(OH)_3^{2-}$
Cr	0.00005	—
Mn	0.002	Mn^{2+}; $MnSO_4$
Fe	0.01	$Fe(OH)_3$ (s)
Co	0.0005	Co^{2+}; $CoSO_4$
Ni	0.002	Ni^{2+}; $NiSO_4$
Cu	0.003	Cu^{2+}; $CuSO_4$
Zn	0.01	Zn^{2+}; $ZnSO_4$
Ga	0.00003	—
Ge	0.00007	$Ge(OH)_4$; $Ge(OH)_3O^-$
As	0.003	$HAsO_4^{2-}$; $H_2AsO_4^-$; H_3AsO_4; H_3AsO_3
Se	0.004	SeO_4^{2-}
Br	65	Br^-
Kr	0.0003	Kr (g)
Rb	0.12	Rb^+
Sr	8	Sr^{2+}; $SrSO_4$
Y	0.0003	—
Zr	—	—
Nb	0.00001	—
Mo	0.01	MoO_4^{2-}
Tc		
Ru		
Rh	—	—

Table 5–1 Continued

Element	Abundance mg/l	Principal species
Pd	—	—
Ag	0.00004	$AgCl_2^-$; $AgCl_3^{2-}$
Cd	0.00011	Cd^{2+}; $CdSO_4$
In	<0.02	—
Sn	0.0008	—
Sb	0.0005	—
Te	—	—
I	0.06	IO_3^-; I^-
Xe	0.0001	Xe (g)
Cs	0.0005	Cs^+
Ba	0.03	Ba^{2+}; $BaSO_4$
La	1.2×10^{-5}	—
Ce	5.2×10^{-6}	—
Pr	2.6×10^{-6}	—
Nd	9.2×10^{-6}	—
Pm	—	—
Sm	1.7×10^{-6}	—
Eu	4.6×10^{-7}	—
Gd	2.4×10^{-6}	—
Tb	—	—
Dy	2.9×10^{-6}	—
Ho	8.8×10^{-7}	—
Er	2.4×10^{-6}	—
Tm	5.2×10^{-7}	—
Yb	2.0×10^{-6}	—
Lu	4.8×10^{-7}	—
Hf	—	—
Ta	—	—
W	0.0001	WO_4^{2-}
Re	—	—
Os	—	—
Ir	—	—
Pt	—	—
Au	0.000004	$AuCl_4^-$
Hg	0.00003	$HgCl_3^-$; $HgCl_4^{2-}$
Tl	<0.00001	Tl^+
Pb	0.00003	Pb^{2+}; $PbSO_4$
Bi	0.00002	—
Po	—	—
At	—	—
Rn	0.6×10^{-15}	Rn (g)
Fr	—	—
Ra	1.0×10^{-10}	Ra^{2+}; $RaSO_4$
Ac	—	—
Th	0.00005	—
Pa	2.0×10^{-9}	—
U	0.003	$UO_2(CO_3)_3^{4-}$

(From R. A. Horne, *Marine Chemistry*. New York: Wiley Interscience, 1969. After E. D. Goldberg.)

ocean. Fats and oils, being immiscible in water, constitute a minor phase in the ocean. Bubbles of air constitute the bulk of the gaseous phase in the ocean.

We can regard the ocean as a chemical *system* consisting of *reservoirs* of chemical substances connected by *pathways* along which those substances are transferred. The amount, or mass, of chemical substance in a reservoir is expressed as a concentration. Several conventions exist for concentration. Most describe the mass per unit volume or the relative number of molecules in a unit volume. Weight percentage is a useful concept as well. The transfer of material along pathways is described in terms of a *flux:* the amount (mass) transferred through a unit area in a unit time.

Fluxes in the Ocean

If the transfer is by means of fluid flow, it is termed *advection*. The advective flux of a liquid is the product of its density and its velocity of flow:

$$\text{Mass flux of liquid} = \text{Density} \times \text{Velocity}$$

For most purposes of chemical oceanography, seawater density is expressed by the approximate value 1 g/cm^3. The advective flux of a chemical species, A, dissolved in seawater is the product of the concentration of the species (written, by chemical convention, as [A]) and the velocity of flow of seawater:

$$\text{Flux} = [A] \times \text{Velocity}$$

Solid particles are transported to the ocean as suspensions in rivers. Within the ocean, turbulent motion moves particles of sediment and organic debris. Ultimately, gravity carries an advective flux of particulate material to the sea floor. The particulate flux of a chemical species, B, is the product of the concentration of the species in the particular phase, [B], the concentration of particles in space, ϕ, and the velocity of the motion of the particles:

$$\text{Flux} = [B] \times \phi \times \text{Velocity}$$

Where the concentration of a dissolved chemical species in the ocean is not uniform, transport by *diffusion* occurs. In diffusion, dissolved particles (ions or molecules) move from a region of high concentration to a region of lower concentration by virtue of their energy of motion. Their rate of travel is governed by the magnitude of their energy of motion (influenced strongly by temperature) and by the frequency with which they can collide with neighboring particles; this is characterized by a *coefficient of diffusivity*, D. The diffusive flux is determined by (1) the diffusivity coefficient, (2) the difference between the concentrations of the chemical species, C, at the region of high concentration and the region of low concentration, and (3) the distance separating the regions. The diffusive flux is expressed as:

$$\text{Diffusive Flux} = D \, \frac{([C]_{\text{high}} - [C]_{\text{low}})}{\text{Distance}}$$

Two kinds of diffusive flux are found in the ocean. In the absence of turbulence, the diffusive flux follows the equation above, which is called Fick's first law of molecular diffusion. Fickian diffusion takes place slowly and is most effective over relatively short distances. If turbulence is present, the diffusive flux is minor compared to that of turbulent mixing.

Turbulent mixing of masses of water resembles a diffusive transport process, and the appropriate coefficient in the flux equation in such a case is a coefficient of *eddy mixing*. Mixing by turbulent eddies is quite rapid and takes place over distances of tens or hundreds of meters in the open ocean.

The flux of a gaseous species is diffusive; transport between the gaseous and aqueous phases resembles the Fickian equation except that an exchange coefficient analogous to diffusivity characterizes the process.

Transport

The flux summed over the area through which flow occurs is called *mass transport*. The transport of water in a river is the product of the river velocity, water density, and cross-sectional area of river channel where the transport is measured. Assuming unit density of water, the mass transport of water can be expressed as:

$$\text{Mass transport} = \text{Velocity} \times \text{Area} = \text{Volume flow rate}$$

Mass transport of a dissolved chemical species is found as the product of its concentration and the volume flow rate of the solution:

$$\text{Mass transport} = \text{Concentration} \times \text{Volume flow rate}$$

The mass transport of a chemical species in particles suspended in a stream is similarly:

$$\text{Mass transport} = \text{Concentration in particles}$$
$$\times \text{Particle concentration} \times \text{Volume flow rate}$$

Transport between phases is defined in terms of material produced or removed within the volume of a reservoir. If a chemical species, E, is produced (or consumed) within a reservoir at a rate, k, that is proportional to its aqueous concentration, the apparent transport into (or from) the reservoir is equal to:

$$k \times [E] \times V$$

where V is the volume of the reservoir.

This simple expression describes many dissolution and precipitation reactions. It also describes the natural growth of organisms where the mass transport represents the uptake of biochemical materials and $-[E]$ represents the concentration of the material removed by the organisms. The mass of radioactive chemical species, F, removed by radioactive decay is described by the same equation:

$$\text{Mass removal} = -\lambda \times [F] \times V$$

where λ is the *radioactive decay constant*. The mass of a new chemical species produced by radioactive decay of its parent species, N, is:

$$\text{Mass production} = \lambda \times [N]$$

If a chemical species, S, is transported between the solid and aqueous phases by *adsorption* or *desorption*, the transport by adsorption is often described by the expression:

$$\text{Adsorption transport} = K \times [S]^n \times V$$

where K and n are adsorption coefficients. Each kind of transport is important locally in deciding the distribution of chemical species in the ocean. The diagram in Fig. 5-1 illustrates the way in which each kind of transport is important.

We are able to learn much about the ocean's chemistry by applying two fundamental principles to mass transport in a system of reservoirs and pathways that we construct to represent the ocean, atmosphere, and sea floor, such as shown in Fig. 5-1. The first is the principle of *continuity*, or the law of conservation of mass (a special form of the first law of thermodynamics regarding the conservation of energy). This principle asserts that the sum of the transports into a system must equal the sum of the transports out of the system, or else the amount of material in the system will change. The second principle involves the concept of *steady state*. A steady state exists in a reservoir when the concentration of the species in the reservoir is not changing: that is, transports in and out of the reservoir sum to zero. The understanding of the distribution of chemical species in a system is facilitated if we can assume that

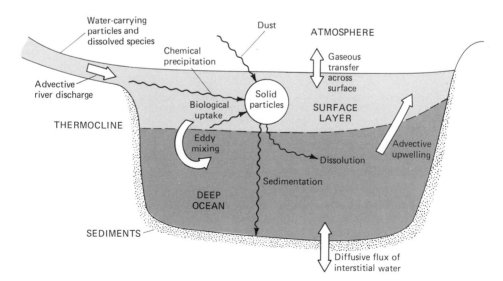

Figure 5-1 Distribution of transport types in the ocean.

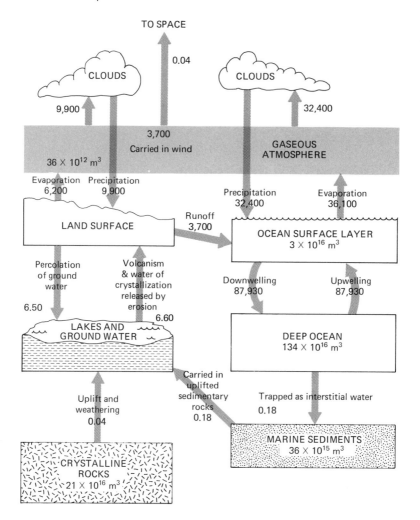

Figure 5-2 Diagram of transport of water in the earth system. Transport is shown in units of $10^{10} m^3/yr$.

transport processes in a system operate long enough to approach a steady state. The longer the residence time of a species in a reservoir, the more closely the steady state distribution describes the actual distribution of the species in the reservoir.

Let us now apply these principles to some simple cases to illustrate the technique of *system modeling*. The first chemical species to be modeled is water and we will consider its distribution in the ocean, the atmosphere, and the solid earth (Fig. 5-2). The ocean is viewed as containing two reservoirs, the surface layer above the permanent thermocline and the deep water below. The

Table 5–2 Calculation of Residence Time of Water in Earth's Reservoirs

Reservoir	Quantity in reservoir	÷ transport in (or out)	= residence time
Deep ocean	134×10^{16} m³	879×10^{12} m³/yr	1524 yr
Ocean surface layer	3.6×10^{16}	1240×10^{12}	29
Atmosphere	36×10^{12}	423×10^{12}	8.5×10^{-2}
Marine sediments	36×10^{15}	0.18×10^{10}	2.0×10^{7}
Crystalline rocks	21×10^{16}	0.04×10^{10}	5.2×10^{8}

atmosphere also contains two reservoirs, the gaseous atmosphere and clouds. The solid earth includes reservoirs of water in marine sediment, in rocks of the earth's interior, and in and on the surface of the land.

The transport of water between each reservoir is shown in Fig. 5-2. We can deduce several facts about the system if we assume it is at steady state. First, it is clear that the transport of river flow must be about as large as the transport of water in the atmosphere because atmospheric precipitation is the source of river waters. Second, the transport of upwelled water must exactly equal that of downwelled water because water is neither gained nor lost by such mixing. Further, we see that the transport of interstitial water is quite small, as is the difference in transport in and out of the surface material of the land. Such small transports are not easily resolved; however steady state in the marine sediment reservoir implies that the transport of water in uplifted sediments must equal the transport into marine sediments. Steady state in the entire system predicts that the amount of water lost to space must equal the amount cycled through the surface layer of the land.

The residence time of water in each reservoir is calculated in Table 5-2. Water remains for the least time in the atmosphere; it is cycled through the atmosphere almost twelve times per year. The residence time of water in the surface layer of the ocean is somewhat longer (28 years), and water resides in the deep ocean almost 1,000 years before being mixed to the surface. Water is trapped in crystalline rocks for a half billion years but remains in sedimentary rocks only 20 million years before reaching the earth's surface.

Now let us consider a model of the distribution of dissolved chemical species. The system of interest is defined somewhat differently to take advantage of pathways and reservoirs that we know are important. A solid particulate phase is included because we know that many elements reach the sea borne on dust and suspended in rivers and are removed to marine sediments as settling particles and fecal pellets. A diagram of the system is shown in Fig. 5-3. The dissolved species modeled in this system are of three sorts. Those that tend to be virtually depleted from the surface layer of the ocean by biological processes are called *limiting* elements. Nitrogen, phosphorous, and silicon, the nutrient elements, are of this sort. Elements that are not depleted in surface water are *nonlimiting*. Sodium, potassium, strontium, chlorine, and

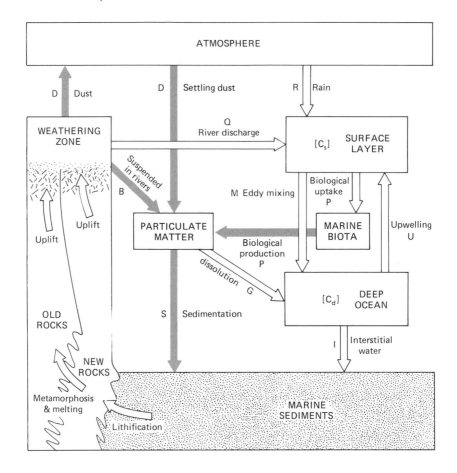

Figure 5-3 Diagram of the system for modeling the transport and distribution of dissolved chemical species in the world ocean. Solid arrows represent suspended particle pathways. Capital letters refer to transport along each pathway affecting ocean reservoirs. (C_s) and (C_d) represent the concentrations of the modeled chemical species in the surface and deep reservoirs.

bromine are notable examples. Those elements that are only partially depleted in surface water by biological processes are termed *intermediate*. Calcium, carbon, barium, and radium are of this sort; they are all involved in the precipitation of calcium carbonate (barium and radium act chemically similar to calcium in the carbon cycle).

The amounts of several important elements carried along the pathways of the transport model are presented in Table 5-3; the transports are expressed in units of 10^{14} g/yr. We note that rain is an important bearer of volatile chemical

Table 5–3 Composition of the Ocean Reservoir and Pathways

Element	Dissolved species	Mass transports in and out of the ocean (in units of 10^{14} g/yr)					Concentration in ocean water (ppb)	
		Airborne		Riverborne		Marine sedimentation	Surface	Deep
		Rain	Dust	Dissolved	Suspended			
K	K^+	8.3	0.13	0.90	0.58	1.30	380×10^3	380×10^3
Na	Na^+	4.8	0.05	2.52	0.36	1.20	105×10^5	105×10^5
Mg	Mg^{2+}	1.3	0.07	1.62	0.28	1.60	135×10^4	135×10^4
S	SO_4^{2+}	5.3	0.01	1.44	0.05	0.65	885×10^3	885×10^3
Cl	Cl^-	3.2*	–	3.06	0.0	0.96	190×10^5	190×10^5
N	NO_3^-	1.1	–	–			0	500
	NH_4^+							
Si	$Si(OH)_4$	–	1.4	2.52	11.16	13.68	94	3,000
P	PO_4^{3-}	–	0.004	0.005			3.5	70
Ca	Ca^{2+}	2.9	0.11	5.34	0.61	5.66	396×10^3	400×10^3
Ba	Ba^{2+}	–	0.004	0.01	0.04	0.25	10	30
C	organic	4.0	0.08	2.80	0.70	0.30		$\left.\rule{0pt}{2.2em}\right\}\,280 \times 10^2$
C	inorganic	2.5	0.04	3.90	0.20	1.60		
Al	?	–	0.41	0	3.01	3.03		10
Fe		–	0.24	0	2.00	2.00		10
Ti		–	0.02	0	0.13	0.13		1
Mn	Mn^{2+}	–	0.003	0	0.03	0.73		2

*Value for rain over a landmass. Over the ocean, the value is greater than ten times this value but the excess probably represents settling sea spray.

129

species, Cl, S, N, and C (as CO_2). Also, it bears to the sea large quantities of the major ions derived from sea spray. Dust supplies small but significant quantities of elements in proportions found in the composition of an average rock, actually a shale. Silicon, aluminum, iron, potassium, and calcium are most abundant in dust. Their concentrations evidence that their sources are quartz, feldspar, and ferromagnesian materials (see Appendix). River water is the principal bearer of calcium and carbon species, both inorganic (as bicarbonate) and organic. Substantial amounts of the major ions of seawater are borne by river water also. The material suspended in river water contains elements in roughly the proportions that occur in shale. The suspended load of a river is the major source of silicon, albeit in particulate form.

The concentrations of elements in the ocean reservoirs also are presented in Table 5-3. There is some uncertainty about the exact concentrations shown in this table, but the orders of magnitude indicate that the distribution of elements in the pathways and reservoirs is not uniform in every case. It is clear that fractionation of certain elements occurs. The degree of fractionation of an element between reservoirs can be determined from the ratio between the concentrations of the element in the two reservoirs to be compared. Fractionation of one element relative to another also is determined by comparing the ratio of concentrations of the pair of elements in each of two reservoirs.

The distribution and fractionation of limiting elements in the ocean reservoirs are revealed by constructing a steady state mass balance of the reservoirs in the system model. The transports into and out of each reservoir are tabulated to derive balance equations that describe steady state in that reservoir (Table 5-4). The ocean surface layer receives transport of dissolved species from river runoff, Q, and rain, R. The particulate transport to the ocean is suspended in rivers, B, and in settling dust, D. The marine biota removes dissolved material from the surface layer as biological uptake, P, and contributes a particulate

Table 5-4   Steady State Balance in Reservoirs in the Ocean System of Dissolved Chemical Species

Transport in		Transport out
Surface layer reservoir		
Q + R + U	=	P + M
Deep-ocean reservoir		
G + M	=	U + I
Particulate matter reservoir		
D + B + P	=	S + G

transport as organic production, P, to the reservoir of particulate matter. The sediments at the ocean bottom receive a transport of particles, S, and trap a transport of interstitial water, I, during sedimentation. Exchange of water between the surface layer and deep ocean causes transport as upwelling, U, and as eddy mixing, M. Transport is expressed as the product of [Cs], the concentration of the species of interest in the surface layer reservoir and M, the water transported by eddy mixing. Similarly, the transport, U, is the product of [Cd], the concentration in deep water, and M, since the transport of water by eddy mixing and upwelling must be equal.

The mass balance at steady state requires that, for the surface layer, the following equation must hold:

$$Q + R + M \times [C_d] = P + M \times [C_s]$$

Transport in = Transport out

and for the deep layer the equation below must hold simultaneously:

$$G + M \times [C_s] = I + M \times [C_d]$$

Transport in = Transport out

The balance of particulate mass provides a third equation:

$$D + B + P = S + G$$

These three equations can be solved to evaluate any three unknowns (transport or concentration), provided all other transports (or concentrations) are known. If not all are known, an additional equation must be stated for each additional unknown. For example, an equation relating particle dissolution to biological production permits solving for a fourth unknown. We see at once that, for the entire system, the mass transport of chemical species into the surface of the ocean must equal that lost to sediments.

The time required to remove 100 percent of the amount of an element being introduced into a reservoir is defined as the residence time, τ, of the element in that reservoir. The residence times of several elements are listed in Table 5-5. The differences in residence times measure the fractionation of elements produced by chemical and biological processes in the ocean.

The steady state assumption is not always valid in the system we have been treating. Figure 5-4 demonstrates that carbon (as CO_2 gas) is not at steady state but instead is increasing in concentration in the atmosphere reservoir. Consequently carbon must be treated in a *dynamic model*, one in which concentrations or transport rates change with time. Such models are of particular importance because they provide the means of predicting the state of the system in the future if changes are induced in the system either naturally, deliberately, or inadvertently. We will demonstrate a dynamic model of carbon because the concentration of atmospheric CO_2 in the future will have a profound influence upon the climate of the earth.

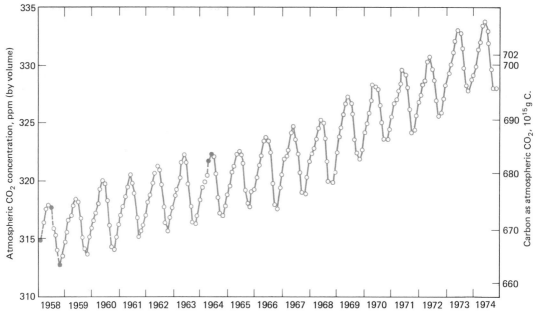

Figure 5-4 Variation in the CO_2 content of the atmosphere. The black dots are interpolated values. The oscillations are seasonal; peaks occur between winter and spring, while low CO_2 content occurs between summer and fall. An increase in the mean CO_2 content of the atmosphere is unmistakably evident. (Reprinted by permission of *American Scientist,* journal of Sigma Xi, The Scientific Research Society)

Table 5–5   Residence Time of Elements in the World Ocean

Ion	Residence time, million yrs	Residence time, mixing cycles
	Entire ocean	Entire ocean
Na^+	200	125,000
K^+	8	5,000
Rb^+	0.12	75
Cs^+	0.04	25
Mg^{2+}	40	25,000
Ca^{2+}	2	1,250
Sr^{2+}	12	7,500
Ba^{2+}	0.02	12.5
$PO_4{}^{3-}$	0.2	125
Si	0.6	375
$SO_4{}^{2-}$	20	12,500
U	0.8	500
Total carbon	0.3	188
Alkalinity	0.1	63
$CO_3{}^{2-}$	0.015	9
H_4SiO_4	0.2	125

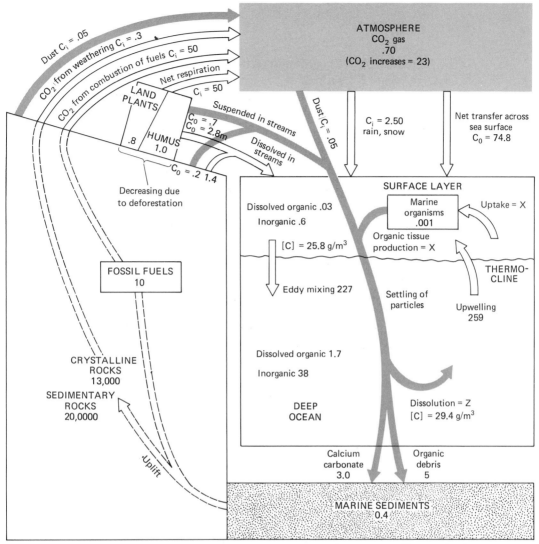

Figure 5-5 Diagrammatic model of the carbon system. Reservoir sizes are given in units of 10^{18} g C. Transports are in units of 10^{14} g C per yr. The symbol [C] represents the concentration of carbon in any form. C_i and C_o represent inorganic carbon and organic carbon. Shaded arrows represent transport in particulate form. The unmeasured transports X, Y, and Z are calculated using information in Table 4-11.

The carbon model is shown in diagrammatic form in Fig. 5-5. A distinction is made in the model between organic carbon (carbon in organic tissue or organic molecules) and inorganic carbon (CO_2, H_2CO_3, HCO_3^-, and CO_3^{2-}) because carbon from each source follows a different pathway and is measured differently. The numerical values shown in Fig. 5-5 are estimated and are subject to refinement as our study of the ocean, earth, and atmosphere progresses.

The increase in the CO_2 content of the atmosphere is about 1 ppm, or 24×10^{14} g C per year. No sources of appreciable CO_2 exist within the atmosphere, so we can deduce that CO_2 is introduced into the atmosphere faster than it is being removed. Transport of CO_2 into the atmosphere is via the following pathways, ranked in order of magnitude of transport:

1. Combustion of fossil fuels; coal, oil, gas (50×10^{14} g C/yr), Fig. 5-6
2. Net oxidation of the terrestrial biomass because of deforestation (50×10^{15} g C/yr is assumed, but estimates vary widely)
3. Weathering of rocks (0.3×10^{14} g C/yr)
4. Dust carried to atmosphere, primarily from desert regions.

Most of the removal of carbon from the atmosphere must occur along the direct exchange pathway to the ocean, considering that precipitation and dust transports are only 2.55×10^{14} g C/yr. The net transport of carbon (as CO_2) into the ocean from the atmosphere is almost 75×10^{14} g C/yr, or about 1.7 moles of C per square meter of ocean surface per year. Additional carbon (about 7.65×10^{14} g/yr) is introduced through precipitation and streams. The transport of carbon into the ocean is by means of:

Net transfer to the ocean	74.8×10^{14} g C/yr
CO_2 dissolved in precipitation	2.5×10^{14} g C/yr
Carbon dissolved in stream runoff	4.2×10^{14} g C/yr
Carbon in materials suspended in stream	0.9×10^{14} g C/yr
Carbon in settling dust	$\underline{0.05 \times 10^{14}}$ g C/yr

Total input to ocean 82.45×10^{14} g C/yr

The ocean can be considered to be near steady state because no variations in total carbon content similar to those changes in the atmosphere (Fig. 5-4) have been observed. This permits us to deduce that the total input to the ocean is equal to the total transport of carbon out of the ocean. The only pathway for carbon removal from the ocean is the settling of particles to the ocean floor and their incorporation in marine sediments. Small (negligible), amounts are removed by the biomass of the world fishery and are precipitated on carbonate reefs.

The carbon reaches the sediments in the form of carbonate shell material and organic detritus. Estimates of carbon in marine sediments and sedimentation rates indicate that the removal of carbon to sediments is only about 3.5×10^{14} g C/yr. What happens to the other 79×10^{14} g C/yr? The answer to that question is the subject of considerable research. If the excess carbon transport to the ocean remained there, an annual increase in the average dissolved carbon concentration of 0.0058 g C/m^3 would occur. Such an increase would be virtually imperceptible even over several decades.

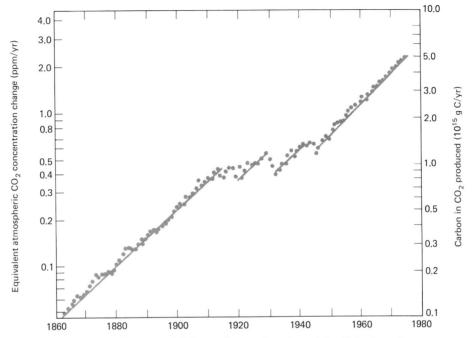

Figure 5-6 Production of CO_2 gas by combustion of fossil fuels and cement manufacture. Note logarithmic scale on vertical axes. (Reprinted by permission of *American Scientist*, journal of Sigma Xi, The Scientific Research Society)

However, the question whether the transfer across the sea surface can proceed at a rate of about 75×10^{14} g C/yr must be considered. We have seen that the flux of CO_2 across the sea surface is described by the equation

$$\text{Flux} = D \times \frac{([CO_2]_{d\,=\,0} - [CO_2]_{d\,=\,z})}{z}$$

where D is the molecular diffusion coefficient and z is the thickness of the surface skin of the ocean over which molecular diffusion, the slowest transfer mechanism in the sea, occurs. Neither of these quantities is known with exactitude. Estimates are:

$$D = 6 \times 10^{-2} \text{ m}^2/\text{yr}$$

$$z = 1.7 \times 10^{-5}\text{m}$$

Substitution of these values yields a flux of 18.9 g/m² yr or a transport of 381 $\times 10^{14}$ g C/yr, a value rather exceeding that of 75×10^{14} g C/yr. So it appears that CO_2 can be transferred from the atmosphere to the ocean at rates that more than keep pace with the rate of increase of CO_2 in the atmosphere.

Accepting, then, that the transport into the ocean totals 82.45×10^{14} g C/yr we now proceed to consider how the carbon is distributed within the ocean.

The calculations show that the excess transport of CO_2 from the atmosphere to the ocean could occur by diffusion across the sea surface. However, it has been determined that only one-tenth of the excess can be accommodated by the surface reservoir because the dissolved CO_2 reacts with carbon species already in the ocean and causes $CaCO_3$ to dissolve. Exchange between the surface layer and deep ocean will permit most of the excess CO_2 to dissolve in the ocean eventually. It is instructive to consider how the concentrations of carbon in the upper layer and deep ocean would change in response to the added excess carbon transport. For this purpose we will assume that all the excess is accommodated by the ocean. The carbon is in the form of dissolved inorganic carbon: 87 percent as the bicarbonate ion, 10 percent as the carbonate ion, and 1 percent as dissolved CO_2 and undissociated carbonic acid. The transport across the thermocline is based upon the concentrations of total dissolved carbon, [C], in the surface and deep ocean and the volume transport of seawater across the thermocline. The distribution of carbon within the ocean reservoirs is deduced by balancing the transports in and out of the surface layer and deep layers of the ocean (Table 5-6). The equations in Table 5-6 can be solved to show that

$$X = 42.5$$

and

$$Z = 39.95$$

The excess transport to the surface layer of the ocean is S = 71 and the excess transport to the deep ocean is D = 7.95. The sum of these is 78.95, the difference between the total transport into the ocean and the total transport out. The excess transports are involved in the water exchange across the thermocline. We can compute the change in concentrations of carbon dissolved in the surface and deep reservoirs by noting that

$$\text{concentration change} = \frac{\text{transport}}{\text{reservoir volume}}$$

The increase in the dissolved carbon concentrations in the upper 100 m of the ocean should be 0.2 g $C/m^3/yr$, and 0.0006 g $C/m^3/yr$ would be the increase in the dissolved carbon concentration in the deep ocean if all the excess carbon transport from the atmosphere were to dissolve in the ocean. This does not quite happen, but it is evident that the excess carbon transported from the atmosphere to the ocean should tend to accumulate in the surface layer if the model properly predicts transport behavior.

The organic production, X, predicted by the model is 42.5×10^{14} g C/yr. Estimates of production in the ocean, however, average 155×10^{14} g C/yr. This matter will be discussed further in Chap. 13.

The technique of modeling chemical systems in the ocean can be applied to any element for which sufficient data exist. Several interrelated models may be considered. For example, the carbon system is related closely to the systems of N, P, Ca, and O in the ocean. We shall return to this subject in the chapters on biology.

Table 5–6   Balance of Transport of Carbon in Ocean Reservoirs in Units of 10^{14} g C/yr

Transport in		*Transport out*	
Surface layer of ocean			
Stream discharge	4.2		
Precipitation	2.5	Eddy mixing	227
Net transfer across		Uptake by organisms	X
sea surface	74.8		
Upwelling	259.0		
Total in	340.5	Total out	227 + X

Balance equation: Excess transport to surface water $= S = 340.5 - 227 - X = 113.5 - X$

Deep layer of ocean			
Eddy mixing	227	Upwelling	259
Dissolution of			
particles	Z		
Total in	227 + Z	Total out	259

Balance equation: Excess transport to deep ocean water $= D = 227 + Z - 259 = Z - 32$

Particulate balance in entire ocean			
Suspended in streams	0.9	Carbonate incorporated in sediments	3.0
Settling dust	0.05	Organic debris incorporated in sediments	0.5
Organic production	X	Dissolution of organic debris	Z
Total gain	X + 0.95	Total loss	Z + 3.5

Balance equation: No net transport to particulate state, so $X + 0.95 = Z + 3.5$

The inclusion of lateral transport in the ocean system model provides a powerful tool for the study of circulation and mixing processes in the world ocean. The modeling of the fractionation and distribution of certain chemical species called *geochemical tracers* serves to establish the pathways and transport (or flux) rates of the ocean's circulation and mixing.

Our concept of such a model is shown in Fig. 5-7. The source of most of the water of the ocean is the Norwegian area; water from this region fills the Atlantic Ocean basin. Local chilling along the Antarctic shelf, particularly the Weddell Sea, adds surface water to the bottom of the South Atlantic. This Antarctic bottom water mixes with the North Atlantic Deep Water (NADW) as it proceeds to fill the Indian and Pacific ocean basins. Surface currents return upwelled water back toward the Norwegian Sea to complete the circulation. Superposed on this circulation is the pattern of *sources* and *sinks* of chemical species and biological cycles discussed previously.

The pattern of circulation and distribution of chemical species is determined by means of tracers, i.e., chemical species or properties that can be traced

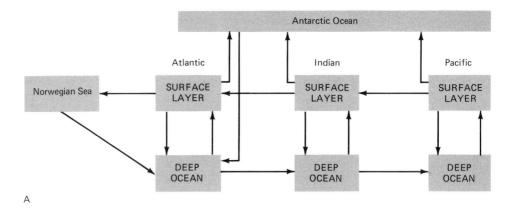

A

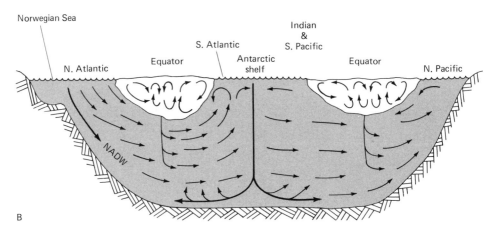

B

Figure 5-7 (A) Model of circulation and mixing transports in the world ocean based upon interpretation of the distribution and fractionation of geochemical tracer species. (B) Pictorial representation of the actual flow being modeled in (A). North Atlantic deep water (NADW) is discussed in detail in Chapter 8.

from their points of origin (sources) along the pathways in the ocean system to their points of removal (sinks) from the system. Radioactive tracers have the advantage of disappearing at known rates by radioactive decay. Their distribution in the ocean system is a result of decay as well as transport by circulation and mixing. In this regard they serve to establish the rate of transport by providing the dimension of time for the model. We shall examine this important effect presently, but first let us consider the use of stable tracers. We have seen that temperature and salinity serve to identify water masses and the degree of mixing of discrete water masses. The dissolved oxygen content of deep water has been used to trace the circulation of water once it has left the surface; a combination of 9 × molar concentration of nitrate + molar concentration of dissolved oxygen (the ratio of nitrate formation to oxygen consumption in the sea) is another stable tracer of water movement.

The stable isotope of oxygen, O-18, is useful as a tracer of water masses because it fractionates from O-16 upon passing through evaporation–precipitation cycles according to the temperature in its region of formation. Precipitation in high latitudes is enriched in O-18 relative to that in the tropics. Consequently, a combination of O-18 content and salinity serves to identify a mass of water once it has left its region of formation.

Some stable tracers are used to estimate transport rates in the ocean. Rates of transport to sediments are determined by measuring accumulation of particulate matter bearing chemical species involved in biological metabolism. The rate of invasion of atmospheric CO_2 into the sea is determined by measuring the total dissolved inorganic carbon, the alkalinity, and the pH of seawater.

The most important tracers for determining transport rates are the radioactive isotopes of elements involved in the circulation and mixing along the pathways of the ocean system. In order to use a radioactive species as a tracer, we must know several things about it. First, we must know how, when, and where the species forms. Carbon-14 (C-14), for example, is produced constantly in the atmosphere by cosmic ray bombardment of nitrogen atoms. Uranium-238 on earth was formed at the time of the event that formed our solar system. Hydrogen-3, or tritium, as it is called, was formed by nuclear bomb explosions in the 1950's.

Next, we must know how fast the radioisotope decays and what its daughter products are. Such information is available from the study of radiochemistry. Carbon-14 decays at a rate such that half of it disappears in 5,700 years. Half of what remains decays away in the following 5,700 years, and so on. This interval is termed the half-life of the radioisotope. The decay process is described by stating that the rate of disappearance of a radioisotope is proportional to the amount remaining at any moment:

$$\text{Rate of change of mass of isotope} = -\lambda \times \text{Mass remaining}$$

where λ, the decay constant, has a value of 1/8,200 years for C-14. The decay constant, λ, signifies that on the average a C-14 atom lasts for 8,200 years before decaying.

The daughter product of C-14 is ordinary N-14. The daughter products of uranium and thorium are themselves radioactive and they in turn decay to form series of decaying radioisotopes that eventually decay to lead.

Finally, we must know the ratio between the radioisotope and its stable chemical counterpart at its source and in each reservoir in our system. Also, the total amount of the tracer species, stable plus radioactive, must be known. Carbon-14 is produced at a rate in the atmosphere that balances its rate of decay there, so the C-14/C-12 ratio of the source is known.

The mixing rate along a pathway is determined by comparing the isotope ratios rather than the species concentrations in a mass balance equation. For example, the rate of exchange of water between the surface layer of the ocean and the deep ocean is determined by using the C-14 tracer in the expression:

$$\text{Transport rate} = \frac{\text{Volume of deep ocean} \times \lambda}{\left[\left(\dfrac{\text{C-14/C-12 ratio in the surface layers}}{\text{C-14/C-12 ratio in the deep ocean}}\right) - 1\right]}$$

Artificial radioisotopes produced by nuclear explosions can be used as tracers in a simple manner because they are detectable at extremely small concentrations and because we know the times of origin of the decaying species. We need only to measure isotope concentrations along a pathway, correct for the decay, and, because the moment of entry of the isotope into the ocean system is known, we may obtain directly the rate of change of concentration by mixing. Tritium (H-3), introduced into the Atlantic Ocean by bomb tests, has become distributed by mixing as shown in Fig. 5-8. Note that the penetration into the deep ocean is less extensive in the equatorial region where the permanent thermocline prohibits vertical exchange. The ratio of He-3 (formed from the decay of H-3) to H-3 is a measure of the time elapsed since water

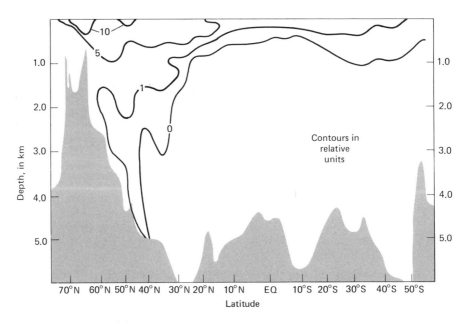

Figure 5-8 Distribution of Tritium (H–3) in the Atlantic Ocean, indicating the extent to which bomb-produced material has penetrated the deep ocean over a period of about 10 years. The dark area represents the relief of the sea floor. (After A. L. Hammond, *Science*, Vol. 195, No. 14, January 1977, p. 165. Copyright American Association for the Advancement of Science.)

Table 5–7 Tracers of Chemical Transport in the Ocean

Stable tracers	
Species or property	Uses
Temperature vs. salinity	Water mass identification, motion, and mixing
Dissolved oxygen	Bottom water motion
Dissolved oxygen + (9 × nitrate)	Water mass identification
Nutrients	Biological uptake, vertical mixing
Alkalinity and total inorganic carbon	Interaction of CO_2 with calcareous sediments and CO_2 assimilation rate of the ocean
Particulate material	Settling rate
O-18 and salinity	Water mass identification, motion, and mixing

Radioactive tracers	
Species	Uses
C-14	Vertical advection and mixing, horizontal mixing at thermocline
Rn-222	Vertical mixing near bottom and near surface
Ra-228	Horizontal mixing, turbulent mixing near bottom
He-3	Horizontal mixing in the deep ocean
Sr-90	Mixing at the thermocline, settling rate of particles
Cs-137	Mixing at the thermocline, settling rate of partcles
H-3	Mixing at thermocline, potentially transport of surface water
Ra-226	Vertical advection and mixing
Pb-210	Incorporation in particulate matter
Si-32	Mixing at thermocline, potentially

bearing these isotopes left the surface in about 1954. Other bomb-produced isotopes used as tracers of water motion and particle settling are Sr-90 and Cs-137 which were introduced into the ocean from the atmosphere in rainfall. Studies of the distribution of Cs-137 and H-3 indicate that water formed in the Pacific north of Japan sinks to 100 m and then spreads laterally 1,000 miles with little vertical mixing. Studies with STD probes (see Chap. 16, page 443) suggest that much of the water in the region of the thermocline is formed by such a process.

C-14 is also produced by nuclear explosions; it is introduced into the ocean by gaseous transfer from the atmosphere.

Some radioactive isotopes enter the ocean from the sea floor and are useful as tracers of transport in the deep ocean. Radium-228, radium-226, and radon-222 are three such tracers. They are formed by the decay of thorium-230 which precipitates when U-238 dissolved in seawater decays. Rn-222 diffuses into the bottom water and is mixed with a small additional amount formed by the decay of Ra-226 which has also dissolved and diffused from the sediments. The distribution of Rn-222 in the bottom water is a measure of the mixing transport in the lowermost 100 meters of the deep ocean. The distribution of Ra-228, Ra-226, C-14, and possibly Si-32 (the latter two form in the stratosphere) are also useful in this regard. Studies with these isotopes show that the degree of turbulent mixing of bottom water is enhanced if the density is constant with depth rather than varying with depth, as is observed at the thermocline.

Ra-228 produced from the decay of Th-232 in shallow continental sediments is useful to trace the horizontal motion and mixing in the surface layer of the ocean. The ratio of He-3 to He-4 in the ocean is high over the East Pacific Rise where basalts enriched in He-3 form new oceanic crust. Pb-210 and Th-228, produced by the decay of radium dissolved in seawater, seem to be removed from the ocean by particulate matter in some sort of process resembling the way in which the concentrations of heavy metals are regulated in the ocean.

The tracers used for studying transport pathways are summarized in Table 5-7.

reading list

BROECKER, W. S., *Chemical Oceanography.* New York: Harcourt Brace Jovanovich, Inc., 1974. 214p.

GOLDBERG, E. D., ET AL., EDS., *The Sea, Ideas and Observations on Progress in the Study of the Seas*, Vol. VI. New York: John Wiley, 1977. Chaps. 17, 18, and 19.

WOODWELL, G. M., "The Carbon Dioxide Question," *Scientific American*, CCXXXVIII, No. 1 (January 1978), 34–43.

important physical properties
of seawater

6

The physical nature of the world ocean is determined largely by the physical properties of seawater. In particular, the forces that cause circulation of water in the ocean arise from changes in the physical properties of that water. Temperature and salinity directly affect the density, buoyancy, and stability of seawater and, consequently, the motion of water in the ocean basins. The physical properties of seawater also strongly influence the behavior of heat and light in the ocean, thereby controlling thermal and radiant energy in the sea. Because so many oceanic processes are affected by the characteristics of seawater, we must examine each property in some detail.

6.1 *Pressure*

Pressure in a fluid, such as water, acts in all directions at any point in the fluid. A fluid flows from a region of high pressure to a region of low pressure; the greater the pressure differential, the greater the speed of flow. Pressure has virtually no effect upon the volume of water because water is almost incompressible. However, the volume of a compressible fluid (a gas) depends upon pressure.

In the ocean, *hydrostatic pressure*, which is the pressure arising from the weight of overlying water, is described by the hydrostatic equation:

$$\text{Pressure } (P) = \rho g z \text{ (units are force/unit area)} \qquad [6\text{–}1]$$

where ρ = the density of seawater (approximately 1.03 g per cu cm), g = 980

143

cm per sec^2 (acceleration due to gravity), and z = the depth below the surface of the ocean in centimeters. Calculations show that hydrostatic pressure in the ocean increases by one atmosphere for each 10 m of depth below sea level. Therefore, in the deepest part of the ocean (about 10,000 m), the pressure is about 1,000 atmospheres. It is necessary to consider such excessive pressures in oceanographic work. Divers must take precautions because pressure affects gases dissolved in the blood. Water-sampling bottles must be opened before they are lowered to great depths in the ocean because their walls are not constructed to withstand the tremendous pressure. Furthermore, watertight instrument housings containing air must be designed to withstand the extreme pressures at great depths in the ocean.

6.2   *Density of Seawater*

The density of seawater varies with changes in temperature, salinity, and, to a minor extent, pressure. Most changes in density occur at the sea surface where solar heating, cooling, precipitation, and evaporation cause the greatest fluctuations in temperature and salinity.

As pressure increases, the density of seawater increases; however, this density increase is slight because seawater is practically incompressible. It is only in the greatest ocean depths that this pressure effect is measurable, and even there the changes are small.

When ions are added to a fixed volume of water, its mass increases. In just this way, an increase in salinity produces an increase in the density of seawater (Fig. 6-1). Salinity changes also affect the temperature at which seawater freezes. As water salinity increases, water must be colder to freeze (Fig. 6-2). Thus, seawater freezes over a range of temperatures rather than at a single temperature. For seawater of average salinity, freezing begins at approximately −2°C. As ice begins to form, however, the remaining brine becomes more saline (sea ice is essentially free of ions) and must reach an even lower temperature to freeze.

The effect of temperature on the density of seawater is more complex than that of pressure or salinity. The density of most seawater (where salinity is greater than 25 parts per thousand) decreases with an increase in temperature (Fig. 6-3), so that cold seawater is more dense than warmer water that has the same salinity. Seawater with salinity less than 25 parts per thousand (brackish) becomes less dense if cooled below the temperature at which it reached maximum density.

The combined effects of temperature and salinity on the maximum density and freezing point of water are demonstrated in Fig. 6-4. Pure water reaches its maximum density at 4°C, but saline water reaches its maximum density at a lower temperature. Most seawater (i.e., seawater having a salinity greater

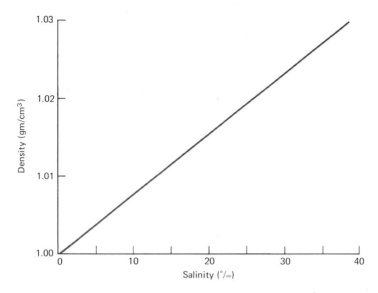

Figure 6-1 Curve showing the variation of density with salinity for water of 10°C.

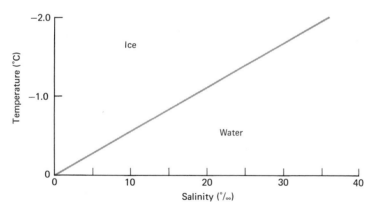

Figure 6-2 Curve showing the variation of freezing point of water as a function of salinity.

than 25 parts per thousand) has no maximum density peak, because it freezes before this peak is reached. In other words, the density of seawater increases with decreasing temperature until it freezes.

Several generalizations about density in the world ocean should be remembered: (1) Seawater has a density between 1.02 and 1.03; in the ocean, density normally increases with depth. (2) Seawater becomes less dense by either

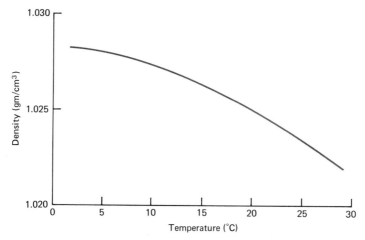

Figure 6-3 Variation of density of seawater (35 ‰) with temperature.

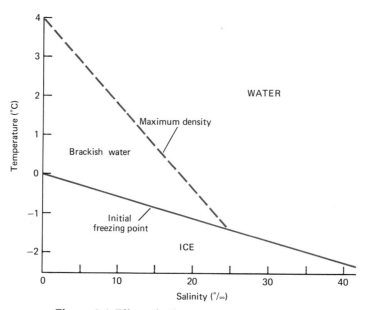

Figure 6-4 Effect of salinity on the temperature of maximum density and the initial freezing point of seawater.

warming or dilution (precipitation or melting of ice), or both. (3) Seawater becomes more dense when it is cooled or when its salinity is increased (by evaporation or formation of ice), or both. (4) Pressure has no effect on salinity. (5) Seawater density is more sensitive to temperature fluctuations than to salinity fluctuations (except near 0°C).

Table 6–1 Stability in the Ocean

	Stability	Instability	Indifferent stability
Density	Increase with depth	Decrease with depth	Uniform
General cases			
Temperature	Decrease with depth	Increase with depth	Isothermal
Salinity	Increase with depth	Decrease with depth	Isohaline
Special cases			
Temperature and salinity	Slight increase with depth of temperature plus large increase with depth of salinity	Slight decrease with depth of temperature plus large decrease with depth of salinity	Change in temperature exactly offset by change in salinity

Stability in the Ocean

Stability in the ocean is governed by the depth distribution of density.* Density, in turn, is governed by the distribution of temperature and salinity. Not only is density more sensitive to temperature changes than salinity changes, but the range of temperatures in the ocean is greater than the range of salinity values. Therefore, temperature is generally the most important factor in determining stability in the ocean.

Several combinations of temperature and salinity can lead to stability, instability, or indifferent stability in the ocean. Table 6-1 shows several examples of such combinations.

Typical density profiles in the open ocean are illustrated in Fig. 6-5. These profiles are largely the result of the temperature distribution. The shape of the salinity profile depends upon geographic location. Areas where the salinity decreases with depth are usually areas where temperature decreases rapidly with depth so that stability is maintained.

The typical density profile describes warm water lying over cold water in a stable configuration. Quite different temperature and salinity conditions produce stability in fiords, estuaries, and landlocked seas. In Puget Sound and the Black Sea, for example, cold fresh runoff from rivers lies over warmer saline water flowing in from the sea. This causes extreme stability and is referred to as the *freshwater lid effect.*

In the open ocean, the shape of the salinity profile is governed by geographic effects on the balance of evaporation and precipitation. In the subtropical zones (20° to 30° latitude), evaporation exceeds precipitation, so surface water

---

*See the Appendix for a discussion of stability.

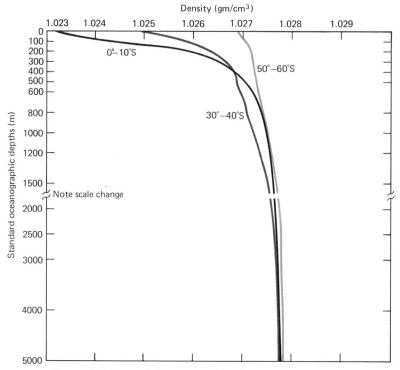

Figure 6-5 Typical density profiles from three regions of the world ocean. Note scale distortion of depth to emphasize the surface regions of the column. (Data after Muromtsev, 1958)

has the highest salinity in the world ocean. The profile of salinity of this surface water shows a decrease with depth. In high latitudes and near the equator, precipitation exceeds evaporation, so the opposite salinity profile prevails, because the water is diluted near the surface. For the entire world ocean, however, evaporation must exceed precipitation since the amount of water on earth is virtually constant (addition of juvenile water is negligible in this case). In other words, total runoff from land plus total precipitation must equal total evaporation.

The evaporation–precipitation balance causes important local effects in estuaries, bays, and lagoons at the periphery of the world ocean. These effects are discussed in detail in the section on inshore oceanography in Chap. 11 (page 318).

Although an unstable density configuration cannot persist in nature, it does occur in a seasonal manner in middle and high latitudes. When instability occurs, a vertical circulation, or *overturn*, takes place, so that stability is restored. Figure 6-6 shows temperature, salinity, and density profiles taken at the four seasons in the open ocean. During the summer (Fig. 6-6C), heating and evaporation lead to stability. In the fall (Fig. 6-6D), cooling at the surface causes the saline water to become more dense than underlying water, so overturn takes place. Mixing by storms tends to destroy the thermocline and

148

enhance the overturn. This process continues throughout the winter (Fig. 6-6A), especially if ice forms at the surface, because the freezing of seawater increases the salinity of the residual brine. By spring (Fig. 6-6B), the warming of surface water and development of a thermocline reestablish a stable density profile that persists through the following summer.

At the continental shelf off Antarctica, ice forms on the surface of the sea every year. Here, therefore, there is an overturn every winter, because the freezing of seawater removes relatively pure water and leaves extremely saline and cold, dense brine that promptly sinks.

In summary, stability occurs when warm water lies over cool water as a result of solar heating at the surface, or when fresh water overlies saline water because of river outflow or excessive precipitation. Instability is usually caused by saline water overlying less saline water as a result of evaporation or freezing at the surface. Instability also results when cool water lies over warmer water because of seasonal cooling at the surface. Indifferent stability exists when the temperature and salinity are uniform with depth. In the open ocean, this condition is invariably caused by mixing as a result of overturn, wind action on the sea surface, and currents. In local areas, such as Puget Sound, tidal currents are instrumental in producing mixing that leads ultimately to indifferent stability.

6.3   *The Ocean Thermocline*

The surface layer of the ocean is separated from the deeper layers of the ocean by a *permanent thermocline* 100 to 700 m deep that persists between the 50° to 60° north and south latitudes. It is shallow and steep at the equator but deeper and more gentle in midlatitudes. It rises to the surface at 50° to 60° latitude and marks the abrupt lateral change between cold polar water descending toward the equator and warm surface water transported from equatorial regions. The permanent thermocline acts as a barrier to the mixing of deep water and surface water. Pollutants, or carbon dioxide dissolved in the ocean at its surface in temperate and tropical regions, are virtually confined to the surface layer of the ocean.

The shallower *seasonal thermocline* develops in the midlatitude regions of the ocean. It develops in the spring, persists in the summer, and disappears in the fall and winter when cooling and storm-wave mixing occur.

The shallowest detectable thermocline is the *diurnal thermocline* that develops as the sun warms the surface of the ocean during the day. It disappears at night when the surface cools.

Thermoclines play an important role in many processes in the ocean, as we shall see. The chemistry, biology, and physics of the world ocean are influenced profoundly by this phenomenon.

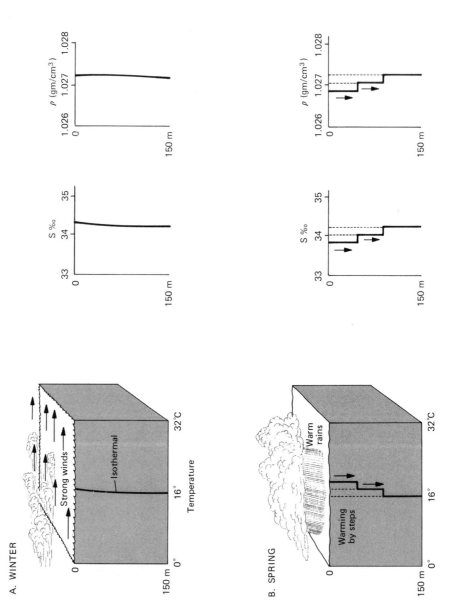

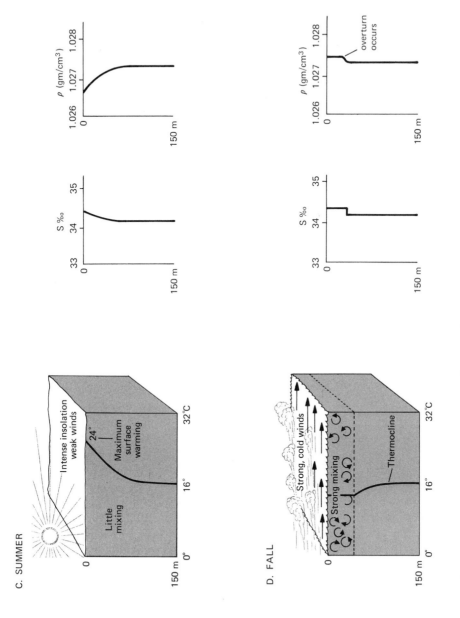

Figure 6-6 Schematic representation of seasonal changes in temperature, salinity, and density with depth in a mid-latitude oceanic area. (After Muromtsev, 1958, and Strahler, 1963)

6.4 *Viscosity*

The viscosity of seawater has an important influence on the motions of the world ocean and upon the nature of the forms of life that float or swim in the sea.

Viscosity arises from the internal friction of a fluid (and may be defined as internal resistance to flow). It represents the ease with which molecules in the fluid move past one another or, alternatively, the ease with which mechanical energy can be exchanged between adjacent molecules. It is fluid viscosity that causes a motorboat to stop when the engine has been stopped. The viscosity of a fluid depends upon the chemical nature of its molecules. Syrup is much more viscous than water, so a boat moving in syrup would come to a stop sooner and in less distance than in water. Viscosity is greatly affected by the temperature of the fluid; the viscosity of a fluid doubles if the temperature is decreased by 20°C. On the other hand, salinity has only a minor effect on viscosity. In fact, the viscosity of seawater is about the same as that of fresh water of the same temperature.

6.5 *Thermal Properties of Seawater*

Water has an unusually high heat capacity, latent heat energy of evaporation, and latent heat energy of fusion. These properties (discussed in the Appendix) are significant when considering the thermal behavior of the world ocean.

Heat Capacity in the Ocean

The ocean can store a great amount of solar thermal energy with relatively small changes in temperature because of its high heat capacity. A comparison of the ranges of temperature observed on land and in the ocean demonstrate this phenomenon quite readily. On land, a range of about 146°C has been observed between Libya (58°C) and Antarctica (−88°C). In the ocean, the range is only 38°C between the Persian Gulf (36°C) and the Polar seas (−2°C). These facts show that the ocean acts as a reservoir of heat energy that becomes neither hot in the summer nor cold in the winter. Because of the lower heat capacity of air, the temperature of air varies considerably from day to night, as well as seasonally. In contrast, the temperature of the water of the world ocean remains relatively constant. Therefore, a thermal gradient (or difference in temperature) usually exists between the ocean and the atmosphere. The ocean exchanges heat energy with the atmosphere rapidly. Consequently, near the ocean, air temperatures are thermostatically controlled. For this reason, the climate of oceanic islands and coastal lands has less temperature variation than the climate of inland areas.

The Latent Heat Energy
of Evaporation in the Ocean

Water's high latent heat energy of evaporation causes large amounts of thermal energy to be supplied to the atmosphere when water evaporates from the ocean. The atmosphere is much more mobile than the sea because of the low viscosity of air, so heat energy from the ocean reservoir can be distributed rapidly over the earth's surface. This energy is released when the water vapor condenses as precipitation in cool regions. Hence, coastal climates are milder than inland climates, especially where atmosphere circulation brings maritime air over cool land.

The Latent Heat Energy of Fusion
in the Ocean

The latent heat energy of fusion is high, so great amounts of heat energy must be released from water before it will freeze. Consequently, relatively little ice forms on the surface of the world ocean, except in extremely cold (heat-deficient) polar regions.

6.6 *Radiant Energy and the Ocean*

The ocean's source of radiant energy is the sun. The sun emits a spectrum of radiation frequencies, of which 50 percent are infrared, 41 percent visible light, and 9 percent ultraviolet, X rays, and gamma rays. The frequencies denote sizes of quanta of energy (called photons). As solar radiation penetrates first the atmosphere and then the ocean, quanta that excite the molecules in air or in water are absorbed. Figure 6-7 shows that an infrared photon is absorbed poorly in molecules in air but quite well in water molecules; that ultraviolet photons are absorbed best by air molecules; and that blue and green photons are least absorbed in both air and water. Therefore, infrared radiation passes through the atmosphere (the gases in the atmosphere, oxygen and nitrogen, are transparent to infrared radiation) but is absorbed by water.

Because infrared photons and some visible light quanta are absorbed into molecules of water in the same way as thermal energy quanta, either infrared photons or thermal energy excites the water molecules. As a result, absorption of infrared photons increases the heat energy and the temperature of the water. The wavelength of radiant energy emitted by a body is proportional to its temperature, so the earth emits radiation that has its peak wavelength in the infrared. Infrared photons are strongly absorbed by water molecules; consequently, much of the radiant energy emitted from the ocean (and land) is absorbed by water vapor or clouds in the atmosphere. Fig. 6-8 compares the incident radiant spectrum emitted by the sun (temperature = 5,700°C) and absorbed by the ocean with the spectrum emitted by the ocean at 20°C.

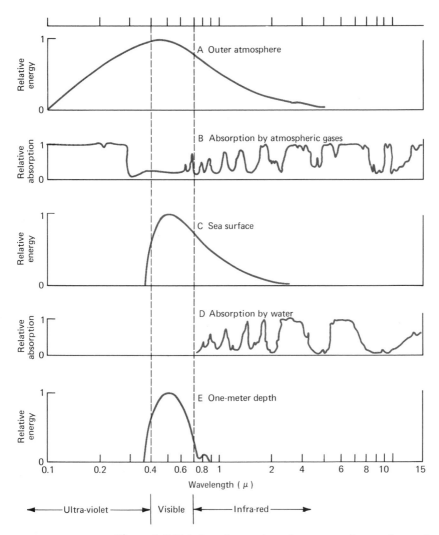

Figure 6-7 Relative change in solar energy due to absorption as it passes through the earth's atmosphere and penetrates through one m of seawater. (A) Energy spectrum of solar radiation reaching the outer atmosphere; (B) Absorption due to the principal absorbing gases in the atmosphere; (C) Energy spectrum of solar radiation reaching the sea surface; (D) Absorption by seawater; (E) Energy spectrum of solar radiation reaching one m depth. (Adapted in part from Miller, Merrill Books Inc., and Sverdrup et al., Prentice-Hall, Inc.)

Infrared radiation is so strongly absorbed by water that the incident solar infrared (0.8 to 2.5 μ) radiation does not penetrate the ocean deeper than about 1 m. Consequently, solar heating occurs in only the upper few meters of the world ocean, and heat energy is carried deeper only by conduction and vertical mixing. The general picture of the distribution of temperatures in the ocean is shown in Fig. 6-9.

154

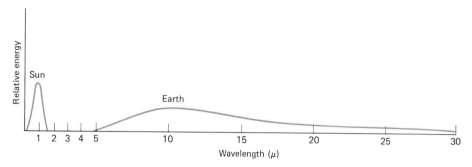

Figure 6-8 Comparison of emitted radiation of the sun and earth.

Blue green light is absorbed least. It does not cause much thermal excitation of molecules, but it is used for plant photosynthesis. It penetrates to about 100 m in the open ocean and to about 10 m in harbors and other nearshore areas. Fig. 6-10 shows how radiant energy of several frequencies is absorbed at a particular location in the world ocean. Below about 100 m, there is virtually no penetration of light, because near-total absorption of radiant energy occurs at this depth. The zone between the surface and the depth of total absorption is called the *photic,* or lighted, *zone.*

The blue green color of the ocean is caused by the minimum absorption of

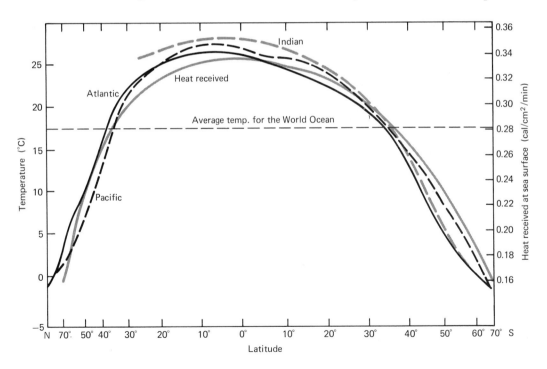

Figure 6-9 Mean zonal distributions of surface temperature for the three ocean basins and heat gain through the sea surface as a function of latitude. (Data from Sverdrup et al., Prentice-Hall, Inc.)

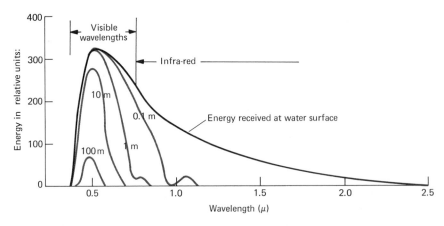

Figure 6-10 Energy spectrum of solar radiation at the water surface and at various depths. (After Sverdrup et al., by permission of Prentice-Hall, Inc.)

blue green light. Blue green light can be transmitted into, scattered, and transmitted out of water without being absorbed.

Sometimes, however, the color of the ocean is not blue green. For example, dissolved organic matter of yellowish brown color gives a green or greenish brown color to the ocean. There are red tides, caused by dinoflagellates (very small marine organisms) that impart a reddish tint to the ocean. In certain locations, such as off the coast of Norway, microorganisms called *coccolithophore* sometimes concentrate and impart a milky white color to the ocean. Suspended sediment may cause a muddy coloration near rivers and along shores where wave action is strong. As these sediments are carried to sea and sink, they form layers of suspended sediment called nepheloid layers. These layers are composed of extremely fine particles held in a temporary, stable (nonsettling) suspension. They scatter light much better than does seawater and are detected by this difference at great depths in the ocean. Determining their distribution provides information on sedimentation processes in the deep ocean.

The transparency of seawater is important to plant life in the ocean and it is a subject of concern to biological oceanographers. It is measured in terms of the transmission of light introduced artificially in water at depths below the photic zone and in terms of the depth of disappearance of a white disk 30 cm in diameter viewed from the surface. The transparency of water in the world ocean is quite variable, as is seen in Table 6-2.

6.7 *Appearance of the Ocean*

The appearance of the ocean depends upon the viewer's vantage point, the roughness of the sea surface, and the degree of cloudiness. Near the sea surface the ocean appears a beautiful azure color where the view angle to the water

Table 6-2   Transparency of Seawater in the World Ocean

Ocean basin	Area	Depth of disappearance of 30 cm secchi disk, m	
Atlantic	Sargasso Sea	66.5	(max)
	Equatorial zone	40–50	
Indian	Trade Wind Region	40–50	
Pacific	Trade Wind Region	45	(max)
	Barents Sea	45	(max)
	S.W. Mediterranean	40–50	
	Aegean	50	(max)
Seas	Adriatic	30–40	
	Black Sea	28	
	Caspian	11–13	
	North Sea, English Channel	6.5–11	

From G. M. Smirnov, *Oceanology, An Engineering Presentation*, 1974. Moscow: Vysshaya Shkola, Publishers 342p. (Reported in *Ocean Sciences* (newsletter), XVII, No. 11 (March 14, 1975), published by Nautilus Press, Washington, D.C.)

surface is steep. At a distance the sea appears blue or gray depending upon whether the sky is clear or clouds are reflected from the surface. If the sea surface is rough, more light is scattered to the viewer by *specular reflection* than if the sea surface is smooth. On a cloudy day the light is gray and the sea has a molten lead appearance, but on a clear day the sky's blue color (caused by *Tyndal scattering* of sunlight by molecules of air) adds to the blue light refracted and scattered from the ocean.

The appearance of the ocean from a distance (for example, from an airplane, a satellite, or even the moon) is blue, the color of the light least scattered or absorbed by the ocean or atmosphere. Other frequencies of radiation are present, but in smaller proportion. Satellites bearing multispectral scanners view the ocean's radiation in narrow-frequency bands (Fig. 6-11) to discriminate specific features in the ocean. The red band (0.5–0.6 μ) rejects blue and green light, thereby enhancing kelp (red brown algae) and suspended sediment. The yellow green band (0.4–0.5 μ) emphasizes plankton blooms and suspended sediment. Reflected solar infrared radiation is useful for delineating the wetlands at the edge of the sea. The thermal infrared radiation (5–20 μ) emitted by the ocean is an indicator of the sea surface temperature. Thermal infrared scanners are used to map the temperature field and detect upwelled (cold) water, industrial and municipal effluent discharges (warm), and currents (either warm or cold) in the ocean (Fig. 7-3). Microwave frequencies (20–1,000 μ) emitted from the ocean are used for remote sensing of thermal activity because they are not absorbed by water vapor or clouds and can be used in any weather.

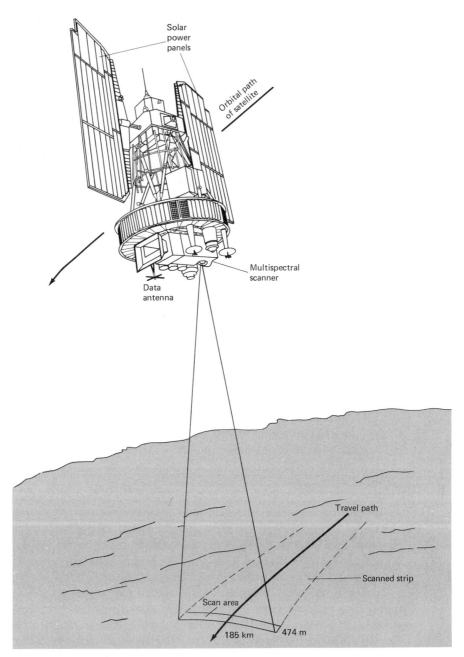

Figure 6-11 A multi-spectual scanner mounted on an earth observation satellite. The scanner sweeps the scan area as it moves over the travel path and produces a continuous image of the scanned strip. The light entering the scanner is broken into 4 components of the visible and solar infrared spectrum and an image is constructed from each. The data are relayed to earth where photographic products are prepared. The scenes shown in Figs. 7-22 and 8-2 were obtained with such a system (NASA LANDSAT).

6.8 *Sound Energy in the Sea*

The ocean is virtually opaque to most forms of radiant energy. Fortunately, an exception to this is acoustic or sonic energy which can penetrate the deepest parts of the ocean and even travel across the largest ocean basin. If enough sonic energy is provided, sediment and rock layers beneath the sea floor can be penetrated.

Sound travels rather rapidly in water, about 1,450 m per second. This is almost five times faster than the speed of sound in air (about 350 m per sec). The reason for the disparity in sound velocities lies in the different densities and elasticities in the two media. The velocity of propagation of sound is equal to

$$\sqrt{\frac{\text{Elasticity}}{\text{Density}}}$$

Seawater is about 1,000 times denser than air but is 150,000 times more elastic. This is the same as saying that air is 150,000 times more compressible than water.

The exact speed of sound in seawater depends upon the temperature, pressure, and salinity of the water. The variation in the speed of sound with temperature and depth is shown in Fig. 6-12A. Variation in water salinity is accommodated by applying the appropriate correction obtained from the curves in Fig. 6-12B.

Alternatively, the speed of sound in water can be calculated from the following equation:

At the sea surface, the sound speed, C_0 is (approximately):

$$C_0 \text{ m/sec} = 1449.2 + 4.623T - 0.0546T^2 + 1.391(S - 35)$$

where T = temperature of seawater, °C, and S = salinity of seawater, ‰.

The most common use of sonic energy in oceanography is to "see" the ocean bottom and to "see" into the ocean bottom. This is accomplished by taking advantage of the principles of reflection of sonic energy at discontinuities in the medium of travel. These occur wherever there is an abrupt change in the properties of the medium that causes a corresponding change in the velocity of propagation of sound. Discontinuities are found at the air–sea interface, the water–sediment interface, the contacts between layers of sediments or rocks having distinctly different physical properties, and the thermocline or any other interface between layers of seawater having markedly different densities. Schools of fish, whales, masses of plankton, and gas seeps often also form velocity discontinuities.

The effects of the thermocline upon the speed of sound in the sea are illustrated in Fig. 6-13. The reversal of speed values associated with the thermocline causes two important effects upon the transmission of sound energy in the sea. If a source of sonic energy is located at a depth near the

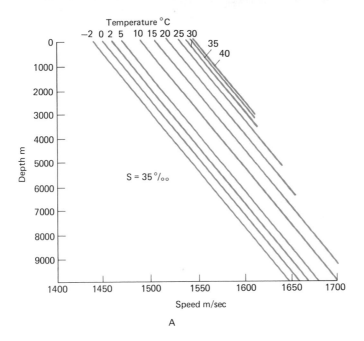

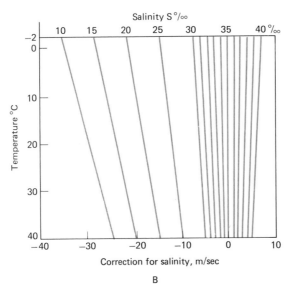

Figure 6-12 (A) Speed of sound in water of salinity = 35 ‰; (B) Speed of sound correction, m per sec. (Used with permission of McGraw-Hill, Inc.)

sound speed minimum, the energy is channeled laterally at that depth because the seawater bends the travel paths of sound toward the channel much as does an acoustic lens. Also, if a sonic energy source is located below the minimum, the travel paths are bent downward to produce an acoustic shadow zone at shallower elevations. The former effect is used to locate aircraft downed at sea. An explosive charge is detonated at the depth of the sound speed minimum.

160

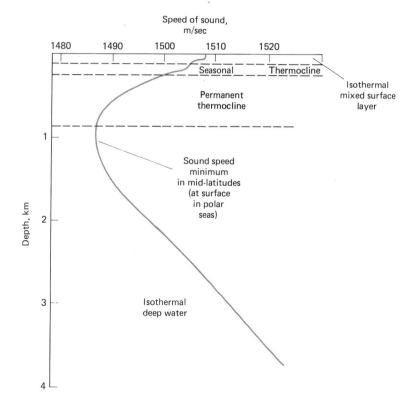

Figure 6-13 The variation of the speed of sound with depth in the sea. (Used with permission of McGraw-Hill, Inc.)

Listening stations on-shore record the time of arrival of the sonic pulse and calculate the location of the explosion. The latter effect is used by submarines to avoid detection by ships listening at the surface.

6.9 *Sea Ice*

Types of Ice

Two types of ice are commonly found in the world ocean. The first type is *glacial ice* which is formed in the vast ice sheets that cover Greenland and Antarctica. The ice is transported to sea to drift as icebergs over great distances before melting. The second type is *sea ice* and is the result of the freezing of seawater in cold climates.

The formation of sea ice depends primarily on the surface salinity, vertical salinity distribution, water depth, temperature, winds, currents, and sea state. Because of these factors sea ice can take on a number of forms and physical properties. For example, with a calm sea state and rapid cooling the sea surface is frozen into a clear, uniform sheet of ice. When waves disturb the sea surface, ice crystals are disturbed by the shearing water motion; a solid ice sheet

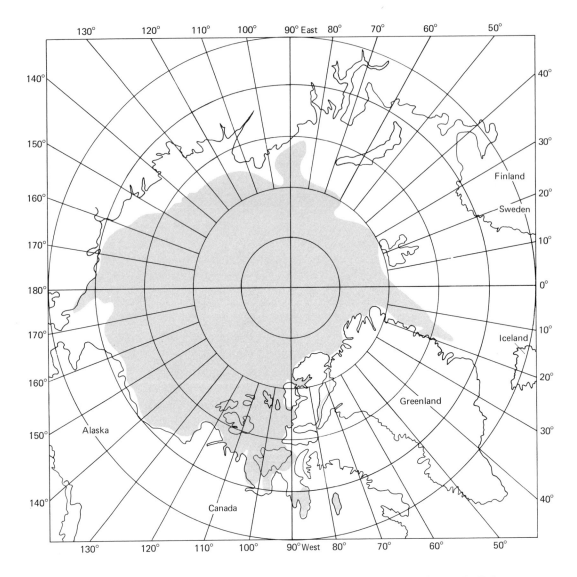

Figure 6-14 Mean ice conditions, September 1 to 15. (After H.O. Pub. No. 705, U.S. Naval Oceanographic Office, Washington, D.C.)

cannot form, and instead, individual ice crystals form thin plates that have a more or less vertical orientation. Under these conditions the sea surface appears slushy or soupy and is called *grease ice* and *slush ice*. Further freezing with continued water motion results in the formation of flat disks 30–100 cm in diameter called *pancake ice*. These forms represent early stages in ice formation. As freezing continues a solid ice sheet is formed that when young may be 2 to 3 cm thick, but may increase over the winter to 2 to 3 m thick. In shallow water along coastal regions ice sheets are called *fast ice*.

162

Under the influence of winds and currents ice sheets are broken up and drift extensively. Pieces of drifting ice undergo many transformations. They often collide, freeze together, break up, pile up, and are placed under great stress by winds and currents. *Pack ice* is the name given ice sheets that have been piled up, sometimes to thicknesses exceeding 20 m. Pack ice covers large areas of the Arctic and Antarctic oceans.

Distribution of Ice

The distribution of ice in the polar oceans varies seasonally; however, vast regions are covered throughout the year. In the Arctic Ocean permanent ice covers about 70 percent of the ocean basin and is concentrated primarily in Siberia and North America (Fig. 6–14). This ice cover is called the *polar ice cap*. Ice rarely forms around the western coast of Norway because of the existence of the relatively warm North Atlantic Current and Norwegian Current that flow along those shores (see Fig. 8–3).

During the winter months packed ice extends southward along the Greenland coasts and the eastern side of North America. This winter ice distribution and its subsequent melting back between March and July give rise to great numbers of icebergs that drift southward along the Labrador coast and the Grand Banks of North America. These icebergs are navigationsl hazards. In 1913 (after the sinking of the *Titanic* due to a collision with an iceberg) the U.S. Coast Guard formed the International Ice Patrol Service to chart the occurrence and drift of major icebergs in the sea lanes.

The ice in the Antarctic Ocean is distributed around the Antarctic continent in a nearly symmetrical pattern (Fig. 6–15). This distribution reflects the symmetry of the circumpolar currents and the zonal climatic patterns; the permanent ice pack extends almost uniformly to 60° south latitude. Because of the massive accumulation of ice on the Antarctic continent, the icebergs originating from the Antarctic ice sheet can be enormous. In 1953 a tabular iceberg was sighted off Antarctica that rose 30 m above sea level and was 40 km wide and 145 km in length.

Formation and Composition
of Sea Ice

The properties of sea ice depend on a number of factors that include the rate of formation and the chemical composition of the original seawater. As discussed in Sec. 6.2 and shown in Fig. 6–4, the initial freezing point of sea ice for 35‰ seawater is $-1.9°C$. The first ice crystals to form are pure water and are needlelike or platelike in appearance. The crystals eventually join together forming cavities trapping the brine that existed between the ice crystals. The size of the cavities and hence the amount of brine that is trapped within the ice crystal network depends upon the speed of ice formation. The slower the ice forms the larger the water crystals and the smaller the cavities.

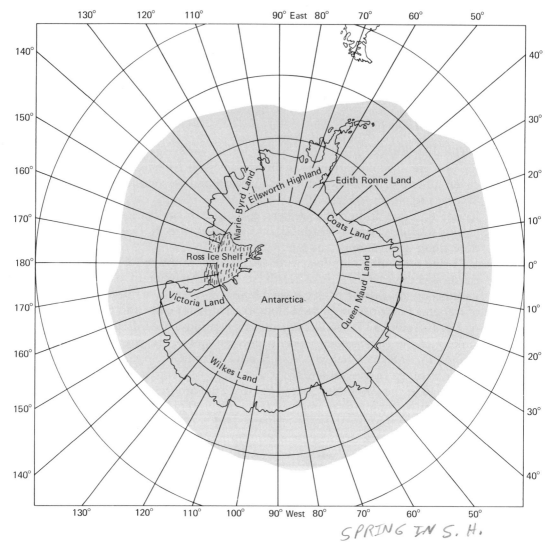

Figure 6-15 Mean ice conditions, October. (After H.O. Pub. No. 705, U.S. Naval Oceanographic Office, Washington, D.C.)

This mode of formation (that includes initial crystals of pure water and subsequent trapping and freezing of seawater) leads to the observation that the salinity of sea ice is always less than the salinity of the original seawater from which it formed. Analysis of many sea-ice samples shows that the freezing of seawater with a surface salinity of 30‰ leads to sea ice whose salinity may vary from about 5.6‰ to 10.2‰ depending on the rate of freezing. The density of this sea ice is approximately 0.92 g per cu cm.

reading list

CHRISTIANSEN, G. S., AND P. H. GARRETT, *Structure and Change*. San Francisco, Calif.: W.H. Freeman and Co. Publishers, 1960. 608p.

Conference on Physical and Chemical Properties of Sea Water, National Academy of Sciences–National Research Council Publication 600. Washington, D.C., 1959. 202p.

KRAUSKOPF, K., AND A. BEISER, *The Physical Universe*. New York: McGraw-Hill, 1960, 536p.

URICK, R. J., *Principles of Underwater Sound*. New York: McGraw-Hill, 1975. 384p.

atmospheric circulation   7

The radiant energy of the sun reaches the world ocean by passing through the atmosphere. Figure 7-1 shows that 19 percent of the energy is retained in the atmosphere. Most of the energy retained in the atmosphere is absorbed directly by atmospheric dust, water vapor, and ozone; and a small amount of energy is absorbed by clouds. Considerable energy is scattered back into space from clouds; small amounts are back-scattered from air, dust, haze in the atmosphere, and from the sea surface. The rest of the energy, about 52 percent, penetrates the earth's surface (of which 72 percent is ocean) and is absorbed as heat by the surface water.

The energy absorbed by the atmosphere and surface layers of the ocean maintains the two media at temperatures that, on the whole, have changed little during recorded history. This long-term steady state exists because the ocean, land, and atmosphere release a total amount of thermal and radiant energy that just balances the solar energy incident on the planet. The energy leaving the earth is mostly long-wave radiation from clouds, water vapor, and CO_2. A small amount is radiated directly from the ocean to space (Fig. 7-2).

Most long-wave (infrared) energy radiated from the ocean is converted to heat in the lower atmosphere. It is added to heat carried from the ocean to the lower atmosphere by conduction and convection and to the latent heat involved in the evaporative transfer into the lower atmosphere of surface water from the ocean. The net effect is that while the ocean is heated from above and made stable, the atmosphere is heated from below and made unstable. The instability leads to atmospheric circulation which has a profound effect on the world ocean.

166

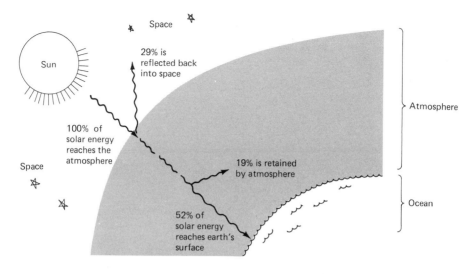

Figure 7-1 Fate of incident, short-wave solar energy in traveling from the sun to the earth's surface.

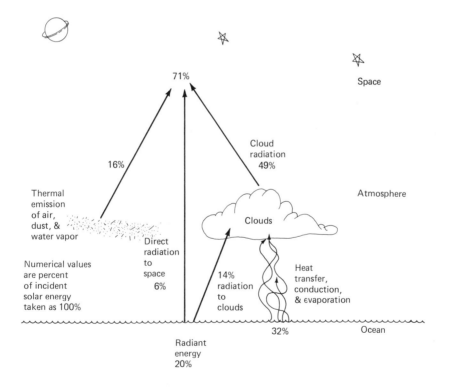

Figure 7-2 The energy flux from the ocean and atmosphere. Transfer of heat and emission of long-wave (thermal infrared and microwave) radiation.

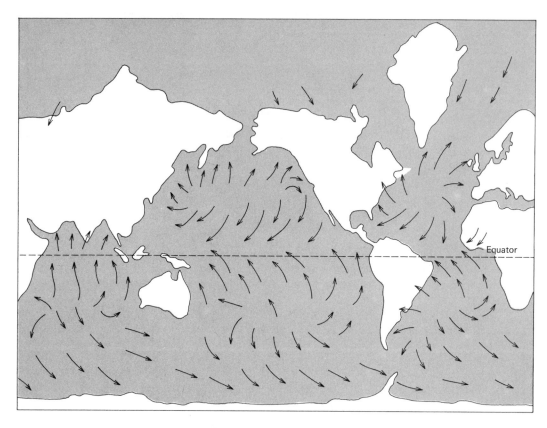

Figure 7-3 Surface winds over the world ocean (average for July). (After U.S. Navy Hydrographic Office Publication No. 9, 1958)

The physical interaction between the atmosphere and the ocean is critically important to many oceanic phenomena. Winds in the lower atmosphere are responsible for waves, surface currents, mixing of the surface layer of the ocean, and the exchange of energy in the form of heat and water vapor. Particulate matter ranging from mineral grains, seeds, and spores to carbon and silica spherules that are the byproducts of industrial combustion are transported out to sea through atmospheric circulation. An understanding of this circulation, therefore, is a necessary part of the study of oceanography.

At first glance, the pattern of surface winds over the world ocean (Fig. 7-3) appears to be somewhat confused and difficult to interpret. This wind pattern can be understood, however, by first considering winds that might be found on a theoretically nonrotating, water-covered globe, and then considering winds on a rotating globe on which continents are present.

7.1 *Winds on an Ideal Earth*

We assume for this discussion that the earth is motionless and is covered with water. Surrounding this earth is the atmosphere, whose lower portions are in contact with the sea and are therefore saturated with water vapor. The water and the atmosphere are heated by solar radiation. This heat becomes more intense near the equator. The air in the vicinity of the equator is heated relative to the surrounding air; its density will decrease, and it will rise. This motion will cause surface air from higher latitudes to flow toward the space left by the rising equatorial air. Actually, the rising air represents a region of relatively low atmospheric pressure. Air, like any fluid, flows toward a zone of low pressure. The equatorial air rises to an altitude determined by its density (i.e., it seeks its own level) and begins to spread laterally toward the poles. A commonly observed analogy to this phenomenon is smoke discharged into still air. The smoke ascends from the stack to a level determined by the density of the smoke and the density gradient in the lower atmosphere. At that level it begins to spread laterally (Fig. 7-4).

As equatorial air rises into a region of lower atmospheric pressure it expands, its temperature decreases, and it becomes saturated with water vapor to the extent that condensation occurs.

This imaginary system is shown in Fig. 7-5. The equatorial surface regions of the globe are characterized by warm temperatures, relatively low atmos-

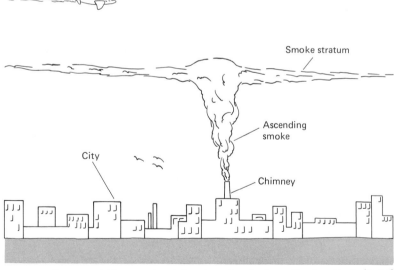

Figure 7-4 The smoke rising to a level where its density is less than that of the air below and greater than that of the air above.

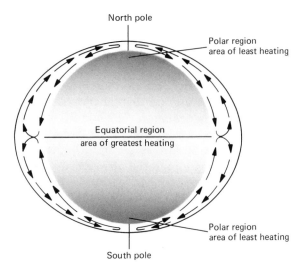

Figure 7-5 Ideal atmospheric circulation for a uniform, nonrotating, nonrevolving earth. (After U.S. Navy Hydrographic Office, Publication No. 9, 1958)

pheric pressure, clouds, and rainfall. In the polar regions, the temperatures are low, surface atmospheric pressure is high, and water vapor content is low, which causes precipitation to be low.

7.2   *The Rotating Earth*

We must next consider the effect of the earth's rotation on the pattern of wind at the surface of the ocean.

The fact that the earth is rotating and that we are rotating with it has a startling influence on the way in which we visualize the motion of an object. One example is the movement of the stars as observed from earth. Just because the stars trace a circular path across the sky does not mean that they are actually moving in a circular path.* We only see their motion relative to us. If we could free ourselves from the rotation of the earth, the stars would not appear to move in this manner. For example, the stars do not change positions relative to each other as they circle the sky (constellations have maintained their identities throughout history). It is important to emphasize that the direction of motion as observed by an individual is a relative thing, depending

---

*Readers are referred to the Reading List at the end of this chapter regarding the historical development of scientific thought on the motions of the stars and planets in the solar system.

not only on the motion of the object but on the vantage point of the observer.
Newton's second law of motion

$$F = Ma \qquad\qquad [7\text{-}1]$$

states, in part, that a force, F, acting on an object having a mass, M, causes
that body to accelerate at a rate, a, in the direction of the impressed force. If
a force is applied to an object at rest it will be accelerated and the motion will
be in a straight line when viewed from a place fixed with respect to the stars.
If an object is in a state of constant motion (not accelerating) and a force is
applied from the side, then the object will be accelerated in the direction of
the applied force and hence will change its direction—that is, be turned from
its previous direction. Thus, any object whose path of movement is curved, or
increasing or decreasing in velocity (when viewed from a place fixed with
respect to the stars) is being acted on by a force.

In viewing the motion of an object we encounter a problem because we are
forced to use a reference position that is on the earth and that rotates with the
earth. As a result, observations are difficult because an object moving in a
straight line (with respect to the stars) past the earth would appear to an
observer on earth to follow a curved path. You can verify this by imagining
yourself to be riding a carousel, while a person at the center is playing catch
with another person standing on the ground at some distance away from the
carousel. If the ball is thrown toward the center of the carousel at the instant
everyone is aligned in a straight line, it would appear that you would be able
to intercept the ball. However, in the time it takes the ball to reach your
position, you have moved in such a way that the ball appears to pass your
side. From your rotating vantage point, you would testify that the ball was
following a curved path, whereas the person standing on the ground to catch
the ball would testify as to its rectilinear motion. Furthermore, you would
conclude that a force had to be acting on the ball to account for its continual
change in direction with respect to your position. Note that if the carousel has
a counterclockwise rotation, the apparent curvature is to the left. A clockwise
rotation causes an apparent curvature to the right.

Our vantage point on the earth is a rotating one. Thus, if we want to
describe the motion of an object on the earth by using Newton's second law,
his equation of motion must be adjusted to describe the apparent curvature of
the object's path. We make the adjustment by stating that a force is acting on
the object, because a moving object deviates from rectilinear motion only
when a force is applied to it. So, to the equation of motion, we add an
apparent, or fictitious "force" that acts at an angle 90° from the direction of
motion and accounts for the observed deviation. This fictitious force is called
the *Coriolis* effect, and it adapts Newton's second law to observations of motion
made on the rotating earth. Mathematically, the Coriolis effect is stated as
follows:

$$F_c = 2w \sin \phi\, v \qquad\qquad [7\text{-}2]$$

where F_c = force per unit mass due to the Coriolis effect, w = angular rotation of the earth (a constant) in degrees per unit times, ϕ = degrees latitude, and v = velocity of the moving body.

Four additional statements can be made about the Coriolis effect:

1. It is an apparent force. It cannot do work or initiate motion (when $v = 0$, $F_c = 0$). It can only account for the altered motion that we observe because of our rotating vantage point.

2. A moving object deviates to its right in the northern hemisphere and to its left in the southern hemisphere.

3. For a given velocity, the magnitude of this force increases with latitude, being zero at the equator ($\sin 0° = 0$) and maximum at the poles ($\sin 90° = 1$).

4. At any given latitude (except the equator), the greater the velocity, the greater the force.

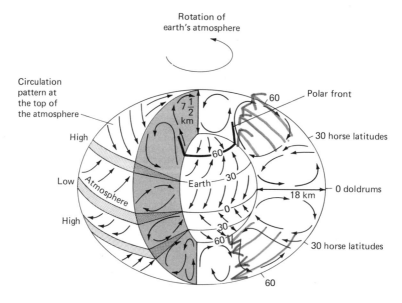

Figure 7-6 Simplified diagram of the general circulation of the atmosphere. Air rising from the equator spreads toward the poles, is deflected eastward, and accumulates at 30° latitude to form the subtropical high-pressure belts. Note the eastward flow of air everywhere at high elevations. This gives rise to the jet stream. (After Strahler, 1963, and U.S. Hydrographic Office, Publication No. 9, 1958)

Note that this effect is only important to the equation of motion when the motion involved is of a global scale. In most scientific work and laboratory experiments, Coriolis effects (apparent curvature of motion) are insignificant. Marine and atmospheric scientists deal with movements on a worldwide scale so they must include the curvature of motion in their equations.

Applying this concept to our rotating earth, we find that as the equatorial air rises and begins to move toward the poles, it would appear to follow a path that is curved to the right in the northern hemisphere and to the left in the southern hemisphere. As a result, there is a system of high-altitude westerly winds at the midlatitudes (Fig. 7-6). Since the northward (or southern) component of flow has been decreased, air tends to accumulate, causing high-pressure regions to occur between 20° and 30° latitude. These subtropical high-pressure belts modify the circulation within the lower atmosphere in such a way that air sinks at about 30° latitude and flows toward both the equator and the poles. The air that sinks spreads laterally. That air that moves toward the equator is warmed subsequently and rises, thus completing a tropical circulation system (Fig. 7-6). The surface air moving in a poleward direction from 30° latitude tends to flow over the more dense polar air existing north of 50° to 60° latitude. The confluence between these two air masses is called the *polar front*. It represents a region of highly changeable weather conditions caused by the interaction of relatively warm and moist subtropical air with cold, dry air from the higher latitudes. The net result is the formation of another cell of moving air that rises at about 60° latitude and sinks at the poles.

Figure 7-7 illustrates the winds that result from differential solar heating on a water-covered, rotating earth. A more realistic picture is obtained by including three circulation cells in each hemisphere (called Hadley cells). Rotational effects are represented by the deflection of surface winds to the right in the northern hemisphere and to the left in the southern hemisphere.

This pattern of surface winds forms six zones or belts that travel obliquely toward the poles or toward the equator rather than due north or south. These belts of winds encircle the earth latitudinally and are named the *trade winds*, the *prevailing westerlies*, and the *polar easterlies*.

It is worth noting the climatic conditions that result from the observed air circulation. In the regions of rising air, the climate is characterized by:

1. Low atmospheric pressure (rising low-density air)
2. Much rainfall and cloudiness
3. Light and variable winds (doldrums).

In the zones of sinking air, there is:

1. High atmospheric pressure (sinking dense air)
2. Cool and dry air, leading to excessive evaporation and low rainfall
3. Light and variable winds (horse latitudes).

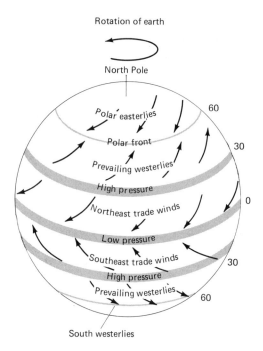

Rotation of earth

North Pole

Polar easterlies   60

Polar front   30

Prevailing westerlies

High pressure

0

Northeast trade winds

Low pressure   30

Southeast trade winds

High pressure

Prevailing westerlies   60

South westerlies

Figure 7-7 Wind and pressure patterns on a rotating earth.

The regions of convergence or divergence of surface winds and the common names given to these areas are also shown in Fig. 7-6. Generally, the *doldrums* are characterized by calms or light winds; the *horse latitudes*,* by light and variable winds; and the polar front region, by strong winds. In fact, sailors used to call winds in these polar areas the "roaring forties" and "furious fifties."

7.3 The Effects of Continents on Atmospheric Circulation

The inclusion of continental masses on a water-covered, rotating earth modifies the model of atmospheric circulation in two ways. First, the surface winds tend to form closed, horizontal cells over the ocean. Second, the distribution of land between the northern and southern hemispheres causes the Hadley cells over the ocean to be shifted northward. As a result, the meteorological equator is shifted 5° to 10° north of the geographical equator. These two effects produce the model of atmospheric circulation shown in Fig. 7-8. A comparison

---

*"It is related that ships carrying horses from Spain to the New World were becalmed in this high-pressure belt and, running out of feed, had to dispose of part of their cargo. At times the sea was littered with the bodies of these horses." From H. R. Byers, *General Meteorology* (2nd ed.). New York: McGraw-Hill, 1944. p. 222.

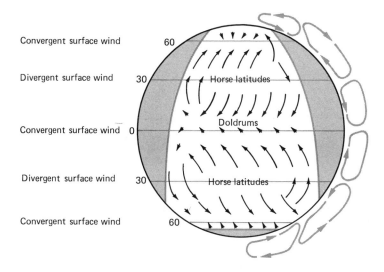

Convergent surface wind

Divergent surface wind

Convergent surface wind

Divergent surface wind

Convergent surface wind

Figure 7-8 The continental land masses tend to cause the surface winds to form closed cells over the oceans.

between Figs. 7-3 and 7-8 reveals a striking similarity between the actual and theoretical pattern of surface winds. However, other effects also influence atmospheric circulation. But such effects have only minor influences on the global pattern of atmospheric circulation. Even though they are negligible in the model, they do produce local modifications of the pattern of surface winds.

7.4 *Some Local Modifications*

Because of the low heat capacity of rock in relation to water, temperature ranges on continental masses are much greater than that of surface water in the ocean (see Chap. 5 and Appendix). During the summer, the land mass becomes much warmer than the adjacent ocean. Consequently, the overlying air is heated; it rises and produces the circulation pattern illustrated in Fig. 7-9A. Moist air from over the ocean moves onto the continent to replace the air rising there. The rising air is cooled, becoming super-saturated, and causes precipitation. During the winter, the land mass is cooler than the adjacent ocean. Air over the land mass is cooled and sinks. This sinking air is relatively dry; and as it pushes out over the ocean, it increases the evaporation of surface water.

In India, where these effects are pronounced, they are called *monsoons* (Fig. 7-9B). The summer monsoon prevails from April to September and is characterized by southwest winds and tremendous rainfall in coastal regions. (During

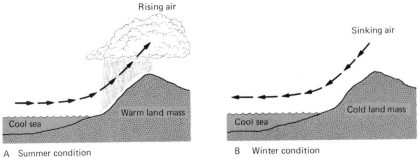

Rising air

Sinking air

Warm land mass

Cold land mass

Cool sea

Cool sea

A   Summer condition

B   Winter condition

Figure 7-9a Monsoonal wind condition resulting from differential heating between a land mass and adjacent sea. This occurs because of the different heat capacities of rock and seawater. The summer condition is characterized by high rainfall on the windward slopes. The winter condition is characterized by high evaporation over the sea. The west coast of India is a famous example of this condition.

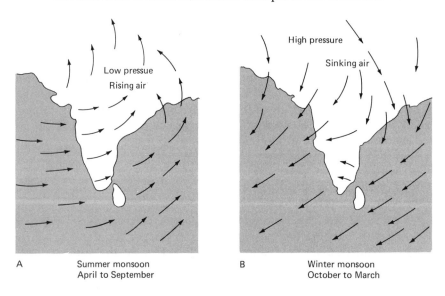

Low pressue
Rising air

High pressure

Sinking air

A   Summer monsoon
         April to September

B   Winter monsoon
         October to March

Figure 7-9b Summer (A) and winter (B) monsoon wind patterns in the Indian Ocean.

the month of July 1861, 366 in. of rainfall were recorded at Cherrapunji, a village in Assam, India.) During the winter monsoon, the climate is hot and dry, and the winds blow from the northeast for the remainder of the year. The Indian Ocean responds to the reversals in the monsoons by a seasonal change in surface currents.

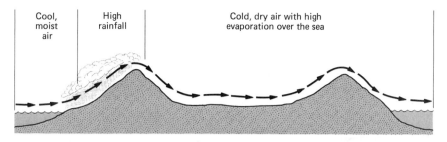

Cool,
moist
air

High
rainfall

Cold, dry air with high
evaporation over the sea

Figure 7-10 The effect of a westerly wind (mid-latitude wind belt) on the climatic conditions existing over a continent (winter condition). A section through the 40th parallel across the United States would fit this example.

7.5 *Diurnal Effects*

In coastal areas, daily monsoonlike winds are observed. A steady *onshore breeze* is maintained during the day because the land is warm relative to the ocean. At night, the land is cooler than the ocean, and so a steady *offshore breeze* blows. Throughout the world, this condition is understood by fishermen—they use the offshore breezes early in the morning to sail out to the fishing grounds and return in the afternoon with the onshore breezes.

The local modifications of the pattern of surface winds by continental topography explain the difference in climate between the east and west coasts of a continent, especially in the temperate zones in winter. As seen in Fig. 7-10, the west coast is characterized by a cool, wet climate, whereas the east coast suffers from much colder conditions, even though both areas are at the same latitude.

7.6 *Surface Salinity as Related to Global Wind Characteristics*

The wind belts (Fig. 7-7) with their associated high and low pressure zones have a significant influence on the physical properties of the surface waters of the world ocean. This influence is best illustrated by observing the latitudinal variation of the salinity of seawater. We have noted that regions of low pressure (at approximately 0° and 60° latitude) are associated with high rainfall, and that regions of high pressure (30° latitude) have low rainfall. This fact can be illustrated by plotting average values of precipitation and evaporation as a function of latitude (Fig. 7-11). The controlling effect that evaporation-precipitation values have on surface salinity is seen in Fig. 7-12. This figure is a plot of net evaporation (evaporation minus precipitation) and surface salinity versus latitude. The climatic influence on the sea surface is obvious. In the following chapter, other effects of the wind on the sea surface will be discussed.

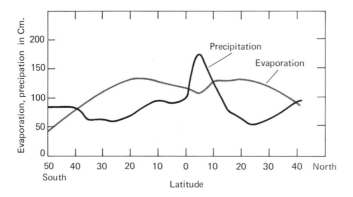

Figure 7-11 Latitudinal variation of average precipitation (P) and evaporation (E) over the world ocean. (From Sverdrup, Johnson, and Fleming, 1942)

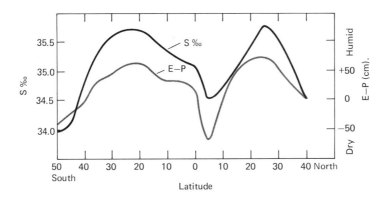

Figure 7-12 Comparison of average surface salinity and net evaporation (E–P) for the world ocean as a function of latitude. (After Sverdrup, Johnson, and Fleming, 1942)

7.7 *Perturbations in Global Weather—Storms at Sea*

Although it is the general circulation of the earth's atmosphere that is responsible for the large-scale circulation and surface circulation of the world ocean, it is departures from the general pattern that produce many of the features of the ocean that we observe. The most profound of these departures are storms. It is storms that produce the high winds and large waves that hamper shipping, attack our coasts, and make life miserable for sailors and oceanographers at sea. Storm waves create the most dramatic and rapid changes in the configuration of our coastlines and beaches. Such waves are of concern to engineers that design coastal and offshore structures and to shipping companies that plan optimium routes for their vessels. Storm waves cause the intense mixing in the surface water that triggers the annual productivity cycle described in a later chapter.

Major storms at sea are of two types: extratropical and tropical. Extratropical storms are prominent in winter weather patterns in the temperate latitudes of the earth. Tropical storms, called hurricanes, cyclones, or typhoons (from the Chinese *tai fung,* meaning supreme wind), occur in the part of the tropics lying more than 5° of latitude from the equator.

Extratropical Storms

These storms usually form at the polar front where cold, dense polar air moving southwestward meets warm temperate air moving northeastward. A perturbation at the polar front can cause the development of a local low pressure zone as shown in Fig. 7-13A and B. The perturbations are caused by ordinary variations in the winds near the polar front or by variations caused by coastlines, especially coastal mountains.

A local cyclonic circulation develops around a pressure low (Fig. 7-13B). Cyclonic circulation is clockwise in the southern hemisphere and counterclockwise in the northern hemisphere. A cold front separating the intruding polar air from temperate air extends from the pressure low for 500 to 3,000 km. A warm front develops where temperate air is shoved over a wedge of dense polar air by the cyclonic circulation. The cold front rotates about the low pressure center faster than the warm front does (Fig. 7-13C), so eventually it overtakes the warm front and forms an occluded front (Fig. 7-13D). If the air behind the cold front becomes warmed slightly, the cold front rides up over the cold polar air beyond the warm front and the occluded front that forms is of the warm type. If on the other hand the intruding polar air remains relatively frigid, it intrudes into air lying beyond the warm front, lofts the warm front, and forms a cold-type occluded front at the sea surface (Fig. 7-14).

The low pressure center moves generally westward in both hemispheres. Its rate of travel is intermediate between the wind speeds in the cold air and those in the warmer air but closer to those in the warmer air. During its travel the occluded front extends farther and farther until the low pressure cell is completely surrounded by cold air, and the warm air is lofted so high that it chills, falls, and mixes with the cold air. The pressure in the center becomes less distinct from that of the surrounding air and the storm system dissipates (Fig. 7-13E).

The severity of the storm is determined by the contrast between pressures

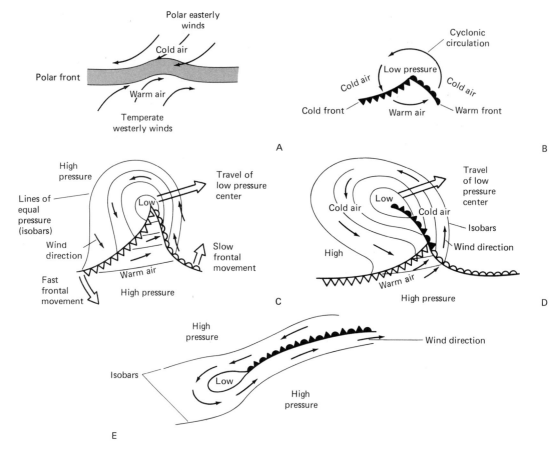

Figure 7-13 Formation and development of extratropical storm winds in the northern hemisphere. (A) A perturbation in the wind field occurs at the polar front. (B) Cyclonic circulation begins and the cold and warm fronts form. (C) The cold front begins to overtake the warm front. (D) Formation of an occluded front. (E) Complete occlusion and deterioration of the storm system. The wind speed is proportional to the spacing between isobars. Close spacing corresponds to high wind speeds. (Used with permission of McGraw-Hill, Inc.)

in the low and in surrounding air. Wind speeds of 140 kph (75 kts) are not uncommon. The storms are most frequent in the winter when temperature contrasts across the polar front are at a maximum. The winds associated with these storms produce winter waves. Summer swells in the northern hemisphere are produced in the southern hemisphere where it is a time of winter storms.

The paths of the low-pressure centers are governed by the distribution of high-pressure systems surrounding them. High-pressure cells over deserts on

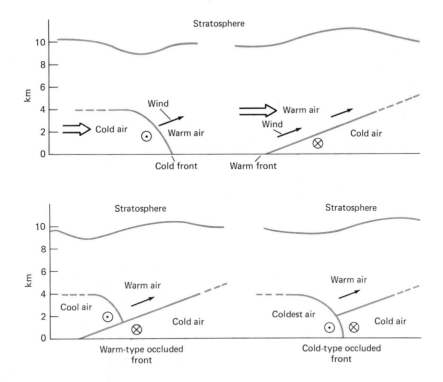

Figure 7-14 Front profiles looking north or east in northern hemisphere. The symbol ⊙ represents wind blowing at the observer, ⊗ represents wind blowing away from the observer. (Used with permission of McGraw-Hill, Inc).

land or in lower temperate regions are particularly effective in steering their motion. The fronts that sweep cyclonically around the low-pressure (Fig. 7-15) centers extend equatorward as far as 15° latitude (in extreme cases). The passage of a cold front or especially of an occluded front is marked by a sudden change in wind direction and in wind speed. The winds experienced at a fixed site at sea during frontal passage are shown in Fig. 7-16.

Tropical Storms

The most severe storms of the world ocean are the tropical cyclones. They bear different names in various ocean basins, but their genesis and morphology are the same. In the Atlantic they are hurricanes, in the Pacific, typhoons, and in the Indian Ocean, cyclones. They are called Willy Willy in Australia and Baguio in the Philippines.

These storms form where trade winds from one hemisphere of the earth are diverted to meet the trade winds of the opposite hemisphere. Diversion is

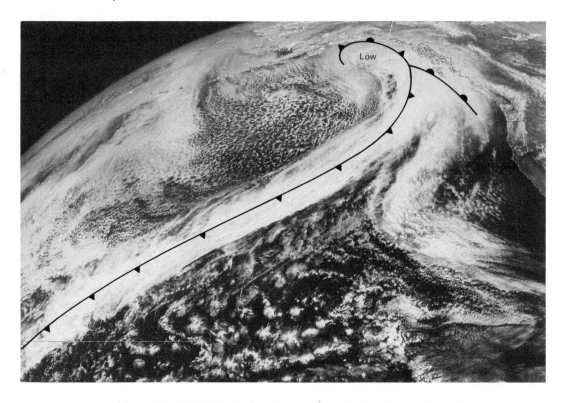

Figure 7-15 Satellite photo of an extra tropical cyclone with well-developed cold front and occluded front. Area is the Gulf of Alaska and the Northeast Pacific Ocean, March 10, 1977. (NOAA Photo)

usually produced by a continental mass and the seasonal shift of the global pattern of air circulation; the monsoon winds are also instrumental in the western Pacific and Indian ocean basins.

The boundary between the northeast trade wind belt and the southeast trades shifts north and south seasonally as shown in Fig. 7-17. The boundary is usually in the northern hemisphere except in the western Pacific and Indian oceans in February. Wherever the trade winds cross the equator, the Coriolis force deflection reverses. In areas where tropical storms generate, the deflection reversal is severe enough to bring the trade wind from both hemispheres into virtual opposition.

Tropical cyclones form when a perturbation of the wind field is caused by a shear-produced eddy or by a disturbance in the upper atmosphere. This leads to a local lowering of the barometric pressure at sea level that causes a convergence and attendant rising of air warmed at the surface of the ocean. A cyclonic circulation develops rapidly as the rising air lowers the barometric pressure even more. Air sweeps inward and upward in an ascending helix

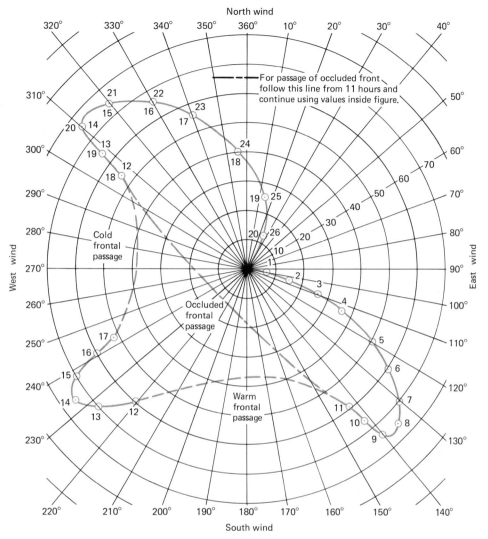

Figure 7·16 Diagram showing the wind speed and direction from which the wind blows at each hour during a frontal passage at hours 11 to 12. The site of observation is at the center of the diagram. This diagram represents an idealized northern hemisphere extratropical storm system bearing winds at 140 km per h. (From: Oceanographic Service, Inc., Goleta, CA)

until wind speeds exceeding 300 kph are developed. The fastest winds at the sea surface travel in a circular band surrounding an "eye" of exceedingly low pressure and light variable winds. The eye is from 10 to 30 km in diameter; most are usually about 25 km in diameter. The band of extreme winds is from 300 to 400 km wide. A satellite photo of such a storm system is shown in Fig. 7-18.

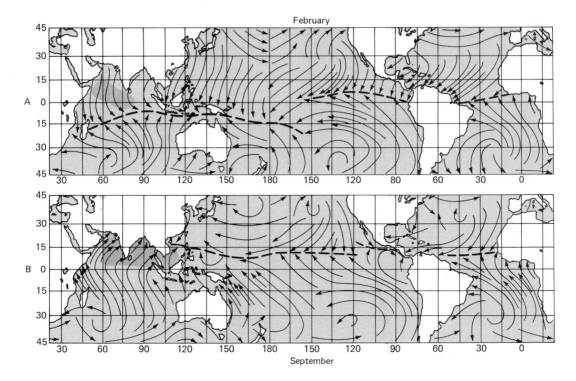

Figure 7-17 The winds over the world ocean during the tropical storm seasons of the (A) southern and (B) northern hemispheres. The dashed lines represent the boundary between the northeast and southeast trade wind belts. The shaded area shows the area of influence of the monsoons upon trade wind circulation. (After Byers, *General Meteorology*, Courtesy McGraw-Hill)

The areas where tropical cyclones form, their time of maximum occurrence, and the regions affected by these storms are given in Table 7-1. The parts of the world ocean affected by tropical cyclones are shown in Fig. 7-19.

Once formed, the tropical cyclone drifts westward enclosed in the trade wind belt. Its rate of travel is on the order of 10 to 30 kph. As the storm progresses, its rate of travel increases. Eventually it moves poleward with the global atmosphere circulation pattern, and its speed and direction of travel become erratic (see Fig. 7-20). Occasionally the eye becomes stationary for several hours, moves in a looping path, or speeds along at 90 kph.

When the tropical cyclone reaches land or moves into a region of relatively cold surface water it loses energy. Frictional retardation at the land surface (which is three to ten times as rough as the sea surface) slows the winds, and surrounding air is drawn into the eye. The pressure in the eye rises and the storm dissipates. Over cold water the storm is deprived of the thermal energy

Figure 7-18 Satellite photo of tropical storm. The eye at the center of low pressure is clearly visible. (NOAA Photo)

Table 7–1 Distribution of Tropical Cyclones in the World Ocean

Ocean	General region	Places of origin	Principal paths	Months of greatest frequency	Cyclone-free months (tropical)
Northern hemisphere					
Atlantic	West Indies	Cape Verde Islands and westward Western Caribbean	Through West Indies and northward to United States or Atlantic or into Mexico, Honduras, etc.	August, September, October	December to May, inclusive
Pacific	Southwestern North Pacific	Marshall Islands Philippine Region South China Sea	Through or near Philippines and northward toward China, Japan, etc.	July, August, September, October	February to April, inclusive
	West Coast of Central America	Gulf of Tehuantepec to Revillagigedo Islands	Northwestward to lower California or halfway to Hawaiian Islands	September, October	December to May, inclusive
Indian	Bay of Bengal	Southwestern part; other parts of Bay	Clockwise path into India or Burma	June to November, inclusive	January to March, inclusive
	Arabian Sea	Laccadive—Maldive Islands Sri Lanka region (?)	Clockwise into India or Gulf of Oman. Other doubtful paths	June, October, November	January, February, March, August (?)
Southern hemisphere					
Atlantic	None	None	None	None	All months
Pacific	Northwestern South Pacific	West of Tuamotu Islands Coral Sea	Westward to Coral Sea, counterclockwise along Australian coast or toward New Zealand	January, February, March	July, August, September
Indian	Madagascar-Mauritius	Cocos Islands and westward	Westward, then counterclockwise southward near Madagascar	January, February, March	July, August, September
	Northwestern Australia	Timor Sea	Counterclockwise along Australian coast	January to March, inclusive	July to September, inclusive

(From H. R. Byers, *General Meteorology*, New York: McGraw-Hill, 1944, p. 418, Table XX.)

(latent heat of condensation) that drives it, and it begins to dissipate, although not as rapidly as over land.

The circular winds in the tropical cyclone generate waves that move radially away from the eye. The waves moving from the forward right quadrant of the storm (in the northern hemisphere) tend to be greatest because they are longest under the influence of the wind.

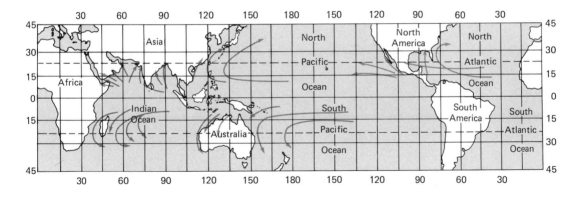

Figure 7-19 Paths of tropical cyclones in the world ocean. Note that no tropical cyclones occur between 5°N and 5°S latitudes. (From Byers, *General Meteorology*, courtesy McGraw-Hill)

At a site in the path of a tropical cyclone the winds build rapidly at first; they build less rapidly as maximum winds approach. The wind dies abruptly as the eye passes, and then maximum winds from the opposite direction spring up as abruptly as the eye moves away. The winds decrease gradually until the storm has passed well away from the site. The behavior of the wind at such a site is shown by the diagram in Fig. 7-21.

Not all perturbations creating local low pressure in the generating regions of tropical cyclones reach intensities that merit the title of hurricane or typhoon. Far more of these disturbances do not bear winds exceeding speeds of 65 kph (34 kts): Such systems are called tropical depressions. Systems with winds from 65 to 120 kph (35 to 65 kts) are called tropical storms.

Local Winds at Coasts

The coast represents a zone of transition between terrestrial winds and maritime winds. The physiography of the coast often alters the regional wind field (Fig. 7-22) to produce increased wind speeds or calm areas. The change in the frictional roughness of the surface over which the air moves causes rapid changes in the wind speeds as they pass to or from the sea. In regions with mountainous coasts the regional air circulation accumulates air up to elevations of the major mountain passes. Air spills through the passes in the mountains and descends the leeward slope to the sea as jets of high velocity wind. Frequently the air is warmed as it descends to regions of lowered pressure. The variety of names given to this orographic circulation is presented in Table 7-2.

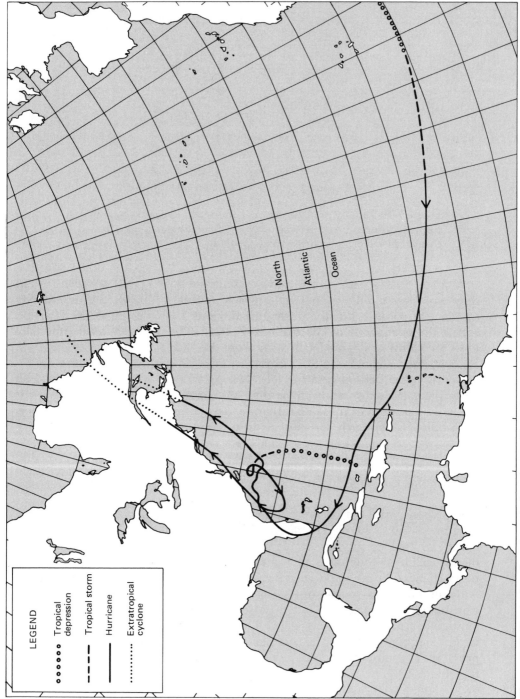

Figure 7-20 Typical paths of tropical cyclones. Note that some cyclones start as tropical depressions and eventually become extratropical cyclones.

LEGEND

∘∘∘∘∘ Tropical depression

- - - Tropical storm

——— Hurricane

∙∙∙∙∙ Extratropical cyclone

North Atlantic Ocean

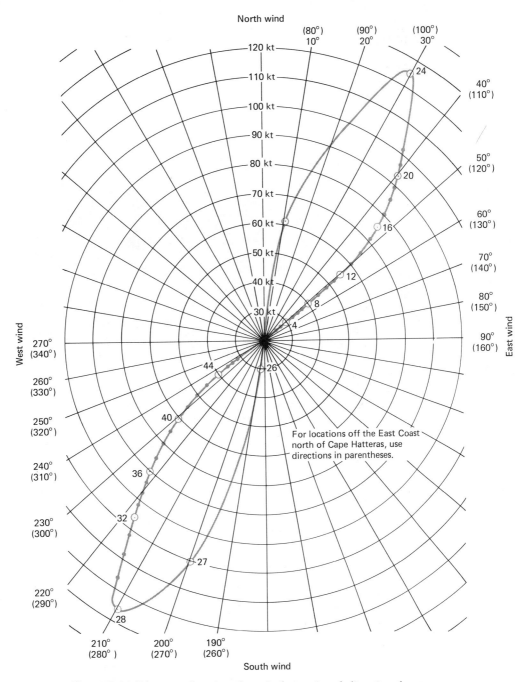

Figure 7-21 Diagram showing the wind speed and direction from which the wind blows at each hour during the approach and passage of an idealized northern hemisphere tropical cyclone whose eye arrives between the 25th and 26th hours. The maximum winds reach a speed of 240 km per h. (From: Oceanographic Services, Inc., Goleta, CA)

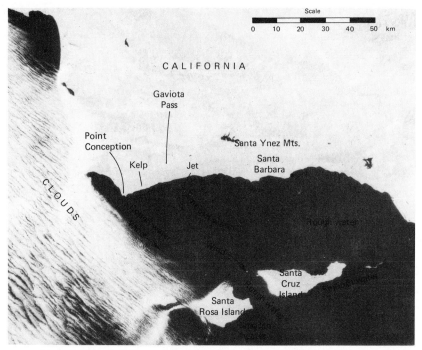

Figure 7-22 Satellite image of a part of the coast of southern California. A northwest wind curves around the mountainous headland at Point Conception. Air accumulates north of the mountains and a jet of wind spills through Gaviota Pass. The high winds roughen the sea surface, increasing its specular reflections. The path of the wind and the Gaviota wind plume are clearly visible. (From: Oceanographic Services, Inc./NASA)

Table 7–2 Orographic Winds

Name	Region applied	Name	Region applied
Santa Ana	Southern California	Pampero	Argentine coast
Föhn	Alps	Bora	Eastern Mediterranean
Tehauntepecer	Mexico & Central America	Zonda	Andes
Mistral	Western Mediterranean	Fall wind	General term
Williwaw	Aleutian coast	Sirocco	Northern Africa

Waterspouts

The marine equivalent to the tornado is the waterspout (Fig. 7-23). This funnel of rapidly rotating winds develops in unstable air that accompanies the squall line associated with cold fronts. Water is drawn up into the funnel, hence the name. Although awesome in appearance, a waterspout seldom causes damage because it is relatively rare at sea or it dissipates quickly upon reaching shore.

Figure 7-23 Waterspout just offshore of Santa Barbara, California.

reading list

BOLIN, B., *The Atmosphere and Sea in Motion*. New York: Rockefeller Institute Press in association with Oxford University Press, 1959. 509p.

BYERS, H. R., *General Meteorology* (2nd ed.). New York: McGraw-Hill, 1944. 645p.

DONN, W. L., *Meteorology, with Marine Applications* (2nd ed.). New York: McGraw-Hill, 1951. 465p.

Interaction Between the Atmosphere and the Oceans, National Academy of Sciences–National Research Council Publication 983. Washington, D.C., 1962. 43p.

KRAUSKOPF, K. B., *Fundamentals of Physical Science* (4th ed.). New York: McGraw-Hill, 1959. 653p.

STEWART, R. W., "The Atmosphere and the Ocean," *Scientific American*, CCXXl, No. 3 (September 1969), 76–86.

oceanic circulation

8

8.1 A Description of Currents in the Ocean

The water in the world ocean is always in motion. A variety of motions exists, each differing in the size and shape of its path and in the length of time that motion persists. Water circulates by following paths as large in scale as hemispheric, as in the North Pacific Ocean basin, and as small as the paths of eddies in the surf zone. Table 8-1 demonstrates the extent and diversity of the scales of circulation in the world ocean. The currents observed at any location in the ocean are a complex mixture of motions of several scales.

If currents are observed over a substantial interval of time, the pattern of water motion changes depending upon the temporal scale associated with each current component. Analyses of ocean currents show components that are either steady, periodic, episodic, or random. The relationship between temporal scales and size scales of ocean currents is shown also in Table 8-1, which shows that certain generalizations regarding currents can be made. Steady flow is associated with oceanic gyral circulation. Seasonal changes in coastal currents are periodic; changes in current speed and direction every 6 to 12 hours are related to tidal circulation; and wave action produces current changes 5 to 25 sec apart. Periodic changes on the order of 15 hours in current direction only is related to inertial flow (i.e., flow that is no longer driven by forces that initiated the motion). Episodic changes in currents usually are related to storms or other atmospheric phenomena. Such episodes last from a few hours to several days. Random changes in current speed and direction are largely a result of *turbulence* in the sea.

192

Table 8–1   Circulation in the World Ocean

	Type of flow	*Temporal nature of flow*
1.	*Oceanic gyres*	
	Flow around the north hemisphere and south hemisphere, parts of the Atlantic and Pacific ocean basins.	Steady, with turbulence of all sizes
	a. Narrow, swift, meandering streams at western edge	Steady
	b. Wide, steady flow along coastal boundaries	Steady
	c. Diffuse, weak circulation at the center of gyres	Random
2.	*Thermohaline circulation of water masses*	Steady
3.	*Boundary flow—local oceanic currents*	
	a. Part of the ocean gyres at boundaries, either coastlines or equatorial regions	Steady or seasonal
	b. Counter current between main oceanic circulation and boundary	Steady or seasonally periodic
	c. Undercurrents—relief flow under parts of major oceanic currents	Steady, locally seasonal
	d. Flow in straits or in restricted channels between seas and the ocean	Steady, locally seasonal
4.	*Coastal currents*	
	a. Local response of oceanic circulation to irregular coastal geometry; large turbulence eddies	Episodic to random
	b. Rings, closed circular currents detached from meanders in oceanic streams	Periodic at 1 revolution every 200–300 hrs
	c. Tidal streams	Strongly periodic
	d. Inertial currents caused by earth's rotation acting upon steady or decelerating currents in the ocean	Periodic change in direction
	e. Upwelling	Episodic
5.	*Localized currents*	
	a. Estuarine circulation	Steady plus tidal periodicity
	b. Interisland jet flow	Tidal periodicity
	c. Wind-drift and Langmuir cells	Episodic
	d. Storm surge induced currents	Episodic
	e. Littoral drift currents	Episodic
	f. Turbidity currents	Episodic
	g. Orbital circulation of waves	Strongly periodic at 5–25 sec
	h. Net wave transport	Steady but episodic
	i. Moderate-scale turbulence	Random
6.	*Small scale currents*	
	a. Wave swash	As periodic as waves
	b. Rip currents	Episodic
	c. Small-scale turbulence	Random

Turbulence

Turbulence is of extreme importance in the world ocean because it is the mechanism by which mixing is accomplished. Thermal energy and chemical substances, such as oxygen, carbon dioxide, and plant nutrients, are distributed through the ocean largely by turbulent mixing. Plankton are moved through the surface layers by turbulence and are kept bathed in nutrients by that effect. The transport of sediments in the nearshore zone is initiated and maintained by turbulence induced by breaking waves.

Turbulence is chaotic motion in a fluid and is perceived as an assortment of eddies that change shape and direction of travel in no apparent pattern. It is seen commonly in smoke, clouds, and in stirred liquids, especially liquids into which another colored liquid is poured. In the ocean, turbulence is observed in current measurements as nonsystematic deviations from the average flow. Fig. 8-1 shows a typical current record of steady flow containing turbulent noise. Such a record is analyzed by assuming that the random turbulent deviations from the average flow represent the sum of an unlimited number of harmonic oscillations, each characterized by a discrete frequency. The energy ($\frac{1}{2} mv^2$) associated with each frequency is extracted and plotted against its frequency to produce a spectrum of turbulent energy (Fig. 8-1B). The spectrum portrays the relative abundances of the turbulent components in the flow. If we assume that each frequency component of motion is rotational (turbulent motion follows curved paths), we can regard the frequencies as representing the sizes of the turbulent eddies in the flow. Low frequencies

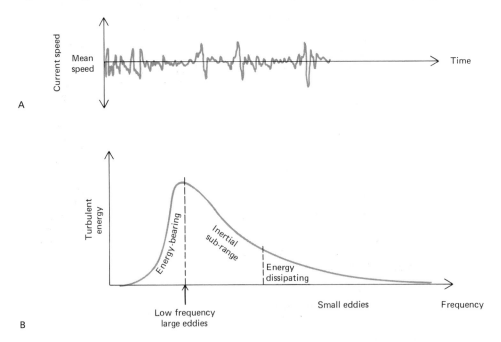

Figure 8-1 A record (A) of current measured at a site showing a steady flow containing turbulence. A turbulence spectrum derived from such measurements is shown in (B). (After B. Kinsman, *Journal of Geophysical Research*, Vol. 66, No. 6, 1961, copyright by the American Geophysical Union)

represent large eddies and high frequencies represent small eddies. We refer to the *scale of turbulence* in terms of the diameter of a circular eddy corresponding to the spectral frequency of turbulence.

Large eddies, called *energy-bearing eddies*, are formed as long as a localized force is applied to water. These eddies then give rise to smaller eddies that move under their own momentum. These eddies, called *inertial eddies*, in turn form smaller and smaller eddies until they become so small that water viscosity converts the energy of their motion into heat. The formation of *energy-dissipating eddies* is the terminal stage in turbulent mixing.

The size of the largest eddy that forms in turbulent flow is determined by the rate that energy is supplied to the flow (by, say, the wind) and the proximity to flow boundaries. In the open ocean, intermediate-scale eddy motions can be quite large, on the order of several hundred kilometers. Near a coast the maximum eddy size is smaller but still appreciable (Fig. 8-2). Eddies the size of large embayments have been observed.

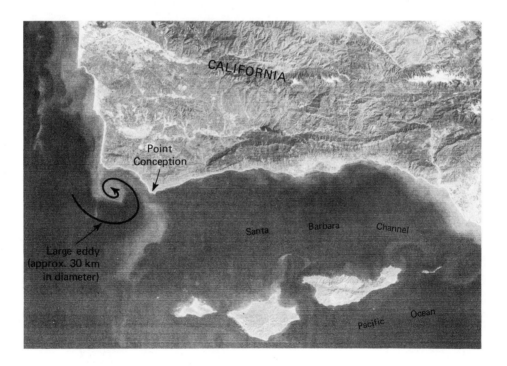

Figure 8-2 A satellite (LANDSAT-1) photo image of a portion of the coast of southern California. Large waves suspended fine sediments in coastal water, and tidal action carried the material into an offshore coastal current. Large eddies are seen where the current passes an irregularity in the coastline. The current has carried the sediment well over 30 km offshore. (Photo from NASA imagery)

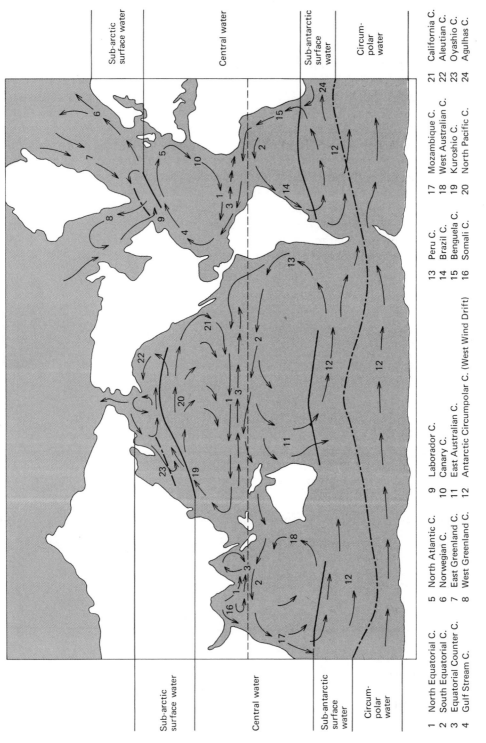

Figure 8-3 Surface currents and surface water of the world ocean. Also included are the major convergences. ⌒ = subtropical convergence (place of origin of Central Water); ⊶⌒ = arctic, antarctic convergence (place of origin of Intermediate Water). ⌒ = surface current.

1	North Equatorial C.	9	Laborador C.	17	Mozambique C.	21 California C.
2	South Equatorial C.	10	Canary C.	18	West Australian C.	22 Aleutian C.
3	Equatorial Counter C.	11	East Australian C.	19	Kuroshio C.	23 Oyashio C.
4	Gulf Stream C.	12	Antarctic Circumpolar C. (West Wind Drift)	20	North Pacific C.	24 Agulhas C.
5	North Atlantic C.	13	Peru C.			
6	Norwegian C.	14	Brazil C.			
7	East Greenland C.	15	Benguela C.			
8	West Greenland C.	16	Somali C.			

Sub-arctic surface water

Central water

Sub-antarctic surface water

Circumpolar water

Eddies in the inertial and energy-dissipating range are usually present near the surface of the world ocean. Only in the depths of ocean (away from the bottom) is the flow virtually free of turbulence of the inertial and energy-dissipating scales.

Surface Currents

Now let us turn our attention to the large scale circulation of the world ocean (we will consider coastal currents in the chapter on inshore oceanography). This circulation is characterized by many steady currents (Fig. 8-3). Short-term fluctuations do exist in the direction and magnitude of the major ocean currents, but, over a period of time, a consistent pattern prevails.

The most conspicuous features in Fig. 8-3 are the large gyres (currents moving in a circle) found in tropical and subtropical regions of each ocean basin. In the northern hemisphere, such gyres move in a clockwise direction, whereas the gyres of the southern oceans rotate counterclockwise. The currents on the western side of the subtropical gyres gain intensity as they flow to higher latitudes. This westward intensification is best developed in the Gulf Stream and in the Kuroshio of the northern Atlantic and Pacific ocean basins, respectively. These currents attain speeds of approximately 250 cm per sec. The currents at the western boundaries of the southern oceans also appear to be intensified, but to a lesser degree than in the northern hemisphere.

Between the major gyres in the equatorial regions of the ocean basins, countercurrents flow in directions opposite to the adjacent currents. Countercurrents do not follow closed paths, as do gyres. They tend to flow along straight paths at low latitudes. The Pacific Equatorial Countercurrent is well developed over the width of the Pacific basin and attains speeds of 50 cm per sec. The Atlantic Equatorial Countercurrent is generally restricted to the eastern Atlantic Ocean basin. The countercurrent in the Indian Ocean basin is not always present, because it is influenced strongly by the monsoons (see Sec. 7.4).

The pattern of movement of the colder water of the Arctic regions is more complex than in the lower latitudes. In the northern hemisphere, water movements appear to be influenced strongly by restrictive continental boundaries. The North Pacific Ocean basin contains its own circulation pattern. It is virtually closed off from the Arctic Ocean basin, and there is relatively little exchange to the north. In contrast, the North Atlantic Ocean basin is open to the Arctic Ocean basin, so great volumes of surface water are exchanged between the two basins. In the southern hemisphere, the largest surface flow in the world, the West Wind Drift, flows from west to east around Antarctica. Here, virtually nothing obstructs the surface currents in the endless expanse of water that surrounds the Antarctic continent.

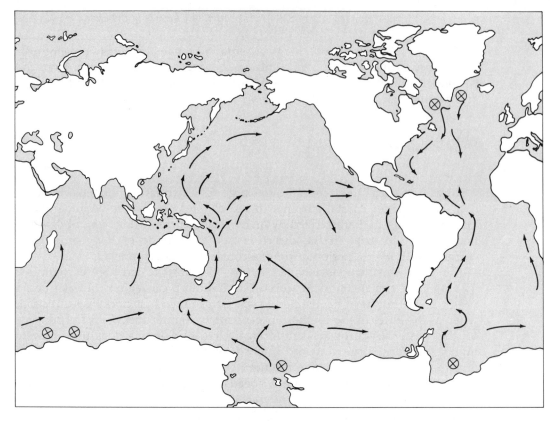

Figure 8-4 Inferred direction of flow of bottom water in the world ocean. ⊗ Area of origin of bottom water. (After Lonsdale, Johnson, Mantyla, and Taft and Jones, Wüst, and Wyrtki)

Deep Currents

Water movements are not limited to the surface of the world ocean. Although surface currents have greater speed and are more distinctly noticeable, they represent less than 10 percent of the water filling the ocean basins. Deep currents, on the other hand, are very difficult to measure because of their remoteness from the sea surface and their low velocity. Nevertheless, motion does exist at all depths.

A variety of methods is used to discern the general nature of deep circulation; the geographical distribution of physical and chemical properties, such as oxygen and temperature, drifting devices, current meters, and bottom photographs, all provide evidence of bottom currents. The evidence produces a somewhat incomplete picture of the deep circulation in the world ocean. The chart in Fig. 8-4 shows distinct areas where deep water forms and then flows toward lower latitudes.

8.2 *The Dynamics of Ocean Currents*

Driving Forces and Circulation Models

The permanent currents of the world ocean (aside from the tidal currents discussed in Chap. 10) are caused by the transfer of energy between the atmosphere and the sea surface. There are two ways in which this transfer occurs. First, kinetic energy is transferred to the sea surface from winds in the lower atmosphere. Second, an uneven distribution of potential energy is produced because cooling or evaporation at the sea surface causes an uneven distribution of mass in the ocean. In both cases, water is put into motion and often both the wind and the climatic effects are involved. It is important to understand that even though seawater is in motion at all depths of the world ocean, currents are produced and maintaned only at the surface.

An uneven distribution of energy in the ocean invariably produces a tendency toward the establishment of a uniform distribution. This is accomplished as energy is transferred from a region of high energy to one of lower energy (see Fig. 8-5). The tendency toward energy transfer is conveniently expressed in terms of a motivating force, and in the ocean the transfer of energy usually occurs as water motion. Two types of forces are associated with water motion. The first type, called *primary forces*, produces and maintains flow; the second type, the *secondary forces*, arises as a result of motion. Primary forces are:

1. The force of the wind exerted on the sea surface through frictional transfer of energy from the atmosphere to the ocean
2. Forces related to the relative differences in the distribution of mass in the ocean, but often expressed in terms of gravity, density, or a pressure gradient rather than as a difference in potential energy.

The secondary forces are:

1. The Coriolis effect arising from the earth's rotation
2. The force of friction which tends to retard motion as kinetic energy is converted to thermal energy.

In order to analyze the interplay of the forces producing ocean currents, we should construct a conceptual model in the form of physical equations. All the forces just listed must appear in an equation that describes the motion of water. The equation would state that the forces of gravity, wind stress, friction, and the Coriolis effect must balance, or else a water particle will accelerate. If the sum of these forces equals zero, then dynamic equilibrium exists and a steady state occurs.

The complete equations that describe water motion in the ocean are too

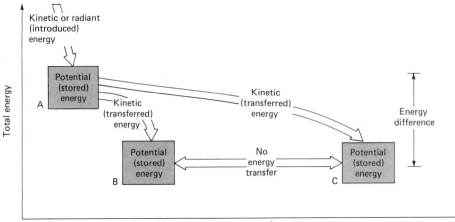

Figure 8-5 An energy budget diagram showing three locations in the ocean. At (A) energy is introduced as radiant energy from the sun or as energy transferred kinetically from the atmosphere. Energy is stored at (A) as a mass, thermal, chemical, electrical, or magnetic potential. The total energy at (A) is the sum of all these forms of energy and it exceeds the total energy stored at (B) and at (C). The same amount of energy is stored at (B) as at (C) but the distance of their separation from (A) is different. Because no difference in stored energy exists between (B) and (C), no transfer of energy takes place between them. Energy is transferred from (A) to (B) and to (C). Eventually, the same amount of energy will be transferred from (A) to (B) as is transferred from (A) to (C) but because (C) lies further from (A) than does (B), the *tendency* for transfer, that is, the *force* that is assumed to drive the transfer, is less in the (A) to (C) transfer. The relationship that applies is stated as:

$$\text{Force} = \frac{\text{Energy difference}}{\text{Distance of separation}}.$$

difficult to solve without simplification. In cases where some of the forces appear to be unimportant, those forces are ignored and the solutions of simplified equations are compared to the natural conditions to determine if the simplifying assumptions are valid. If the comparison is unfavorable, a reevaluation of the problem must be made. This technique helps an oceanographer understand which forces are important in different situations and how various oceanic phenomena interact. Several important examples are given below.

Wind-driven currents.   The first observations of wind-driven circulation were made by Fridtjof Nansen aboard the vessel *Fram* during her historic voyage (1893 to 1896) across the North Polar Sea drifting frozen in the ice. Nansen noted that ice floes did not move in the general direction of the wind but deviated 20° to 40° to the right. In 1902, V. W. Ekman modeled this phenomenon mathematically by equating the force produced by a steady wind blowing over the sea surface (frictional wind stress), the force arising from the earth's rotation (Coriolis), and the force of water's internal friction. He assumed a homogeneous sea (no horizontal pressure gradient forces) without lateral boundaries and a steady state (no acceleration). The mathematical solution of this famous work suggested the following:

1. Under the influence of a steady wind stress, surface water will flow 45° to the right of the wind in the northern hemisphere and 45° to the left in the southern hemisphere

2. At depth, the direction of motion of each water layer deviates to the right relative to that of the overlying water layer, because each lower layer is swept on by the motion of its overlying layer, just as the topmost one is swept on by the wind stress

3. The speed of each succeeding layer is less than the one above because of frictional losses as energy is transferred to underlying layers.

These three conclusions can be illustrated by a logarithmic spiral known as the *Ekman spiral* (Fig. 8-6). As a general rule, the speed of the surface layer is about 2 percent of the wind speed. The Ekman spiral also shows that at some depth the direction of the current moves at an angle of 180° to its surface

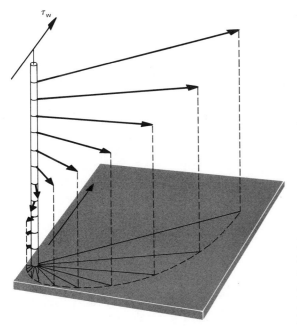

Figure 8-6 Ekman spiral in the northern hemisphere. τ_w is the force (stress) induced by the wind acting on the surface. (From Sverdrup, Johnson, and Fleming, 1942, by permission of Prentice-Hall, Inc.)

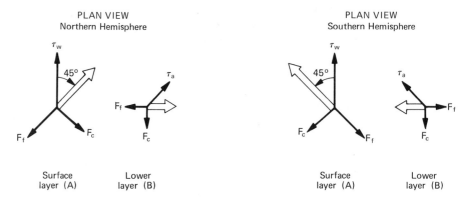

Figure 8-7 Force diagram for a wind-driven current. τ_w = wind stress (a force); τ_a = stress (a force) exerted by surface layer (A) on the lower layer (B); F_c = Coriolis force; F_f = force of friction (coupled with underlying layers). Double arrows represent direction of water motion.

counterpart; the magnitude of this deeper current, however, is much less than that at the surface (approximately 1/23 as great). This depth is called the *depth of frictional resistance*, below which the effects of the wind are considered negligible. A characteristic value for the depth of frictional resistance is 100 m. A force diagram for this model is given in Fig. 8-7.

A very important result of this phenomenon is the average direction in which water is transported. If the direction and magnitude of all the arrows from Fig. 8-6 are averaged, the resultant vector would be oriented 90° to the right of the wind in the northern hemisphere and 90° to the left in the southern hemisphere. Thus, the mean transport of water (called the *Ekman transport*) resulting from a steady wind blowing over the sea surface is oriented 90° to the right of the wind in the northern hemisphere and 90° to the left in the southern hemisphere (Fig. 8-8). To summarize, a piece of paper floating at the surface of the ocean in the northern hemisphere will drift approximately 45°

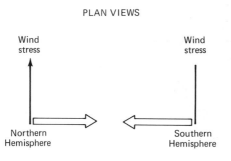

Figure 8-8 Direction of the Ekman transport (double arrows) relative to the wind stress (force) shown by single arrow.

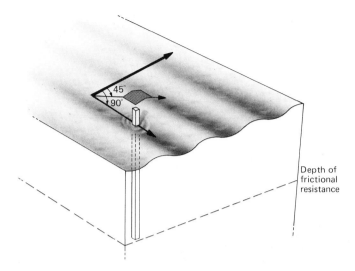

Figure 8-9 Direction of the surface water as compared to the average direction of the total layer of motion due to wind stress. The paper moves in the direction of the surface water whereas the weighted pole represents the average movement. Heavy arrow represents the wind direction.

to the right of the wind direction, whereas a wooden rod 100 m long floating vertically will drift 90° to the right (Fig. 8-9).

Comparisons of the Ekman theory with real observations are exceedingly few because of the difficulty in finding situations where all of Ekman's assumptions hold true and no secondary effects are present. Probably the best evidence in support of this theory is the *upwelling* effect due to Ekman transport in the vicinity of a coastline.

When a north wind blows along the west coast of a continent in the northern hemisphere, for example, water is transported 90° to the right of this wind (to the west), and the surface water moves away from the coast (Fig. 8-10A). This produces a sea surface that slopes slightly upward in the direction of the Ekman transport (Fig. 8-10B). Because of the coastal boundary, the water that moves in to take the place of the water removed must come from depth. The effect, therefore, of this particular wind is to bring cold, slightly more dense water to the surface along the coast (Fig. 8-10B). This phenomenon is called upwelling. If the wind blew in the opposite direction, the opposite effect would occur. The surface water would be "piled up" along the coast and therefore would *sink*. Various combinations of conditions causing upwelling or sinking are possible, depending on the hemisphere, and the shape and orientation of the coast, and the wind direction.

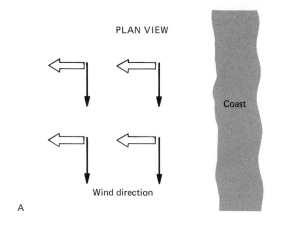

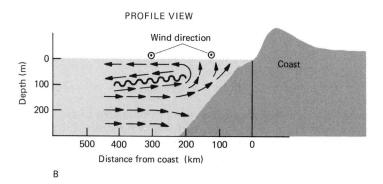

Figure 8-10 The process of upwelling, illustrating the initial effects of a north wind blowing along the west coast of North America. The Ekman transport (shown by double arrows) is to the west. The small arrows in (B) represent direction of water motion. The wavy line is the plane around which the motion exists. The symbol ⊙ indicates a wind moving toward the reader. (Modified from Defant, 1961)

It is probably the secondary effects accompanying this phenomenon that make it so noticeable. Not only can this colder, upwelled water affect the coastal climate and, in turn, decrease the enthusiasm of bathers, but it can also cause a redistribution of local fisheries because of the redistributed temperature and salinity conditions.

In addition, the chemical properties associated with the upwelled water cause another important process. This water comes up from depths of 200 to 300 m, so it is often quite rich in plant nutrients (relative to the surface water). Upon reaching the sunlit surface regions, it usually causes an increased growth of marine plants and *phytoplankton*.

This illustration of the importance of Ekman transport should not lead us to believe that a continental boundary is the only type of obstacle that can cause either upwelling or sinking. Water at the upstream or windward side of an

204

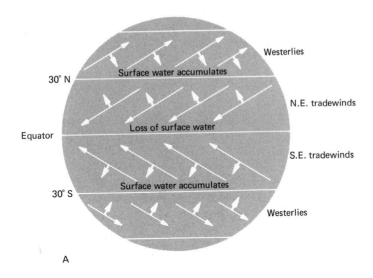

A

Figure 8-11A Movement of surface water resulting from the Ekman transport due to the surface winds over the sea. Short arrows represent the direction of Ekman transport.

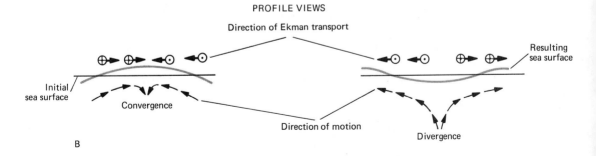

B

Figure 8-11B The shape of the sea surface and water motion associated with a convergence and divergence in the northern hemisphere. The symbol ⊙ indicates a wind moving toward the reader; ⊕ indicates a wind moving away from the reader.

island tends to be in a downwelling condition and upwelling occurs at the leeside of islands that interrupt broad currents or steady winds. Also, as illustrated by Fig. 8-11A, a zonal wind distribution in the global wind belts causes the same results. Note that a *divergence* is somewhat analogous to an upwelling condition in the open ocean (Fig. 8-11B), and a *convergence* is analogous to the sinking condition (Fig. 8-11B). It is important to observe the changes in the shape of the sea surface due to convergences and divergences.

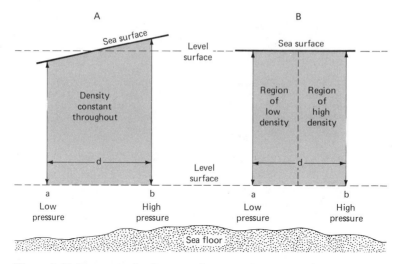

Figure 8-12 Two cases leading to a horizontal pressure gradient in the ocean. Case (A) could represent a situation where the wind blows water against a shore or where lateral variations in barometric pressure in the atmosphere deform the sea surface. Case (B) prevails where lateral changes in salinity and temperature lead to lateral differences in density.

Geostrophic flow. Geostrophic means "earth-turned" and refers to a condition of flow in which a *horizontal pressure gradient force* is balanced by the Coriolis effect. The idea of a horizontal pressure gradient force needs elaboration. First we must describe what is meant by a *level surface.* It is a surface situated such that gravity acts equally at every point upon it.* Now assume that a level surface exists beneath the surface of the ocean. Consider two cases, one where the sea surface is sloping (Fig. 8-12A) and one where the sea surface is level but a difference in density exists laterally (Fig. 8-12B). Let us determine the pressure along the lower level surface in both cases. We see that the pressure at the two points *a* and *b* (which are separated by a distance, *d*) is not equal in either case. This is because pressure, *P*, is

$$P = \frac{\text{force}}{\text{area}}$$

Force = mass × g (note that g is constant along the level surface)

Mass = density × volume

---

*For the purpose of this text you may assume that a level surface is everywhere equidistant from the center of the earth. For a precise definition, it is necessary to solve the universal law of gravitation at every point on the surface to assure that it is a surface of constant gravity.

Hence,

$$\text{Pressure} = g \times \text{density} \times \frac{\text{volume}}{\text{area}}$$

$$= g \times \text{density} \times \text{depth (because depth} \times \text{area} = \text{volume)}$$

In Fig. 8-12A, the depth from the sea surface to the level surface is greater at b than at a. In Fig. 7-12B, the depths are the same but the density at b exceeds that at a. The *horizontal pressure gradient* in each case is found by:

$$\frac{\text{Difference in pressures at } a \text{ and } b}{\text{Distance between } a \text{ and } b} = \frac{P_b - P_a}{d}$$

The force associated with a pressure gradient in the ocean can be derived directly from the horizontal pressure gradient by observing that

$$P_a = \frac{\text{force at } a}{\text{unit area}}$$

$$P_b = \frac{\text{force at } b}{\text{unit area}}$$

so a force equal to $P_b - P_a$ acts at each unit of area along the level surface.

The horizontal pressure gradient force can be understood in terms of an energy budget. In each case the mass over point b exceeds the mass over a. The masses represent stored potential energy, so the energy at b is greater than at a. Therefore, energy tends to be transferred from b to a and this tendency is represented by a force called the horizontal pressure gradient force.

The cases illustrated in Fig. 8-12 depict two principal causes of horizontal pressure gradient forces in the ocean:

1. A slope in the sea surface
2. Lateral variations in seawater density.

Geostrophic flow is established in response to an unbalanced horizontal pressure gradient force. Fig. 8-13A illustrates how a water parcel responds to a horizontal pressure gradient force. Position 1 represents the hypothetical initial condition in which a pressure gradient force (F_p) exists but the parcel has not yet moved. At this moment there is an imbalance of forces and the water parcel will accelerate. Positions 2 and 3 represent various stages in the acceleration of the water parcel when Coriolis effect (F_c) is causing a deflection of motion (this example is drawn for the northern hemisphere). Position 4 is the steady state condition where $F_c = F_p$ and the water parcel is moving at a constant speed parallel to the lines of equal pressure, called *isobars*. This particular representation assumes a frictionless fluid, for simplicity.

Steady state force diagrams for geostrophic currents are shown in Fig. 8-13B.

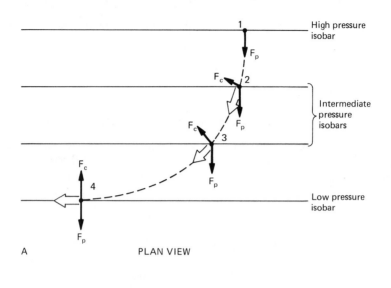

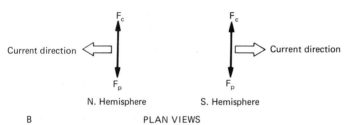

Figure 8-13 (A) In the northern hemisphere particle motion is deflected to the right as it accelerates in response to a pressure gradient. Positions 1, 2, and 3 represent the accelerating phase of the motion. Position 4 represents a steady state. F_p = gravitational force; F_c = Coriolis force; the double arrow points to the direction of motion. (B) Steady-state force diagram for a mass distribution current in the northern and southern hemispheres, respectively. F_p = force of gravity; F_c = Coriolis force.

Surface Circulation

The surface layer of water in most of the ocean is a shallow lens of warm, saline, low-density water floating on an immense volume of colder, less saline water of greater density. Surface water is warmed by large amounts of solar radiation in the subtropical regions and becomes relatively saline by evaporation. The boundary between the surface layer and deep water is marked by a sharp *thermocline*. Because of the sharp density discontinuity at its lower boundary, the surface layer moves in a system of currents that has only a slight physical connection with deep circulation.

The surface currents of the world ocean are driven primarily by zonal wind patterns in the lower atmosphere. Ekman transport tends to move low-density

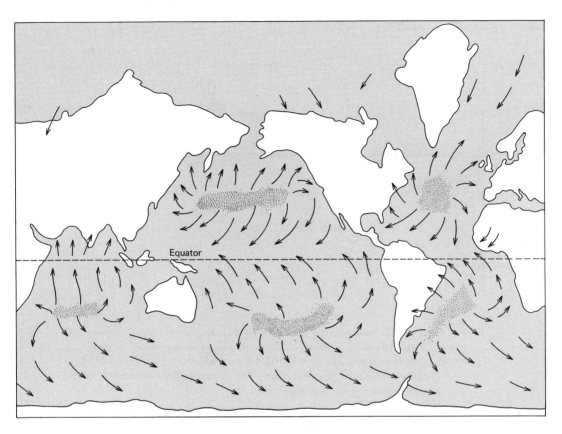

Figure 8-14 Surface winds over the world ocean (average for July). Stippled areas are regions where surface water accumulates due to Ekman transport. (After U.S. Navy Hydrographic Office Publication No. 9, 1958)

surface water at right angles to the wind direction where it accumulates between the wind belts. This is illustrated in Figs. 8-11 and 8-14. It has been calculated that water accumulated in the zone between the trade winds and westerlies causes the sea surface to rise approximately 2 m. The accumulation of water produces sea surface slopes that lead to horizontal pressure gradients and geostrophic flows. Surface circulation, then, is both wind-driven and geostrophic, and a realistic model to describe this flow should include:

1. The wind stress
2. The horizontal pressure gradient caused by surface slope
3. The Coriolis effect.

Friction is omitted because it is negligibly small compared to the other forces in this model. Examples of force diagrams for the North and South Equatorial currents are shown in Fig. 8-15.

The direction of the surface current determined by the forces shown in the

MAP VIEW

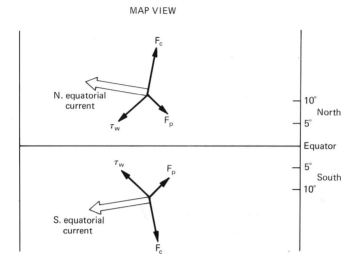

Figure 8-15 Forces acting at the North Equatorial and South Equatorial currents. The flow is steady (nonaccelerating) so the forces in the diagrams sum to zero. τ_w = wind stress force; F_c = Coriolis force; F_p = horizontal pressure gradient force. The direction (but not speed) of the flow is shown by the double arrows.

diagrams in Fig. 8-15 is more or less parallel to the wind direction, but some deflection exists. Deflection is to the right in the northern hemisphere and to the left in the southern hemisphere. The angle of deflection is less than that proposed in the pure wind drift circulation model.

One important current seems to oppose this pattern. It is the Equatorial Countercurrent that is present in all oceans (Fig. 8-3). One simple hypothesis states that this current also is produced and maintained by wind stress, gravity, and the Coriolis effect but in slightly different associations. The asymmetry of the countercurrent about the equator reflects the asymmetry of atmospheric circulation (i.e., it proves the existence of a meteorological equator).

Water driven westward by the trade winds forms the North and South Equatorial currents. These currents pile up water against the east coasts of continents. For example, the inclination of this accumulated water in the Atlantic Ocean basin is thought to be approximately 4 cm per 1,000 km. Most of the surface water turns poleward after reaching the continents. However, some of it flows back toward the east as a countercurrent within the calm (called the *doldrums*) that exists between the trade winds.

Because the development of the countercurrent is determined by the amount of water accumulated, the shape of the continents has an important influence (see Fig. 8-3). The bulge of the northeast coast of South America deflects the Atlantic Equatorial Current northward, so the Atlantic Countercurrent is only of moderate extent. In contrast, the coast of Southeast Asia is shaped like a basin and causes much greater accumulation of water. Hence, the Pacific Countercurrent is well developed and extends across the entire Pacific Ocean basin. In the Indian Ocean basin, the countercurrent is seasonal because of the influence of the monsoons.

The maximum speed of the countercurrent is approximately 50 cm per sec, and the volume transport is about 25 million m^3 per sec. The speed of the North and South Equatorial currents is approximately 100 cm per sec.

Up to this point, we have discussed only the causative forces and the configuration of the surface circulation. In order to complete the picture, a third dimension must be considered—that is, the thickness of the surface layer and the vertical circulation within it.

The lower limit of the thermocline varies between approximately 400 m (at the equator) and 900 m (30° latitude). For practical considerations, however, the lower limit of the active surface can be considered as 200 to 300 m. At this depth in the middle and low latitudes, there is a strong pycnocline below which relatively vigorous circulation is lacking (Fig. 8-16). The thickness of the surface layer varies according to the presence of convergences and divergences produced by circulation. This vertical circulation is caused by the effects of both winds and climate. For example, the force diagram in Fig. 8-15 shows a slight poleward component of the surface flow, which, by itself, would cause a divergence between the North and South Equatorial currents (and likewise a convergence between the equatorial and more northern currents). Superimposed upon this pattern are the effects of climate on the sea surface; that is, the climate causes density changes in the surface water that change vertical circulation within the surface layer. Therefore, at midlatitudes, under the subtropical highs, excessive evaporation causes the surface water to sink because of increased density. In contrast, the density of equatorial water is decreased by the excessive precipitation in the doldrums. Cells of vertically circulating water are produced, and they change the depth of the thermocline as a result of these convergences and divergences.

A schematic diagram of this circulation is represented in Fig. 8-17. Remember that the meridional or poleward circulation (represented by arrows) is indeed very sluggish as compared to the east–west components. This fact does not imply, however, that meridional flow is not important. The equatorial divergences are important biologically because nutrient-rich water is welled up into the sunlit surface regions, enhancing otherwise poor biological growth in the equatorial regions of the world ocean.

By combining Figs. 8-3, 8-16, and 8-17 conceptually, we can visualize the average shape, physical properties, and currents within the surface layer. The picture that results differs, however, from the real ocean. It does not explain

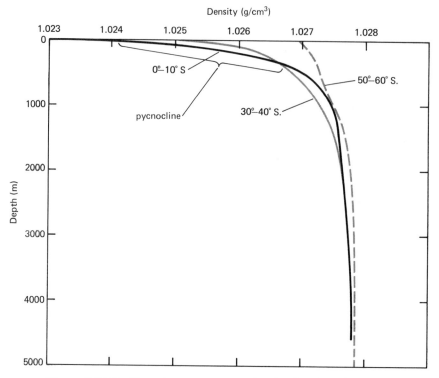

Figure 8-16 Profiles of average water density for three latitudinal zones in the Pacific Ocean. (Data from Muromtsev, 1958)

the presence of strong currents on the western boundaries of the ocean basins. It has been postulated that the westward intensification of the subtropical currents are a result of the following:

1. The force of the wind as it rotates around the surface gyres
2. The friction against continental boundaries
3. The change of the Coriolis parameter with latitude.

An example of a simplified theoretical solution to this combination of forces is illustrated in Fig. 8-18. Note the gross similarities to the major surface current gyres in Fig. 8-3.

Because these currents in the western part of each major gyre are very narrow and yet must transport the same quantity of water as the equatorial currents (except for that lost to countercurrents), they must be deeper and swifter. Within the core of the Gulf Stream, speeds of greater than 200 cm per sec have been measured. Slower speeds still persist at depths exceeding 1,000 m.

In the Pacific, the Pacific Equatorial Undercurrent moves 125 to 150 cm per

PROFILE VIEW

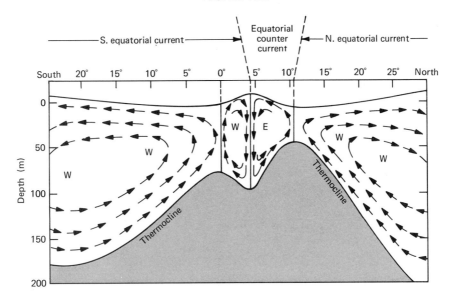

Figure 8-17 Schematic representation of the zonal and meridianal components of the surface circulation in the Atlantic Ocean (the topography of the thermocline is exaggerated in the vertical scale about 1:1 million; that of the physical sea surface even more); W indicates current toward west; E indicates current toward east. (After Defant, 1936)

sec to the east; it lies 100 m under the South Equatorial Current at the Equator. This departure from the simple scheme in Fig. 8-17 is not understood completely.

A narrow, swift current in the world ocean usually follows a meandering path that is constantly shifting about its average course. Frequently the meanders become so distended that they break off the main stream and become small gyres called *rings*. Rings are narrow bands of swiftly flowing water that enclose water either warmer or colder than the water surrounding them. The mode of formation of rings from the Gulf Stream is illustrated in Fig. 8-19. The rings are several hundred kilometers in diameter, extend several thousand meters deep, and rotate at speeds from 1 to 4 km per h. They migrate several kilometers per day and last for 2 to 3 years before dissipating. The rings have no source of energy once they detach from the main stream so they gradually decay by losing energy through viscous friction. Rings have been observed that formed from the Kuroshio (where they are called Siome), from the Antarctic Circumpolar Current, and from the Loop Current in the Gulf of Mexico. They are probably associated with every swift, narrow stream in the world ocean.

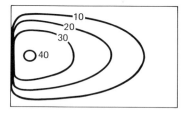

Figure 8-18 Flow in a theoretical ocean. The flow is parallel to the numbered lines (called streamlines). The closer together the lines, the faster the flow between them. The ocean is considered to be rectangular and of equal depth in this model. Wind stress is taken to vary with latitude such that it is at a maximum at the poles and the equator and at a minimum at mid-latitudes. The Coriolis force is taken to increase steadily from the equator to the pole. (After Stommel, 1948, *Trans. Amer. Geophys. Union*, Vol. 29, No. 2)

Deep Circulation

Approximately 90 percent of the volume of the world ocean is contained below the surface layer, even though the currents flowing in this region are produced and maintained within an area that comprises only about 25 percent of the earth's sea surface. In contrast to the surface layer where wind stress is the primary driving force, deep circulation is driven by horizontal pressure gradient forces arising from density differences within the water. These differences are produced and maintained by the climate that exists poleward of the meteorologic and oceanic polar front (note the Arctic and Antarctic convergences in Fig. 8-3). Movements within the deep sea are the result of water sinking because its density has been increased relative to the surrounding water. In the polar and subpolar parts of the world ocean, surface water, cooled strongly by the prevailing climatic conditions or made highly saline by the freezing of sea ice, becomes more dense than the underlying water. As a result, this water sinks to a level at which it is neutrally buoyant with respect to the surrounding water and spreads laterally in the direction of horizontal pressure gradients that may exist. Such circulation is called *mass distribution* circulation. It is also called *thermohaline* circulation because it results from changes in temperature and salinity along global climate belts. Only two forces are influential in this type of motion: the horizontal pressure gradient force and the Coriolis effect. In this respect deep circulation is geostrophic.

Actually, sinking takes place at several distinct places in the subpolar and polar parts of the world ocean. Because these places are at different latitudes, and the climate becomes more severe at higher latitudes, the water that sinks within each of these places has different densities and therefore sinks to different depths. As a result, deep-ocean water is separated into individual *water masses,* each having independent physical characteristics, movements, and origins. Water that sinks at the subarctic convergence (Fig. 8-3) flows to

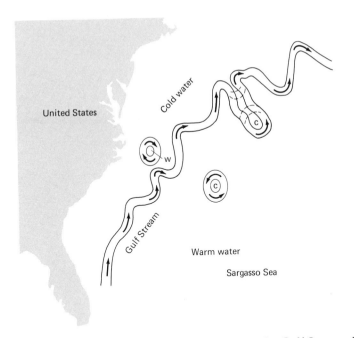

Figure 8-19 The formation of rings in the Gulf Stream. Rings west of the Gulf Stream enclose warm water from the Sargasso Sea. Rings east of the Gulf Stream enclose cold-water cores. The dashed lines indicate the imminent separation of a cold core ring from a distended meander. Warm core rings are short-lived because of limited space between the Gulf Stream and the coast. (From R. K. Kerr, *Science*, Vol. 198, October 1977, pp. 387–389. Copyright 1977 by the American Association for the Advancement of Science.)

relatively shallow depths and forms the *intermediate water mass.* As we might expect, the denser water flowing beneath the intermediate water mass and filling deeper parts of the ocean basins is produced in the higher latitudes where the climate is most severe. Thus, the *deep-* and *bottom-water masses* of the world ocean are derived mainly from the Arctic and Antarctic regions of the world.

8.3   *The Water Masses*

Analysis of the global distribution of water temperature and salinity has shown that immense volumes of seawater can be distinguished by unique characteristics of temperature and salinity. If the temperature of a parcel of water is plotted against its salinity on a graph constructed with appropriate axes, a useful diagram called a *T-S diagram* is obtained. Lines of equal density (represented as $\sigma_t = 1,000 \, (\rho - 1)$) can be drawn upon such a diagram to

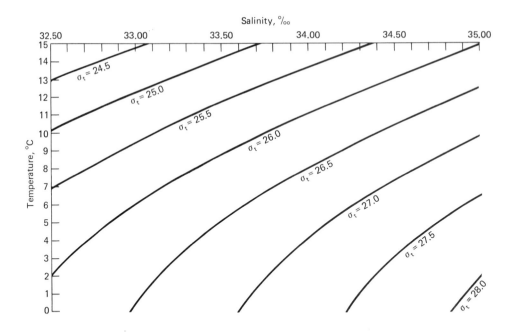

Figure 8-20 Specimen of a blank T-S graph used for plotting the results of seawater analyses. Lines of equal density, ρ, are shown in terms of σ_t where $\sigma_t = 1{,}000\,(\rho - 1)$.

provide a rapid means of determining the density of a water parcel (Fig. 8-20). Figure 8-21 gives some examples of T-S diagrams for various geographic regions and illustrates how *water masses* can be defined and recognized.

Identifiable water masses exist because surface water tends to circulate within rather broad latitudinal zones where it acquires temperature and salinity characteristics determined by the heating, cooling, precipitation, or evaporation conditions. Also, the water that sinks in a region possesses (to varying degrees) the surface water characteristics of that region. Therefore, when a body of water sinks and flows to another area, its physical characteristics may serve as an indicator of its origin. Consequently, a water mass can be traced thousands of kilometers from its origin by observing its temperature and salinity. Eventually, the characteristics of a given water mass will change because it mixes with other water masses; within limits, however, this method of tracing water is a valuable oceanographic tool.

For convenience, surface water has been named in accordance with its geographical location (see Fig. 8-3). *Central water* occurs within the major gyres of the world ocean. Subarctic and subantarctic water lies between the subtropical convergences and the Arctic and Antarctic convergences. The water south of the Antarctic convergence is called *circumpolar water*.

A convenient way to visualize the water mass structure of the world ocean

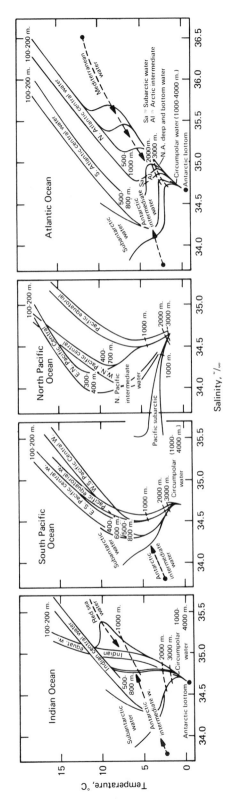

Figure 8-21 Temperature–salinity relations of the principal water masses of the oceans. (From Sverdrup et al., 1942, by permission of Prentice-Hall, Inc.)

217

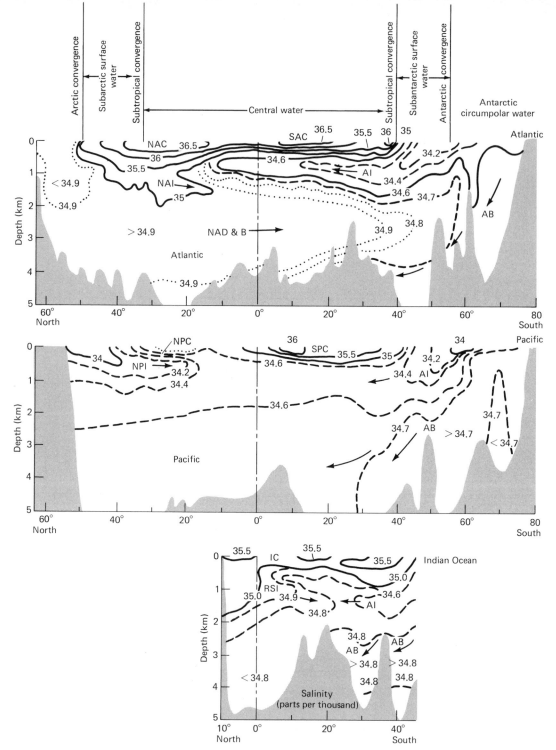

Figure 8-22 Vertical distribution of salinity in the three ocean basins. Arrows indicate general flow directions. Abbreviations for the water masses are given in Table 8-2. (Adapted in part from Dietrich, 1963, and from Wüst, 1950)

is to plot the typical salinity distribution in a longitudinal slice through each of the three ocean basins. Both temperature and salinity should be plotted for a more correct picture; however, the single profiles of salinity are simpler and identify the major water masses adequately (Fig. 8-22). The positions showing flow directions also are included in Fig. 8-22. The actual ranges of temperature and salinity associated with the major water masses are tabulated in Table 8-2.

Table 8–2   Major Water Masses in the World Ocean

Water mass	Temp. °C	Salinity ‰
Central water masses		
N. Atlantic water (NAC)	8–19	35.1–36.5
S. Atlantic water (SAC)	6–17	34.7–36.0
W. North Pacific water (NPC)	6–18	34.0–34.9
W. South Pacific water (SPC)	10–17	34.5–35.6
Indian water (IC)	7–16	34.5–35.6
High latitude surface water masses		
Atlantic subarctic water	4–5	34.6–34.7
Pacific subarctic water	3–6	33.5–34.4
Subantarctic water	3–10	33.9–34.7
Antarctic circumpolar water	0–2	34.6–34.7
Intermediate water masses		
Arctic intermediate water (NAI)	3–5	34.7–34.9
N. Pacific intermediate water (NPI)	4–10	34.0–34.5
Antarctic intermediate water (AI)	3–7	33.8–34.7
Mediterranean intermediate water (MI)	6–12	35.3–36.5
Red Sea intermediate water (RSI)	8–12	35.1–35.7
Deep and bottom water masses		
N. Atlantic deep and bottom water (NAD and B)	2–4	34.8–35.1
Antarctic bottom water (AB)	−0.4	34.7

(After H. U. Sverdrup, M. W. Johnson, and R. H. Fleming, *The Oceans.* Englewood Cliffs, N.J.: Prentice-Hall, Inc., 1942. 1087p.)

Surface Water Masses

Central water mass.   The central water mass is the water between the subtropical convergences at 30° to 35° north and south latitudes (Figs. 8-22 and 8-23). It extends down to the permanent thermocline. This water mass is subdivided into small units that have about the same density but differ in their physical

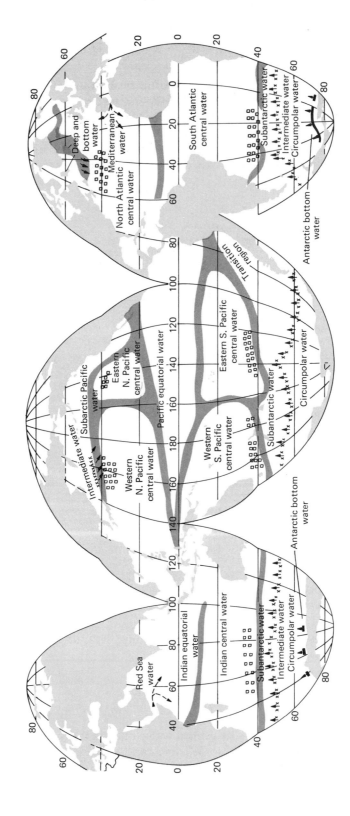

Figure 8-23 The geographic distribution of water masses that have common vertical salinity and temperature distributions, as denoted by their T–S curves. Squares mark the regions in which the central water masses are formed; crosses indicate the lines along which the Antarctic and Arctic intermediate waters sink. (From Sverdrup et al., 1942)

characteristics, depending on their location (Table 8-2). For example, the North Atlantic surface water is the most saline water in the ocean. In contrast, excessive dilution in the North Pacific Ocean basin is illustrated by the low salinities of the North Pacific Central water mass.

To summarize, the central water mass of the world ocean is characterized by temperatures between 6° and 19°C and salinities from approximately 34.0 to 36.5 parts per thousand.

High latitude surface water masses. Surface water masses in the temperate zones between the subtropical and subarctic or subantarctic convergences are called subarctic and subantarctic surface water masses (Fig. 8-23). These water masses are formed at latitudes characterized by cool temperatures and high rainfall, so they tend to be colder and less saline than the central water masses (Table 8-2).

The most extensive surface water mass in the polar regions of the three major ocean basins is the Antarctic Circumpolar water mass that flows from west to east around the Antarctic continent. This water mass extends to a considerable depth (approximately 3.5 km) and has very uniform temperature (0° to 2°C) and salinity (34.6 to 34.7 parts per thousand).

Intermediate Water Masses

Intermediate water masses directly underlie the central water masses and are formed in the regions of the Arctic and Antarctic convergences. They extend to a depth of 1,500 m (Fig. 8-22). Because intermediate water originates in several areas, a precise temperature and salinity value cannot be assigned to one water mass. Actually several water masses can be identified which are characterized by a range of values that vary according to the origin of the water. As in the case of the Central water mass, the Intermediate water mass can be subdivided according to origin and physical characteristics. The subdivisions are given in Table 8-2.

Of these subdivisions, the Antarctic Intermediate water mass is most extensive. This water originates from the subantarctic surface water that surrounds the earth between the subtropical and Antarctic convergences (Fig. 8-23). Because this region is so widespread, the water that sinks mixes to a certain degree and finally becomes the Antarctic Intermediate water mass found in all ocean basins. This water flows northward to about 20° north latitude in the Atlantic Ocean basin and approximately 10° south latitude in the Pacific and Indian ocean basins (Fig. 8-22).

The origins of water masses in the northern basins of the world ocean are restricted by the geometry of the continents and ocean basins in the northern hemisphere. In fact, the formation of the Arctic Intermediate water masses (North Pacific and North Atlantic) is restricted to the western portions of the Pacific and Atlantic basins. In the North Pacific Ocean basin, subarctic surface water cools and sinks to become the relatively dilute North Pacific Intermediate water mass, which has the temperature and salinity range given in Table 8-2. The intermediate water mass formed in the North Atlantic Ocean basin also originates from subarctic surface water which has been cooled in the winter. Because of the high evaporation over the North Atlantic Ocean basin, however, the North Atlantic Intermediate water mass is relatively saline (Table 8-2).

Some water in the world ocean is so homogeneous that it has a single temperature and salinity and can be represented by a single point on a T-S (temperature-salinity) diagram. Such water is called a *water type*. It is thought that the water masses of the world ocean are formed by mixing huge amounts of two or more water types. Two important intermediate water types are formed in the Mediterranean and Red seas. The Mediterranean Sea water type leaves the Straits of Gibraltar with a salinity of 38.1 parts per thousand and a temperature of about 13°C. It flows below the North Atlantic and Antarctic Intermediate water masses, and, even though its temperature and salinity change rapidly, it can be traced over most of the Atlantic Ocean basin.

Much less is known of the Red Sea water type. It has a temperature of about 10°C and a salinity of approximately 35.7 parts per thousand. The water type extends over much of the equatorial and western regions of the Indian Ocean basin.

Deep Water Mass

By far the most conspicuous source of the deep water mass lies in the Labrador and Irminger seas of the western North Atlantic Ocean basin (Fig. 8-23). This water results from the mixing of high-salinity water from the Gulf Stream and subarctic surface water. In the winter, the mixture cools and sinks and it flows below the intermediate water mass. As it moves southward it rises over the more dense Antarctic bottom water mass (Fig. 8-22). Thus, the North Atlantic deep water mass extends completely to the floor of the North Atlantic Ocean north of 30° latitude, but it is sandwiched between the intermediate and bottom water masses south of this latitude. The Atlantic deep-water mass is characterized by a temperature of 3°C and a relatively high salinity of 34.9 parts per thousand.

No deep water mass is formed in either the Pacific Ocean basin (except for small amounts from the Okhotsk Sea) or in the Indian Ocean basin.

Bottom Water Mass

The Antarctic bottom water mass contains the most dense water of the world ocean. It is formed off the Antarctic continent in the winter and spreads northward into all three ocean basins (Fig. 8-23). This water mass has been traced as far north as 30° north latitude (Fig. 8-17).

Freezing plays an important part in the formation of the Antarctic bottom water mass. In winter, large amounts of water are frozen over the continental shelf of the Weddell Sea. The residual brine flows down the continental slope and mixes with approximately equal parts of circumpolar surface water to form a water mass with a temperature of −0.4°C and salinity of 34.7 parts per thousand.

To summarize, the water of the world ocean is arranged in layers that originate at the sea surface at higher latitudes and extend under the surface water in tropical regions. A latitudinal arrangement of the water masses at the surface of the world ocean shows the same arrangement as the succession of water masses with depth (Fig. 8-17). The succession is: (1) central water mass (within the surface layer), (2) intermediate water mass, (3) deep water mass, and (4) bottom water mass. The transition from the central water mass to the underlying intermediate water mass is rather abrupt, but the other boundaries are quite diffuse, and the layers grade into each other.

It should be noted that all of the water masses mix with surrounding water as they flow. Therefore, they slowly change and lose their identities as they move away from their sources. This whole system of oceanic circulation is always in motion; water mixes, returns to the surface to be diluted, evaporated, or cooled, and sinks again to continue the cycle of oceanic circulation. Studies of the distribution of naturally occurring radioactive carbon in the sea (see Chap. 15) indicate that the mixing cycle of bottom water takes about 1,000 to 1,600 years in the Pacific Ocean basin and about half that time in the Atlantic and Indian ocean basins. These mixing times (also expressed as *turnover rates* or *residence times*) are verified by corresponding observations using radium (Ra−226).

The amount of radiocarbon in a body of water depends upon the age of the water and the degree of mixing with masses of water with different radiocarbon concentrations. Bottom water in the Pacific Ocean basin mixes relatively little and it has low concentrations of radiocarbon. These facts indicate that deep water is rather old. The radiocarbon concentrations at the bottom of the Pacific decrease from south to north in a manner suggesting that the water movement from the Antarctic northward proceeds at about 0.05 cm per sec.

Surface water has a residence time of 10 to 20 years and is considerably younger than the deep water in the world ocean. These conclusions are based on assumptions concerning the nature of mixing in surface waters and the exchange of radiocarbon between the ocean and atmosphere.

reading list

MUNK, W., "The Circulation of the Oceans," *Scientific American*, CXCIII, No. 3 (September 1955), 96–104.

NEUMANN, G., AND W. J. PIERSON, *Principles of Physical Oceanography*. Englewood Cliffs, N.J.: Prentice-Hall, Inc. 1966. 545p.

PICKARD, G. L., *Descriptive Physical Oceanography*. Elmsford, N.Y.: Pergamon Press, 1968. 200p.

SVERDRUP, H. U., M. W. JOHNSON, AND R. H. FLEMING, *The Oceans*. Englewood Cliffs, N.J.: Prentice-Hall, Inc., 1942. 1087p.

VON ARX, W. S., *An Introduction to Physical Oceanography*. Reading, Mass.: Addison-Wesley, 1962. 422p.

9.2 General Features and Description of Waves

In order to describe and discuss waves, we must first introduce descriptive terminology. A schematic profile of an ideal surface wave and its component parts is presented in Fig. 9-1.

Most waves move in what is called the *direction of propagation*. The *celerity* is the speed with which a crest or trough moves in the direction of propagation. The *period* of a wave is the interval of time required for successive crests or troughs to pass a fixed point: for example, successive crests of waves with an 8-sec period will pass a fixed point every 8 sec.

The length, period, and celerity of a wave are related. For all progressive (i.e., laterally moving) waves, this relationship can be demonstrated in the formula:

$$C = \frac{L}{T} \qquad [9\text{-}1]$$

where C = celerity or speed, L = wavelength, and T = period. Note that this formula does not state which factors govern the velocity of a progressive wave. It merely relates speed and the wave characteristics.

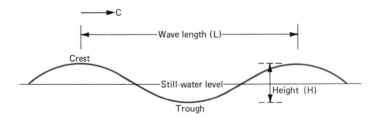

Figure 9-1 Component parts of an ideal water wave consist of speed or celerity (C), wave length (L), height (H), crest, and trough.

9.3 Classification of Waves

Sea waves are classified by (1) the motion of the sea surface, (2) the relationship of the waves to the depth of water, (3) wave origin, and (4) period or other wave property (Table 9-1). In this text, the subject of ocean waves is discussed mainly in terms of origin; however, sometimes it is instructive to consider the other classifications.

The first classification deals with the motion of the wave form (or sea surface). A wave that propagates laterally is a *progressive wave* (Fig. 9-1). An example of a progressive wave is the train of waves that moves away from a

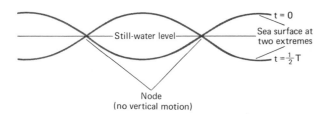

Figure 9-2 Idealized representation of a standing wave. The wave form appears to undulate vertically rather than move in a particular direction.

rock dropped in quiet water. A vertical undulation of the sea surface that does not propagate laterally is called a *standing wave* (Fig. 9-2). Most waves have properties of one of these two classes.

The second classification deals with the relationship of the wave form to the depth of the water. If the water is deeper than 1/2 of the wavelength of a wave, that particular wave is said to be a *deep-water wave*. On the other hand, if the depth is less than about 1/20 of the wavelength, the wave is considered a *shallow-water wave*. This distinction is made because a wave in shallow water is affected by the bottom and therefore has different characteristics than the same wave in deeper water. In the transition zone, where the depth is between 1/2 and 1/20 of the wavelength, the wave characteristics change from deep-water to shallow-water types. This relationship is illustrated in Fig. 9-3.

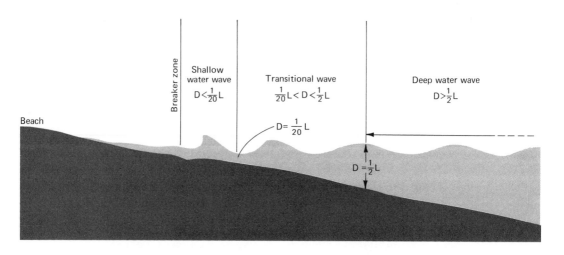

Figure 9-3 In shallow water the characteristics of a wave change with respect to the water depth.

9.4 *Wind Waves*

The waves familiar to most people are those caused by the wind. Waves of this origin occur in many sizes and shapes, ranging from a few centimeters in length and height to hundreds of meters in length and over 30 m high. Where these waves are present, the sea surface can vary from a chaotic surface of

228

breaking waves to a smooth plane interrupted only by a systematic undulation. Let us illustrate the complete spectrum of what can be called *wind waves*. To study their origin, propagation, and breaking characteristics, we shall follow a group of waves from the time they are generated within a storm at sea to the time they break against a beach thousands of kilometers away.

Genesis and Metamorphosis of Wind Waves

As the wind begins to blow over the smooth surface of the ocean, a certain amount of energy of the wind is imparted by friction and pressure fluctuations to the sea surface. Part of this energy forms wind waves. The harder the wind blows, the greater the transfer of energy and the larger the waves. The size of a wave (i.e., its height and wavelength) is determined not only by the force of the wind, but also by its duration and by the distance over which it blows, or its *fetch*. For example, a 15 m per sec (30-knot) wind can produce a wave about 4 m high. However, a 4 m wave does not originate the instant that the wind begins to blow. The first waves to form are *capillary waves* (Fig. 9-4). These waves, in turn, make the sea somewhat rougher and allow more efficient interaction between the wind and the sea surface, thereby increasing the transfer of energy from the wind to the sea. After the 15 m per sec wind has blown for about 5 hours, the largest waves are approximately 3 m high; after

Figure 9-4 Small capillary waves having a wavelength on the order of 1 cm are the first waves that form under the influence of the wind.

**Table 9–2   Minimum Fetch
and Duration Required for Full
Development of Waves Associated
with Various Wind Speeds**

Wind	Fetch	Duration
m/sec (kt)	km	h
5.1 (10)	18.5	2.4
10.2 (20)	140	10
15.3 (30)	520	23
20.4 (40)	1320	42
25.5 (50)	2570	69

(Data from Wolfe et al., *Earth and Space
Sciences*, 1966, D.C. Heath & Co.)

23 hours, the waves will have reached an average height of 4.1 m. No matter how long the wind continues to blow beyond 23 hours, the waves will not become higher, because after that time the dissipation of energy by viscosity is equal to the energy imparted to the sea by the wind. For the given conditions, therefore, some sort of dynamic equilibrium is attained.

Because these waves are progressive, the distance they travel before an equilibrium condition is reached is about 520 km for the 15 m per sec wind. The speed of these waves approaches the speed of the wind.

It can be said that duration and fetch are limiting; that is, for a given wind, a certain duration and fetch are required in order for fully developed waves to occur. Beyond this required time and distance, the waves grow no higher. If, however, either variable is limited, the maximum wave form will not be attained. Table 9-2 shows the minimum fetch and duration required for a fully developed wave at varying wind speeds. The characteristics of fully developed wind waves are given in Table 9-3.

In a storm area where the sea surface is turbulent and filled with spray, whitecaps, and breaking waves, not only are the "mature" waves resulting

Table 9–3   Characteristics of Fully Developed Wind Waves

Wind speed	Average period	Average length	Average height	Maximum height*	Approx. celerity
m/sec (kt)	sec	m	m	m	m/sec (kt)
5.1 (10)	2.9	8.5	0.27	0.55	4.6 (9)
10.2 (20)	5.7	32.9	1.5	3.0	8.7 (17)
15.3 (30)	8.6	76.5	4.1	8.5	13.3 (26)
20.4 (40)	11.4	136.0	8.5	17.3	17.8 (35)
25.5 (50)	14.3	212.0	14.8	30.0	21.9 (43)

*Average of the highest 10 percent of all waves.
(Data from Wolfe et al., *Earth and Space Sciences*, 1966, D.C. Heath & Co.)

Figure 9-5 Under the influence of strong winds the sea surface takes on a chaotic shape composed of many sizes of waves traveling in many directions. (Photograph courtesy Peter B. Taylor)

from the particular wind conditions formed, but also many sizes of waves traveling in different directions (Fig. 9-5) exist. Storm centers generally move at slow speeds, so the larger wind waves they produce propagate from the storm area in all directions, often traveling for thousands of kilometers before being diminished by friction or obstructed by a shoreline.

Away from the storm area, the sea surface has a different appearance. Spray, whitecaps, and breaking waves are absent; to an observer, the sea surface has a smoother appearance than within the storm area. Waves of different lengths disperse in such a way that the longer (therefore faster) waves move ahead of the slower, shorter waves. At progressively greater distances from the storm edge, the wave train continues to disperse until the longer waves may be traveling several days ahead of the shorter waves. Here the sea surface appears smoothly corrugated by waves having very uniform height and wavelength. These waves are of the progressive type and are referred to as *swell* (Fig. 9-6). Of course, all gradations exist between the chaotic sea state existing in a storm and swell conditions occurring thousands of kilometers from the generating area.

Two types of motion are associated with swell: that of the wave form and that of the water. It is important to realize that waves transport only energy, not water. Although the form of the progressive wave (i.e., the actual hump in the sea surface) moves across great expanses of the ocean at relatively high speeds, the water does not accompany the wave form in its travel. Actually,

Figure 9-6 Aerial view looking down on a large ocean swell on the sea surface. Approximate wavelength is 250 m. (Photograph courtesy of Barbee Scheibner)

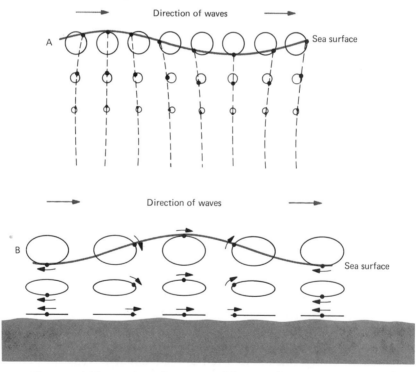

Figure 9-7 The motion of water particles as a wave passes are circular in deep water (A), and flattened ellipses in shallow water (B). The depth of wave disturbance is approximately ½L.

the individual water particles only revolve in vertical circular orbits (Fig. 9-7A). With each complete revolution, energy is transferred to the water lying adjacent in the direction of wave propagation. It is the energy associated with a wave that is passed on continuously, not water particles.

To verify this fact, note how a ping pong ball behaves on the surface of the sea. As a wave passes, the ball moves in a vertical circle as it receives and transmits the energy of the waves (Fig. 9-7A). The motion of a similar ball floating below the surface is the same, except that the radius of the circular orbit decreases with depth. At a depth of approximately 1/2 of the wavelength, the orbital radius is approximately 4 percent of its surface value—a negligible figure. It is said, therefore, that a wave does not exist below a depth of about 1/2 of its wavelength. Waves traveling in water deeper than half the wavelength are considered to be deep-water waves.

The speed (C) at which a deep-water wave travels can be found by the following equation:

$$C^2 = \frac{gL}{2\pi} \qquad [9\text{-}2]$$

where C = celerity, g = acceleration due to gravity, L = wavelength, and π = 3.14. If we combine this equation with Eq. [9-1], we obtain:

$$C = \frac{gT}{2\pi} \qquad [9\text{-}3]$$

or

$$L = \frac{gT^2}{2\pi} \qquad [9\text{-}4]$$

Therefore, a deep-water wave having a period of 10 sec has a velocity of:

$$C = \frac{gT}{2\pi} = \frac{(980 \text{ cm/sec}^2) \ (10 \text{ sec})}{(2) \ (3.14)}$$
$$= 1,560 \text{ cm/sec and a wavelength of} \qquad [9\text{-}5]$$
$$L = CT = (15.6 \text{ m/sec}) \times (10 \text{ sec}) = 156 \text{ m}$$

Note that the speed of swell depends upon the square root of its wavelength (Eq. 9-2). Consequently, in deep water, longer waves move faster or overtake short waves as they propagate from the storm area. We call this process of wave separation *dispersion*. This explains why the first waves to reach a distant beach from a large storm are the longer waves.

Where the depth of water is shallower than 1/2 of the wavelength, a deep-water wave feels bottom and starts the transition to a shallow-water wave. As this happens, the circular orbits of water particles become flattened into ellipses (Fig. 9-7B) and the speed of waves begins to decrease. Since the wave period remains constant, the length of these waves must also decrease. As the

Figure 9-8 Waves traveling great distances ultimately expend their energy on the shorelines of the world. Where the beach is shallow the surf zone extends far offshore. On steep beaches the surf zone is very narrow.

length decreases, the steepness (i.e., the ratio of height to length) increases. When the steepness increases so that the ratio of height to length exceeds 1 to 7, the wave becomes unstable and breaks, forming surf, thus finally expending its energy on some distant beach (Fig. 9-8).*

The speed of a shallow-water wave is found by the following formula:

$$C = \sqrt{gD} \tag{9-6}$$

where D = depth. No dispersion is associated with shallow-water waves, because their speed depends upon depth rather than length or period.

The equations for the celerity of deep-water and shallow-water waves are derived from a general celerity equation that is of a complexity beyond the scope of this text. That equation describes the celerity of waves in any depth of water, including depths between deep and shallow water.

---

*Chapter 11, "Inshore Oceanography," further discusses *shoaling waves*, which influence nearshore sedimentary processes.

9.5 *Wave Spectra*

Interaction Between Waves

The preceding equations describe the nature of waves of a single pure class or type. Look again at Fig. 9-5. The sea surface is disturbed by waves of many heights, directions, and wavelengths. Even in Fig. 9-6 the uniform swell shapes a sea surface disturbed by smaller waves of a variety of lengths and directions of propagation. When the sea surface is perceived instantaneously as in these photographs it is apparent that the sea surface is a composite of many short-crested wave forms, each of which represents a quantity of mechanical energy. The surface appearance of such a real sea is considered to reflect an interference pattern caused by the addition of a large number of small waves of a broad range of periods. The amount of energy each wave represents is indicated by its height according to the relationship:

$$\text{Energy per unit area of sea surface} = \left(\frac{\rho g}{8}\right) H^2 \qquad [9\text{-}7]$$

The energy in a unit area of a sea surface formed by waves of several different heights is proportional to the sum of the square of each individual wave height:

$$\frac{\rho g}{8}(H_1{}^2 + H_2{}^2 + H_3{}^2 + \ldots + H_n{}^2) \qquad [9\text{-}8]$$

It follows that the height of the sea surface disturbance caused by the coincidence of several wave trains is found by taking the square root of the sum of the squares of the heights of the several wave trains:

$$H = [H_1{}^2 + H_2{}^2 + H_3{}^2 + \ldots + H_n{}^2]^{\frac{1}{2}} \qquad [9\text{-}9]$$

This equation says that the total energy represented by the interaction of several wave trains is simply the sum of the energy in each train.

Now this matter of interacting waves can be viewed in another way. We can state that a sea surface that appears to be a confusion of many different wave types (such as that in Fig. 9-5) can be represented as the result of the interaction of many wave trains, each having a distinct height, period, and direction of propagation. In fact we are able to represent the confused sea surface by a *wave energy spectrum* that describes the energy contained in each of the many wave trains that interacts to form the sea surface. If we construct a graph by plotting the energy represented by a small, discrete range of wave periods on a scale of wave periods, the result is a spectral curve such as shown in Fig. 9-9. This curve is called a nondirectional spectrum because it describes the spectrum of all component waves regardless of their direction of propagation. A similar curve can be prepared for each cardinal direction to derive a series of *directional wave spectra*.

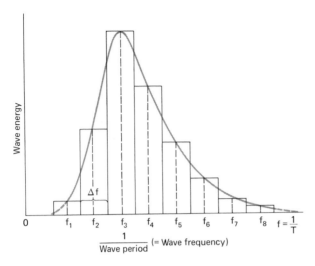

Figure 9-9 Spectrum of wave energy showing frequency (1/T) bands. The sum of the energies in each band, Δf, represents an approximation of the total energy contained in each unit area of the sea represented by this spectrum.

The spectrum of waves has many important uses beyond being a comprehensive description of a real sea surface formed by a chaotic assemblage of waves of many heights, periods, and directions. Several of these uses will be described now.

The spectrum shown in Fig. 9-9 depicts the amount of mechanical energy associated with waves having periods as shown along the horizontal axis. If we add together the energy in each discrete frequency (1/T) band, we obtain the total energy in each unit area of the sea surface that the spectrum represents. This total energy is represented on the spectrum as the area under the spectral curve. Mathematical techniques exist for measuring the area under the spectral curve so that the total energy can be determined conveniently from measurement of waves. An example of this procedure is shown in Fig. 9-10.

The total energy in the waves is a useful indicator of values other than the intensity of wave activity in an area at sea. It can be used to deduce how waves will affect ships and other structures at the sea surface. Here is how it is done: Wave measurements made at many sites in the world ocean have shown that the frequency of occurrence of wave heights follows a consistent pattern. When the frequency of occurrence of wave heights is plotted against wave height as in Fig. 9-11, the curve that results is practically identical to that of the Rayleigh probability distribution law, a fundamental concept in mathematical statistics. This fact allows us to use the properties of that law to predict the nature of the wave heights expected at sea. Some of the relationships obtained from the Rayleigh law are presented in Table 9-4.

The significant height, H_s, is of particular interest because it is the wave height characteristically sensed by an observer at sea; an observer tends to notice only the highest waves. Table 9-4 permits one to predict the highest

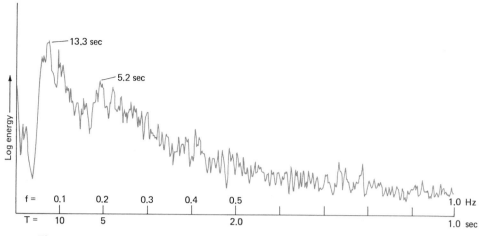

Figure 9-10 An example of a wave record and the wave energy spectrum derived. The spectrum shows two energy peaks: The higher peak is caused by a 13-sec swell, and the lower peak represents a sea having maximum energy in 5-sec waves. This example represents a sea state similar to that shown in the photograph in Fig. 8-6.

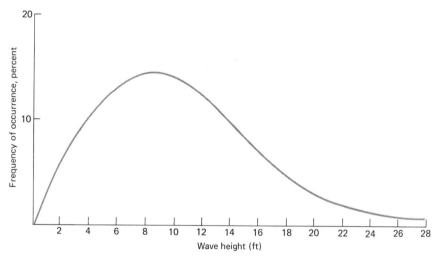

Figure 9-11 The Rayleigh distribution curve. Measurements of the frequency of occurrence of waves having heights within narrow ranges of values tend to conform to this curve. (From Walter H. Michel, *Ocean Industry*, May 1967)

wave, average wave height, and most common wave height in a sea from which the significant height is observed. Also, the significant height is used extensively for predicting waves at sea by assessing the causative wind.

The energy spectrum of waves has an important application in the design of structures in the sea. The response of a ship—for example, the way it pitches—can be tested as a model in a tank in which waves of uniform height

Table 9–4   Wave Height Relationships Derived from the Rayleigh Probability Distribution Law

Height of the most frequent wave	$= 0.70 \sqrt{\overline{H^2}}$
Average height of all the waves	$= 0.89 \sqrt{\overline{H^2}}$
Average of the highest third of the waves (the significant height, H_s)	$= 1.41 \sqrt{\overline{H^2}}$
Average of the highest tenth of the waves	$= 1.80 \sqrt{\overline{H^2}}$

where $\overline{H^2}$ is found by squaring each wave height in a series of wave measurements, adding these values and taking their average value.

and period are generated. Keeping the height the same, several tests with waves of different periods are performed and the amount of pitch is measured in each case. The results of the test are expressed as a curve depicting the amplitude of pitch induced in the ship by a wave of unit height and any period.

Now we can see how powerful a tool the wave spectrum really is, for if we square the test results:

$$(\text{Pitch amplitude/unit height})^2$$

and multiply these values by the ordinates of the wave spectrum, the result is a pitch amplitude spectrum that describes the behavior of the ship in the real sea represented by the wave height spectrum. These operations are illustrated in Fig. 9-12. Other ship motions such as heave, roll, and yaw, as well as accelerations in any direction, can be analyzed in a similar manner using wave energy spectra in conjunction with wave tank model tests. Forces of waves striking a fixed structure can be predicted in a similar fashion.

The design of offshore structures demonstrates the use of wave spectra. Offshore structures are often constructed of welded steel members, and the welded joints are subject to the development of cracks (fatigue) under the repeated impact of waves. The sequence of individual waves attacking a structure is not important; what is important is the number of impacts at each wave height. Fatigue is predicted by deriving an energy spectrum using either actual recorded wave measurements or information on the statistics of wind velocity and the waves that such wind would produce. The spectrum is converted to a stress spectrum from which the average period and significant wave height are calculated. A spectrum is prepared for each sea state likely to occur. The number of stress events expected to occur each year at each wave height (stress level) is determined by dividing the number of seconds in a year by the corresponding wave period. These results are used to calculate the fatigue life of the structure in the sea which has been depicted by the wave energy spectrum.

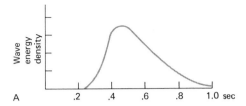

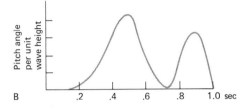

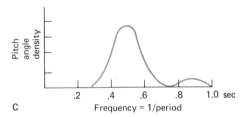

Frequency = 1/period

Figure 9-12 An example of the use of wave energy spectrum (A). The response curve (B) represents the results of the test of a ship model in a wave tank where waves of unit height and various periods were generated. The pitch angle of the ship was measured at each wave frequency (1/T). The values of pitch angles/unit wave height were squared, then multiplied by the wave height spectrum to obtain the pitch spectrum of the ship (C). (From Walter H. Michel, *Ocean Industry*, May 1967)

Wave Prediction

The principles of wave behavior discussed so far are all used in methods for predicting the nature of waves at any site in the world ocean. The starting point in wave prediction is the characterization of the winds producing the waves. The wind velocity, fetch, and duration are obtained by an analysis of meteorological maps constructed by plotting atmospheric pressure, air temperature, winds, and other weather data reported by ships at sea. An example of such a chart is shown in Fig. 9-13. Alternatively, marine weather data can be processed by a digital computer programmed to perform all the steps of wave prediction.

Spectral Method

Wind velocity, fetch, and duration are applied to either of two wave prediction methods. The spectral method uses graphs, each prepared from the spectrum associated with unlimited wind of a specified velocity. Spectra produced by such winds are shown in Fig. 9-14. It is assumed that if the wind fetch or duration is actually limited, the unlimited spectrum (spectrum of the

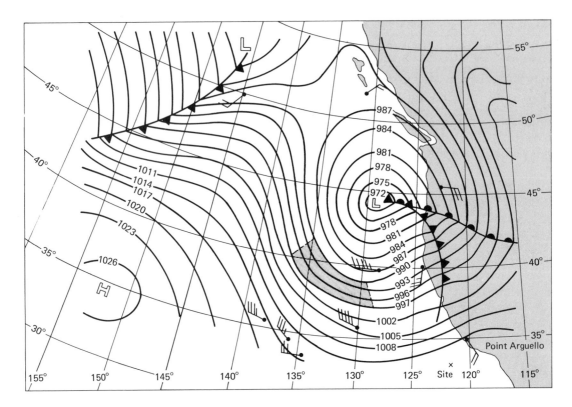

Figure 9-13 A typical weather map of a low pressure system off the West Coast of the United States. Air circulating counterclockwise around the low pressure center (L) reaches speeds of 50 knots 600 miles at sea. The contour lines are isobars on lines of equal barometric pressure in millibars. The barbed lines show the wind speed (10 kts per barb, 5 kts per half barb) reported at the location marked with the dot. The fetch contributing waves to the site X is stippled. (From Shore Protection Manual, Vol. I, pp. 3–23)

fully arisen sea) can be truncated at the longest period that can be developed, because the seas tend to develop by the creation of waves whose periods increase successively with time (Fig. 9-15). The spectra are transformed (by accumulation) so that the total energy per unit area of sea surface can be read directly. Several accumulated spectra are presented in Fig. 9-16. Energy is converted to characteristic wave heights by the convention shown in Table 9-4. The average period of the waves generated by the wind is found by the relationship:

$$\text{Average period (in seconds)} = 0.285 \times \text{wind speed (in knots)}$$

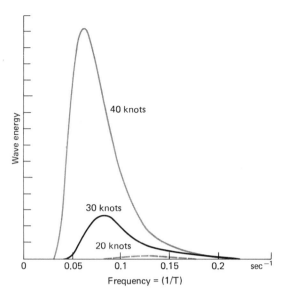

Figure 9-14 Wave energy spectra produced the winds blowing over unlimited fetches long enough to produce a fully arisen sea. No matter how much longer the wind blows, these spectra will not change, provided that the wind speed remains constant at the value shown next to the corresponding spectral curves. Note that high winds produce seas containing waves of longer periods than are present in seas generated by low winds. This is indicated by a shift of the spectral peak (maximum energy) toward lower frequencies (longer periods).

which has been derived empirically from many measurements of waves at sea.

The wave heights and periods predicted by the method just described apply only to waves in the storm area. As the waves move out of their area of generation they are modified by dispersion and angular spreading. Dispersion, caused by the differences in group velocities of waves of differing periods, causes only a restricted band of wave periods to propagate to an observation site within a specified time. Longer-period waves from the upwind edge of the wind fetch have traveled beyond the site, and shorter-period waves from the downwind edge have not yet reached the site, so the energy of the sea surface at the site represents the sum of the energies represented by a wave spectrum truncated to exclude periods higher and lower than those that can be present at the site. The total energy of the truncated spectrum is then a measure of the wave height and period characteristics of the sea at the site.

Angular spreading occurs because the chaotic assemblage of short-crested waves in the storm area represents a composite of energies propagating in many directions. Propagation of wave energy out of the storm area therefore proceeds in many directions. Theoretical considerations and observations suggest that energy propagates out of the storm area according to the cosine squared distribution law:

$$E_\theta = E_\tau \cos^2\theta$$

where E_θ is the percentage of the energy propagating in a direction lying θ degrees from the wind direction, and E_τ is the total energy of the sea surface in the storm area. The width of the storm wind fetch presents a window through which waves traveling in a narrow sector can reach the site. The ratio

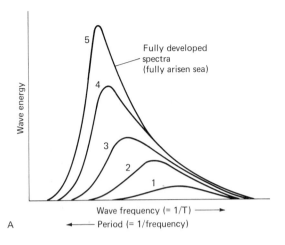

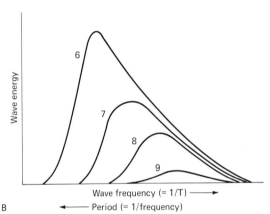

Figure 9-15 Changes in wave energy spectra with time at a site at sea following the sudden appearance of a storm bearing winds of uniform speed. In (A), the spectra grow toward longer periods with successive times 1–5. The spectra broaden and become higher as the wind imparts more and more energy to the sea. The spectra in (B) show the effect of dispersion following sudden cessation of wind at the site. As the long-period waves leave the site the spectra become lower (loss of energy) and shift toward short periods. (From *Principles of Naval Architecture*, J. P. Comstock, ed., p. 621, 1967)

of the sum of the energies in waves passing through the window to the total energy of the waves in the storm area represents the percentage of energy reduction that the waves experience in reaching the site.

The principles of wave prediction described above are formalized in procedures which account for the irregularity of wind speed during the life of a storm, the motion of the storm (hence, the concept of a moving fetch), and the irregular, changing shape of the fetch in real storms.

Significant Height Method

Another approach to wave prediction is based upon a theoretical and empirical consideration of the behavior of the ocean surface under the influence of wind forces. The change of energy in a deep-water wave is expressed in terms of the transfer of energy from wind to water by normal pressure, by drag, and by the transfer of energy away by the wave motion. The equations that describe the budget of energy in space and time are solved to extract the relationships between wind speed, fetch, duration, and wave properties. These relationships are expressed in terms of the ratio of wave celerity to wind speed

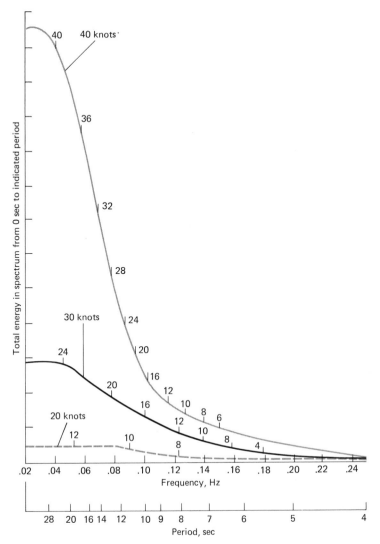

Figure 9-16 Accumulated spectra for steady winds. For each period (or frequency), the total energy of all waves that develop having periods less than that value is shown by the spectral curve corresponding to the generating wind speed. The numbers along the curves indicate the time in hours that the wind must blow to transfer the energy to the sea. The flat part of the curves on the left side of the figure indicates the total energy in the fully arisen sea generated by a steady wind of the indicated speed.

(called wave age) and the ratio of wave height to wave length (steepness). The results of many observations of waves at sea under various conditions of wind fetch and duration were used to extract values of wave age and steepness and to derive the empirical curve shown in Fig. 9-17. This curve yields information that allows theoretical relationships between wave properties, wind duration,

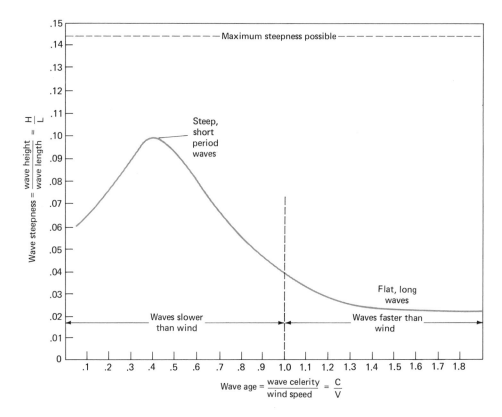

Figure 9-17 Empirical curve fit to wave data obtained from measurements made through the world ocean. Note that the existence of values of wave age greater than one demonstrates that individual wave forms can travel faster than the wind that generates them.

wind speed, and fetch to be cast in the form of wave prediction curves as shown in Fig. 9-18. Deep-water wave prediction is performed by determining the time history of surface winds from weather maps, measuring the fetch size and movement, and using the prediction curve to obtain the height and period of waves being generated in the wind fetch. The prediction of waves that have left the fetch area is made by determining the effect of *wave decay* that is caused when energy is no longer transferred from the wind to the waves but continues to be removed by wave motion.

Very little energy is removed by viscous dissipation. It has been estimated than an 8-sec wave could go around the world ten times, travel longer than 2 years, and still retain 37 percent of its original height if the viscosity of seawater were the only factor removing wave energy. However, if waves are generated in shallow water, the loss of energy through friction with the sea

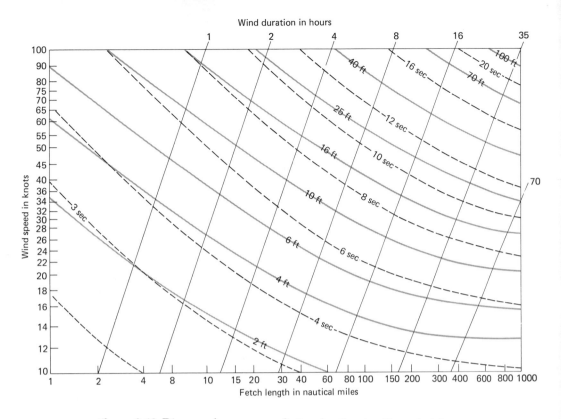

Figure 9-18 Diagram for wave prediction by the significant height method. The wind speed is entered at the left side of the diagram and extended horizontally to the vertical line for the prevailing fetch length curve or wind duration, whichever is intersected first. The significant height in feet and corresponding period in seconds are interpolated to the intersection point from their corresponding curves. (After C. L. Bretschneider, LOOK LAB/HAWAII, 1970)

floor must be included in the wave energy budget equations used to derive wave prediction curves.

Interaction Between Waves and Ocean Currents

Experiments have shown that ocean waves that pass through currents moving across their paths are little affected by the water transport. However, when the waves travel into an opposing current, their steepness and height increase. The effect is more pronounced in waves of shorter period. Short-period waves tend to steepen and break as their steepness (H/L) exceeds 1/7. Waves traveling into a current moving in the same direction tend to lengthen (Fig. 9-19). The amplification of waves by the Agulhas current is shown in Fig. 9-20. This region of abnormally high waves is known to be extremely hazardous to ships plying the waters of South Africa.

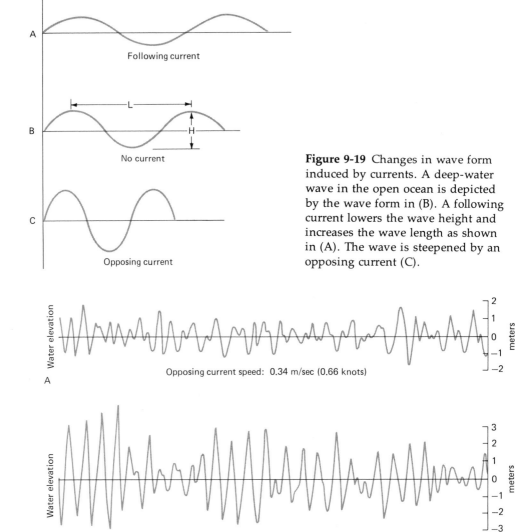

Figure 9-19 Changes in wave form induced by currents. A deep-water wave in the open ocean is depicted by the wave form in (B). A following current lowers the wave height and increases the wave length as shown in (A). The wave is steepened by an opposing current (C).

Figure 9-20 Wave recordings taken nearly simultaneously from two locations southeast of South Africa. Record (A) was taken out of the mainstream of the Agulhas current and record (B) was taken in the mainstream of the current. The amplification of the waves by an opposing current is quite apparent. (From *Mariners Weather Log*, Vol. 76, Jan. 1976, pp. 1–3, NOAA)

9.6 Long-Period Waves

Tsunami

A *tsunami*, or seismic sea wave (often referred to as a "tidal wave," although it has nothing to do with the tides), is a shallow-water sea wave that is caused by submarine crustal movements or the sudden displacement of a large volume of seawater. These waves originate from any of several geologic phenomena: submarine volcanic explosions, submarine landslides, large submarine earthquakes, earth movements (faulting), or even large landslides into the sea.

The physical characteristics of tsunamis are striking. It is because their wavelengths are between 120 and 720 km that they are shallow-water waves. Their speed of propagation, therefore, is determined by the water depth (see Eq. 9-7). In the open ocean (where the average depth is 4,000 m), they can propagate at about 200 m per sec, or 400 nautical mph. Consequently, a tsunami caused by submarine faulting in the Aleutian Islands would require only 5 hours to travel to Hawaii. In the open ocean, a tsunami can pass without being observed because its height is only about 30 cm and its period varies from 10 to 60 min. However, as it approaches shore, such a wave can attain heights of 35 m.

Because of the origin and nature of tsunamis, they can cause great damage and loss of life in certain coastal areas throughout the world. Probably the most widely publicized example of the magnitude and destructive force associated with these waves is that caused by the volcanic explosion of the island of Krakatoa in the Sunda Strait on August 26 and 27, 1883. The resulting waves reached heights as great as 35 m in some of the Indonesian islands. Approximately 32 hours after their formation, the waves were detected in the English Channel; however, because they had traveled almost 20,000 km, their height had decreased to several centimeters.

The rim of the Pacific Ocean is a seismically active area, so the occurrence of earthquakes and tsunamis has been relatively frequent there. One of the factors contributing to the great loss of life caused by these seismic sea waves is the fact that their occurrence cannot be predicted. They arrive on distant shores without much warning. Sometimes a trough reaches shore first, causing an outward rush of water that lowers the water surface to an abnormal degree. Several minutes later, the first of a series of large crests and deep troughs arrives. Each is separated by several minutes, and the entire train of waves lasts several hours. Since 1946, a tsunami warning system consisting of a communications network was formed to transmit warnings of an impending tsunami to Pacific area countries and islands. This system is not the final answer, however, for tsunamis do not occur after all earth tremors or movements. The presence of an earthquake does not necessarily signify a tsunami. Moreover, the exact cause of the tsunami is not known. It seems to be related to both vertical and horizontal displacements of the sea floor as well as to submarine slumping, but there may be other causes. Possibly it will be necessary to place electronic sensing devices on the sea floor to signal automatically the passage of a tsunami—no matter what its cause or origin.

Storm Tides

Storm tides are solitary occurrences of abnormally high water levels caused by a combination of meteorological and oceanic conditions. The primary causes of these waves are violent storms that sweep great amounts of ocean water against coastal regions. The occurrence of a *storm setup* in itself may not have a great damaging effect on a coastal region. Coupled, however, with other phenomena, such as strong winds, large wind waves, high tides, and uncommonly low atmospheric pressure (causing slight sea level increases), storm tides can inundate coastlines and cause great devastation and loss of life.

For example, storm tides as high as 5 m have struck the Texas coast. In 1900, the city of Galveston, Texas, was nearly destroyed. A combination of hurricane-force winds, storm setup, high waves, and low pressure caused flooding of the city; property damage ran into tens of millions of dollars, and over 5,000 people were killed.

9.7   Internal Waves

Internal waves are similar to ordinary sea waves except that they occur within the sea rather than at the surface. They exist at density discontinuities between water layers, especially at the pycnocline. In a homogeneous sea they cannot exist. Internal waves are so long that they must be detected by the periodic rise and fall of *isotherms,* lines connecting equal temperatures on oceanographic data profiles. Figure 9-21 shows how several isotherms vary with depth and time. In this particular example, the period of the oscillations is about 15 min and the amplitude is about 7 m. *Slicks* that are seen on the surface of the ocean are often manifestations of internal wave movement and are generally located above a wave midway between trough and crest (Fig. 9-22).

Internal waves characteristically have greater amplitude and slower speeds of propagation than do surface waves. Internal waves can be found in both shallow and deep ocean water and in large freshwater lakes, such as Lake Ontario. Table 9-5 illustrates the wide variation in the properties of these waves.

Table 9–5   General Characteristics of Internal Waves

	Period	Amplitude	Speed
Shallow	4 min–25 h	2 m	5 cm/sec
Deep	4 min–25 h	100 m	100 cm/sec

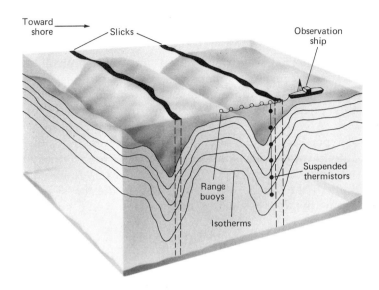

Figure 9-21 Block diagram showing an internal wave propagating toward shore off San Diego. (After Neumann and Pierson, 1966, by permission of Prentice-Hall, Inc.)

Figure 9-22 Photo of surface features associated with internal waves. (Photograph courtesy William McLeish)

The causes of internal waves are varied and not completely understood. Early reports from steamship captains described conditions of "dead water" through which their vessels appeared to move sluggishly. In 1904, V. W. Ekman explained this phenomenon by postulating the existence of near-surface internal waves. A vessel that was traveling at about the speed of an internal wave (100 cm per sec) would have a significant part of its thrust used in generating internal waves at the lower boundary of the relatively fresh upper layer of water—provided the depth of the boundary were about the same as the ship's draft. If the vessel increased its speed, the thrust would again be used to overcome the fluid resistance, and the ship would no longer appear to "stick" in the water.

By now, scientists have discovered that internal waves are, in fact, caused by many phenomena: storms, surface waves, ships, tidal action, wind blowing over the sea surface, or possibly even any transient disturbance that combines with these other conditions.

9.8   *Standing Waves*

In contrast to a progressive wave, where the wave form propagates in a particular direction, a standing wave (also called a *seiche*) is characterized by a surface oscillation that does not appear to move horizontally. Standing waves occur in basins that are closed or almost closed to the ocean. Actually, the ocean basin itself can maintain a standing wave (see the discussion of tides in Chap. 10). The characteristics of a standing wave are related to the nature of the enclosing basin. When an impulse of energy is supplied to the basin of water, the water surface will oscillate up and down by tilting first in one direction and then in the opposite direction, as illustrated in Fig. 9-2. There is a place, called a *node*, where no vertical movement—only horizontal movement—occurs. Maximum vertical movement occurs at points called *antinodes*. Depending upon how, when, and where the energy impulse occurs, a basin may oscillate with several nodes (also illustrated in Fig. 9-2). The period of oscillation of a standing wave depends on the geometry (i.e., the length and depth) of a basin. This relationship is given for a single node in the following formula:

$$T = \frac{2L}{\sqrt{gD}} \qquad\qquad [9\text{-}10]$$

where T = natural period of oscillation, L = length of basin, g = acceleration of gravity, and D = depth.

If energy impulses are supplied to a basin periodically so that the period of the impulses is about equal to the natural period of the basin, the height of the standing wave will increase with time. In other words, the basin will resonate, and the vertical motion of the water at the antinodes will increase. In nature, energy impulses are supplied to the basins by storm surges, sudden changes in barometric pressure, progressive waves, earthquakes, tides, and such transient impulses as landslides. A sudden single impulse causes a series of oscillations that are gradually dampened by boundary friction and viscosity. Such oscillations can be catastrophic if the impulse is large. More severe, however, are cases produced by periodic impulses, such as waves and tides, if they can produce enough resonance to cause the oscillations to build up to dangerously high changes in the sea level at the antinodes (i.e., the shores of the basin).

There is also a kind of single-oscillation wave called a *landslide surge*. A landslide falling into a basin may displace large volumes of water, causing an oscillation that can have devastating effects upon the basin and surrounding areas. Such a landslide surge occurred in Lituya Bay in Alaska in 1958 where 40 million cu m of earth fell into the bay from elevations of 1,000 m. Water rushed 500 m up the mountains on the opposite side of the bay, and a water wave 15 m high surged seaward at a speed of 50 m per sec, carrying several vessels anchored within the bay over a bar located at the entrance. A similar disaster occurred in the Vaiont reservoir in Italy in 1963. A landslide containing 600 million tons of earth created a wave as high as 250 m that overtopped the dam. It swept into the village of Longarone and caused many casualties and great damage.

reading list

BASCOM, W., "Ocean Waves," *Scientific American*, CCI, No. 2 (August 1959), 74–78.

————, *Waves and Beaches: The Dynamics of the Ocean Surface*. Garden City, N.Y.: Doubleday, 1964. 267p.

BERNSTEIN, J., "Tsunamis," *Scientific American*, CXCI, No. 2 (August 1954), 60–64.

BIGELOW, H. B., AND W. T. EDMONDSON, *Wind Waves at Sea, Breakers and Surf*, U.S. Navy Hydrographic Office Publication 602. Washington, D.C.: Government Printing Office, 1974. 177p.

BRETSCHNEIDER, C. L., *Forecasting Relations for Wave Generation*, LOOK LAB/HAWAII, I, No. 3, July 1970.

CHRISTOPHER, P., H. RUSSEL, AND D. H. MACMILLAN, *Waves and Tides*. London: Hutchinson's Scientific & Technical Publications, 1952. 348p.

MICHEL, W. H., "Sea Spectra Simplified," *Marine Technology*, V (January 1968), 17–30.

PIERSON, W. J., JR., G. NEUMAN, AND R. W. JAMES, U.S. Navy Hydrographic Office, *Practical Methods for Observing and Forecasting Ocean Waves*, H.O. Publication No. 603, 1954, reprinted 1971. 284p.

SVERDRUP, H. U., AND MUNK, W. H., U.S. Navy Hydrographic Office, *Wind, Sea and Swell: Theory of Relations for Forecasting*. Technical Report No. 1. H.O. Publication No. 601, March 1947, reprinted 1952. 44p.

U.S. NAVAL HYDROGRAPHIC OFFICE, *Techniques for Forecasting Wind Waves and Swell*. H.O. Publication No. 604, 1951, reprinted 1963. 37p.

WORLD METEOROLOGICAL ORGANIZATION, *Handbook on Wave Analysis and Forecasting*. Publication WMO No. 446, Geneva, Switzerland, 1976.

tides

10

For many of their activities, people must understand the origin and nature of tides and be able to predict the tidal fluctuations of the world ocean. Certain kinds of commerce and industry, reclamation of land from the sea, amphibious military operations, beach recreation, and dispersal of wastes in coastal areas are all dependent upon the tides (Fig. 10-1). The rise and fall of the tides are also important to ocean processes not directly related to humans, particularly coastal morphology, chemical processes, and the life cycles of organisms in coastal regions.

10.1 *The General Nature of Tides*

A tide is the alternate rising and falling of the sea level as a result of the gravitational forces exerted on the earth by the sun and the moon. The regularity of this rise and fall, or *flood* and *ebb*, is associated with the periodicity of solar and lunar gravitational effects. The height of a tide is related to the sum of water displacements produced by these gravitational forces.

The tides propagating through the world ocean are strongly modified as they approach the shallow margins of the continents. However, they are modified with respect only to amplitude and velocity, not to frequency. The influence that a coast exerts on tidal characteristics is determined by coastal size, shape, and bathymetry; therefore, no two locations in the world exhibit the same tidal behavior.

252

Figure 10-1 The village of Manho-ri in Asan Bay, Korea, located on the Yellow Sea. The range is 8.5 m between high tide (A) and low tide (B). Fishing activities here are strongly governed by these spectacular tides.

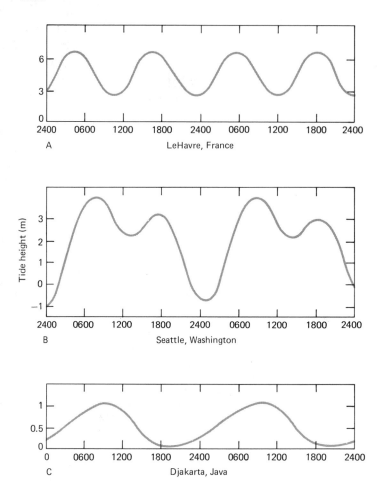

Figure 10-2 These tide curves illustrate semidaily (A), mixed (B), and daily (C) types.

The most obvious tidal fluctuations are those that occur once daily (diurnal) or twice daily (semidiurnal). These fluctuations have either equal or unequal amplitudes, so a wide variety of tide curves is observed throughout the world. Some examples are shown in Fig. 10-2.

Tides with periods longer than 24 hours also occur. If we observe a tide curve over a lunar month, periodic variations in the *tidal range* (the difference between successive high and low tides) become evident. Times of maximum tidal range, called *spring tides,* occur at about 2-week intervals. Times of minimal tidal range, called *neap tides,* also have a 2-week interval but lag behind spring tides by about 1 week. Some examples of spring and neap tides

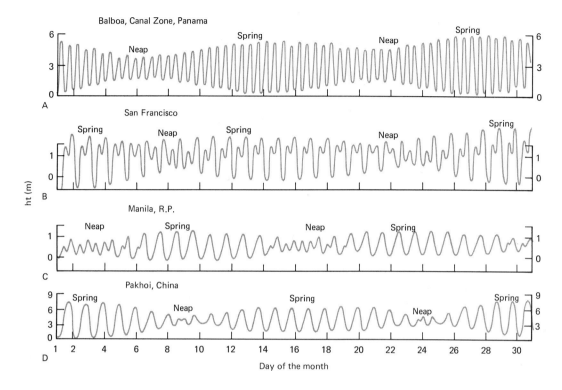

Figure 10-3 Tides at Balboa, San Francisco, Manila, and Pakhoi. The time in days is given on the bottom of the figure. The curves vary from semidiurnal (A), to mixed (B and C during neap tides), to diurnal (D).

from various geographic locations are shown in Fig. 10-3. Notice that the tide at Manila is diurnal except during neap tides, which are semidiurnal (Fig. 10-3C).

Tides flow as shallow-water progressive waves in the open water, but in coastal regions they may act differently. In Chesapeake Bay and Puget Sound, for instance, the tide wave tends to progress as a shallow-water wave whose speed is a function of water depth (according to Eq. 9-6). In other regions, the tides act as standing waves. The most famous example is in the Bay of Fundy in Nova Scotia. Here, large vertical fluctuations occur at the head of a bay while at the mouth of the bay the water level does not change appreciably. The maximum tidal range at the head of the Bay of Fundy is in excess of 15.4 m, whereas the tidal range at the mouth is approximately 3½ m.

Not only the ocean but everything on the earth responds to the gravitational attraction of the sun and the moon. Tides occur in the atmosphere and in lakes. Lake Superior, for example, has a tide of a few centimeters. The earth's crust also responds to tidal forces. The nature of the tides, their magnitude, and periodicity are governed by the positions and motions of the bodies in our solar system. Before proceeding to consider tidal effects on the earth, we must become familiar with some of these motions.

10.2 *The Position of the Earth in the Solar System*

Almost everyone knows a few elementary facts about the earth and its association with the sun: The earth is approximately 149,642,000 km from the sun (93,000,000 miles); the earth completes one revolution about the sun in approximately 1 year; and the earth rotates around its axis in the time defined as 1 day. These three facts provide a basis for a further description of the earth–sun association that is less well known but nonetheless important. Let us study Fig. 10-4.

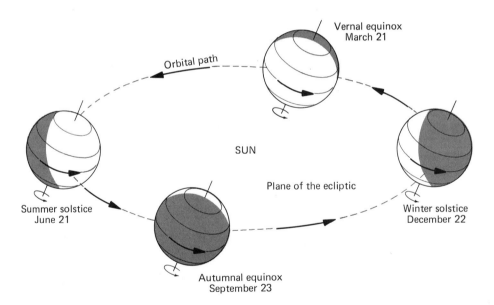

Figure 10-4 The four seasons as related to the earth's orbit around the sun. The earth's axis remains fixed in space and is tilted approximately 23.5° with respect to the vertical. (After A. N. Strahler, 1963)

This figure illustrates schematically four positions of the earth during its yearly orbit around the sun (as viewed from above the north polar axis of the earth). Note the following facts:

1. The earth's orbit traces an ellipse with the sun at one of the foci. The distance between the two bodies is not constant

2. The earth not only revolves around the sun in a counterclockwise direction; it also rotates around its own axis in a similar direction

3. The axis of the earth is not oriented vertically with respect to the orbital plane; it is tilted about 23½° from the vertical

4. The axis of the earth always points in essentially the same direction relative to the stars. During part of the year, the northern hemisphere faces toward the sun; at other times, it faces away.

Because the earth's axis changes position relative to the direct rays of the sun, we have seasons and corresponding differences in the length of day and night. At the summer solstice in the northern hemisphere (about June 21), the earth's axis has the greatest inclination toward the sun, and the northern hemisphere receives the sun's rays most directly. This is the longest day of the year in this hemisphere. Indeed, north of the Arctic Circle there are 24 hours of daylight. When it is summer in the northern hemisphere, however, it is winter in the southern. The shortest day of the year occurs there in June, and there are 24 hours of darkness south of the Antarctic Circle. At the summer solstice in the northern hemisphere, the noon sun is directly over the Tropic of Cancer (23½° north latitude).

At the winter solstice in the northern hemisphere (about December 22), the conditions prevailing on the earth are, of course, the reverse of those at the summer solstice. It is the northern winter (with its corresponding short days) and the southern summer (with long days). At this time, the sun is directly over the Tropic of Capricorn (23½° south latitude).

The vernal and autumnal equinoxes are the times of the year when day and night are of equal length over the whole earth. Day and night are always of equal length on the equator. At the vernal equinox (about March 21), it is spring in the northern hemisphere and autumn in the southern hemisphere. At the time of the autumnal equinox (about September 23), it is autumn in the northern hemisphere and spring in the southern hemisphere. The noon sun is directly over the equator at both the vernal and autumnal equinoxes.

10.3   *The Tide-Producing Force*

The variety of tidal phenomena affecting the earth arises from forces associated with the motion of mutually attracted celestial bodies. The earth, the moon, and the sun are drawn together by forces of gravitational attraction. They are kept apart by the centrifugal forces arising from their orbital motions. The relative positions that these bodies maintain in space are determined by a balance of the opposing forces. The orbits of the moon about the earth and of the earth around the sun are paths along which the balance of forces is realized.

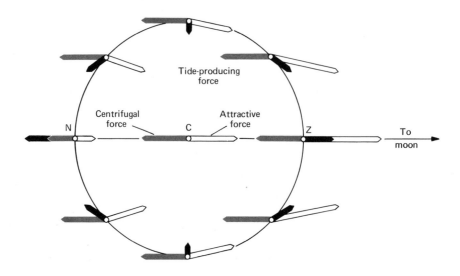

Figure 10-5 Distribution of centrifugal and gravitational (attractive) forces acting on the earth. (Modified after A. N. Strahler)

To discuss the tide-producing force systematically, we must consider the earth-moon system as different from the earth-sun system, and then consider how the force of gravitational attraction and centrifugal force are regulated. The concepts developed for one system will apply to the other system as well. We use the earth–moon system because its tide-producing force is over twice as great as that of the sun. Once the effect of the earth–moon system is understood, the influence of the sun can be added.

The earth and the moon revolve around their common center of gravity, called the *barycenter*, in a counterclockwise direction when viewed from the north polar axis. The moon completes one revolution around the earth every 29.53 days. This motion represents a dynamic equilibrium; that is, the gravitational attraction tending to draw the earth and the moon together is balanced by the centrifugal force arising from their orbital motion about one another. Figure 10-5 shows how the centrifugal and gravitational force vectors are seen to balance at the center of the earth.

Let us now investigate the distribution of gravitational and centrifugal forces on the surface of the earth to find the reasons for tidal behavior in the ocean.

The Force of Gravitational Attraction

One of Newton's laws of motion relates the force of gravitational attraction between two bodies to the product of their masses divided by the square of the distance between them:

$$F_g = \frac{GM_1M_2}{r^2} \qquad\qquad [10\text{-}1]$$

where M_1 and M_2 = masses of attracting bodies, r = distance between objects, and G = gravitational constant.

For the earth–moon system, the product M_1M_2 is constant, so Eq. 10-1 can be expressed as:

$$F_g = \frac{M}{r^2} \qquad\qquad [10\text{-}2]$$

where $M = GM_1M_2$ = a constant. Equation 10-2 describes how the earth is influenced by gravitational forces acting between the earth and the moon. The forces are distributed as shown in Fig. 10-5. On the side of the earth nearest the moon, the distance (r) between point Z and the center of the moon is less than from the center of the earth (point C), so F_g is greater at Z than at C. Point N is farther from the moon than point C; therefore, F_g at point N is smaller than at the center. These differences are small but important, because they lead to the unbalanced forces that are responsible for the tides.

Centrifugal Force

Centrifugal force is the other major force producing tides. Centrifugal force results from the motion of a mass along a curved path. In the case at hand, we are interested in the centrifugal force on the earth as it travels in its orbit about the center of the earth-moon system. The force is directed away from the center of the orbit and may be expressed as:

$$F_c = \frac{MV^2}{r} \qquad\qquad [10\text{-}3]$$

where M = the mass of the orbiting body, r = the radius of curvature of its orbital path, and V = velocity of motion. The value of F_c is the same at all points on the earth, because the orbit of any point on the earth has the same radius as the orbit of any other point of curvature.

We can clarify this fact by considering the analogy of a Ferris wheel (Fig. 10-6). The axis of the Ferris wheel represents the center of the earth-moon system and the gondola is the earth. The orientation of the gondola at different positions is indicated by the seats. If there is no frictional coupling between the Ferris wheel and the gondola, the gondola will remain oriented with respect to the ground as the Ferris wheel revolves. Note that no matter what position is chosen, the orbits of all points have the same radius $(r_1 = r_2 = r_g)$. The centrifugal force acting on all points on the gondola is the same, since this force, F_c in Eq. 10-3, depends only upon the radius if the mass and velocity are constant. The distribution of F_c on the earth is constant and unidirectional

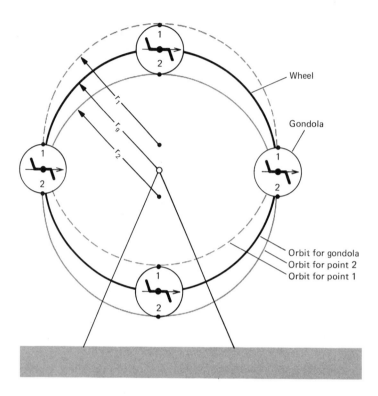

Figure 10-6 Schematic representation of a Ferris wheel in which there is no frictional coupling between the gondola and the wheel. The gondola maintains its position with respect to the ground at all times. The orbits traced by various points on the gondola as it revolves are also included.

because the motion of the earth about the barycenter is similar to that of the Ferris wheel.

It is not necessary to include in this discussion the centrifugal force arising from the rotation of the earth about its own axis. The earth's shape is in dynamic equilibrium with respect to its internal gravitational and centrifugal forces; consequently, there is no resultant force to influence tidal phenomena.

The *tide-producing force* is obtained by resolving the combined effects of the centrifugal and gravitational forces throughout the earth. This resolution is shown in Fig. 10-7. Note that the two regions of intense tide-producing forces exist: one facing the sublunar point (where gravitational forces dominate) and one on the opposite side of the earth (where centrifugal forces dominate). The surface resultant of the tide-producing force is called the *tractive force* (Fig. 10-8). Tractive forces cause ocean water to accumulate, producing *two* tidal highs, one at the sublunar point and another on the opposite side of the earth.

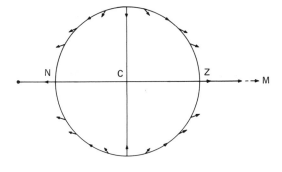

Figure 10-7 Distribution of tide-producing force on a plane of the earth oriented toward the moon. (After Sverdrup et al., 1942)

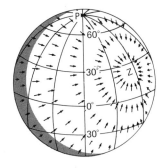

Figure 10-8 Distribution of the tractive force over the surface of the earth. The point Z is facing the moon. (After Sverdrup et al., 1942, by permission of Prentice-Hall, Inc.)

The moon circles the earth once every 29.53 days; during the 24 hours of one rotation of the earth on its axis, the moon completes $1/29.53$ of its revolution about the earth. As a result, the moon appears to return to a point directly overhead in a period slightly longer than one day. The interval is 24 hours and 50 min, the so-called *lunar day*. This phenomenon is illustrated schematically in Fig. 10-9. Note that two high and two low tides sweep the circumference of the earth within the period of the lunar day. Such a tide is called a *lunar semidiurnal tide* and is illustrated in Fig. 10-2A.

Further complexities arise when we try to describe the motion of the tidal bulges with respect to the earth's surface. As the moon revolves around the earth, its declination changes constantly throughout the lunar month. The plane of the moon's orbit is tilted 5°9' with respect to the plane of the ecliptic (Fig. 10-10). Hence, during each lunar month, the declination of the moon's orbit changes continually between positions 28½° above and below the equator. As declination varies, different places on the earth exhibit different tidal behavior. During the time of the month when the moon is at maximum declination every point on the earth exhibits a lunar semidiurnal tide with a period of 12 hours and 25 min. Only at the equator do high and low tides have equal amplitude. Elsewhere, an inequality exists in extreme high and low tidal amplitudes. Tides of this type are called *tropical tides* (Fig. 10-11A).

The tidal curve in Fig. 10-11A actually consists of a diurnal and semidiurnal

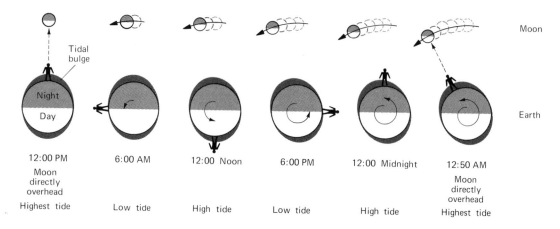

Figure 10-9 Cause of lunar semidiurnal tide constituent.

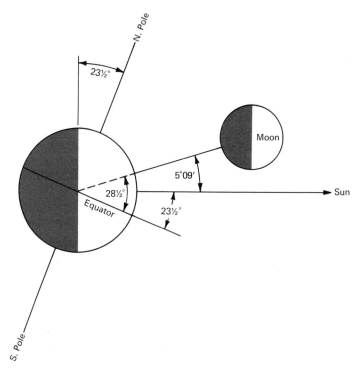

Figure 10-10 The plane of the moon's orbit is inclined 5°09′ with respect to the plane of the ecliptic. Thus the maximum declination of the moon is 28.5° (approximately) with respect to the earth's equator.

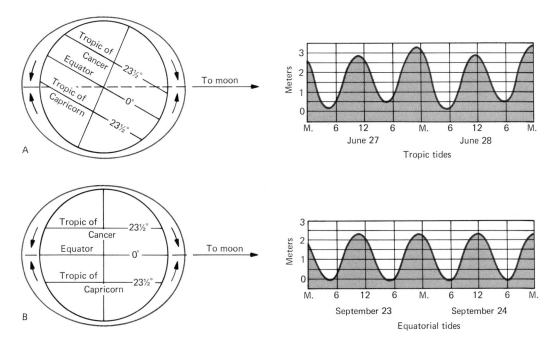

Figure 10-11 The tidal bulges shift with the declination of the moon causing equatorial and tropic tides. The corresponding tidal curves are also shown. (After A. N. Strahler, 1963)

component (Fig. 10-12). No purely diurnal tide exists, but the effect of declination is to add, or superimpose, a small diurnal component onto the existing semidiurnal pattern. The result is a mixed tide in which successive high and low water levels are different. Likewise, every unique movement of the sun or moon adds another tidal constituent onto the basic pattern—a phenomenon that will be discussed in the next section.

The lunar plane shifts to coincide with the earth's equator twice each lunar month. At that time, a somewhat different tidal configuration occurs (Fig. 10-11B). The tidal bulge is oriented symmetrically around the equator, and all portions of the globe influenced by tidal fluctuations are characterized by semidiurnal lunar tides of equal amplitude. Tides of this type are called *equatorial tides* (Fig. 10-11B).

This idealized and, in some ways, unrealistic portrayal of the tides emphasizes several of their important aspects. First, tide-producing forces are related to the combination of gravitational and centrifugal forces within the earth–moon system. Second, two tidal bulges are predicted by this analysis, which agrees with tidal observations. Finally, many tidal configurations are possible, depending on latitude and declination of the moon.

The identical analysis can be applied to water-level changes produced by

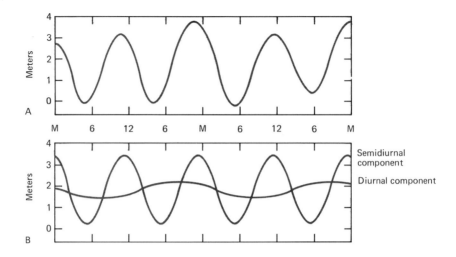

Figure 10-12 Separation of a tropic tide curve (from Fig. 9-10A) into diurnal and semidiurnal components.

the earth–sun system. Certain minor modifications, however, are required: (1) the period of the solar–diurnal tide is 24 hours and of the solar semidiurnal tide, 12 hours; (2) the plane of the sun's ecliptic is inclined away from the earth's equator. This inclination reaches a maximum of 23½° on an annual cycle.

Actually, tidal bulges are shallow-water waves that cannot travel at the speed of the earth's rotation. The result is that the tides are *forced waves:* Their period is dependent on the periodic motions of the moon and the sun, but their speed depends on the water depth (approximately 200 m per sec in the open ocean). As a consequence, high tide does not necessarily coincide with the passage of the sun or the moon. The delay time for the moon is called the *lunitidal interval.* This interval remains approximately constant for a given locality but varies greatly throughout the world.

At certain positions in the moon's orbit around the earth, the tide-producing forces of the moon and the sun combine to cause a very large tidal range, called a *spring tide.* Spring tides occur when the earth, the moon, and the sun are in alignment *(syzygy),* as shown in Fig. 10-13A. Such a configuration occurs every half-revolution of the moon around the earth, or approximately every 2 weeks. When the moon is 90° from the line connecting the earth and the sun (the *quadrature),* the lowest tidal range, the *neap tide,* occurs. These tides are also about 2 weeks apart, but they occur 1 week after each spring tide. Spring-neap variations are called the *lunar fortnightly constituents* of the tide-producing force. The relation to the phases of the moon can be seen in Fig. 10-13B. Spring tides occur at full and new moons, whereas neap tides occur at the first quarter and the third quarter of the moon.

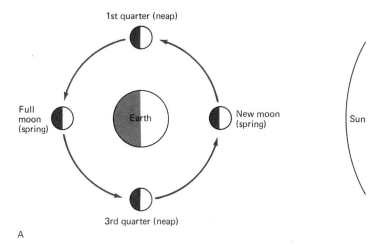

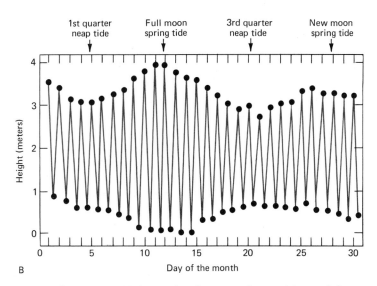

Figure 10-13 Relationship between the positions of the moon and sun with respect to the earth (A) and the occurrence of spring and neap tides as shown in a plot of tidal range over a 30-day interval (B). (After A. N. Strahler, 1963)

10.4 *Tidal Prediction*

When Sir Isaac Newton propounded his theories on gravity, he also introduced the *equilibrium theory of tides*. He assumed a water-covered earth of constant depth that remained in a state of equilibrium with regard to the interplanetary forces of gravity. Accordingly, the great tidal bulges should exactly follow the transits of the sun and the moon across the sky.

However, the tidal behavior envisioned in the equilibrium theory is inaccurate. Although the gravitational influences of the sun and the moon are evident on the earth, the speed at which the tidal bulges traverse the equatorial oceans is less than one-half the speed of the diurnal motions of the sun and the moon. Thus, the equilibrium theory does not deal correctly with the dynamics of water set in motion by the tractive forces.

Once the transport of water is considered, there arise several other complexities that further diminish the applicability of the equilibrium theory. In the first place, it is impossible to set the ocean waters in motion at a speed necessary to maintain equilibrium with the passage of the moon, because the quantity of water to be transported is too great. Second, once water is moving, it is influenced by local factors, such as the shape, size, and depth of the ocean basin. These factors modify tidal motion. Tidal friction and meteorological influences are also important in influencing water motion in the world ocean.

The equilibrium theory is useful only for predicting tide-generating forces and some of the basic tidal configurations that are observed. In addition, spring and neap tides and other long-term tidal variations can be predicted, for they occur at rates slow enough to agree with the theory. But still, actual local tidal motions on the earth cannot be calculated by using the equilibrium theory. As a result, mechanical techniques have been devised to predict the tides. These techniques require that tides be measured in any given place before prediction is possible.

The first step in tidal prediction is a systematic description of the periodic fluctuations of the tide-producing force. For this procedure, the complex orbital motions of the moon and the sun are separated into distinct cycles, or *tidal constituents*. Periodic fluctuations of the tractive forces reflect the combined periodicities of these motions.

Consider, for instance, the earth's revolution about the sun. If the variations in the earth's distance and declination with respect to the sun are neglected, then we could expect a purely semidiurnal tide. However, the distance from the earth to the sun varies; it is minimal during the northern winter (perihelion) and maximal during the northern summer (aphelion). These differences cause the tide-producing force to fluctuate on a yearly cycle. Hence, a perturbation, or tidal constituent, must be added to the basic pattern of the semidiurnal tide.

The declination of the sun also varies on an annual basis. During the summer solstice, the sun's declination reaches 23½° north latitude; at the winter solstice, it reaches 23½° south latitude. These declinational changes introduce another tidal constituent, a diurnal one that has a semiannual periodicity. The constitutent for the effect of solar declination is analogous to the constituent showing the moon's declination (illustrated in Fig. 10-11).

This illustration, although highly simplified, shows how the tide-producing force can be related to the motions that the earth and the moon have with respect to the sun. Individual tidal constituents are sinusoidal and therefore are simple mathematically. Most important, when they are superimposed, a realistic representation of the tide-producing force is achieved. By this technique, called *harmonic analysis,* scientists can describe the combined effect of over 70 tidal constituents having periods from 12 hours to 1,600 years. Some examples are given in Table 10-1. Each tidal constituent is defined by a separate component of the motion of the earth and moon about the sun. Each component contributes a unique tidal fluctuation called a *partial tide.* The sum of partial tides gives the total tidal behavior. Although a great number of tidal constituents exist, not all have influence on every part of the ocean. Depending on its size, shape, and depth, each embayment, coastal area, and even each ocean basin responds to different constituents. For example, the Atlantic Ocean basin responds most strongly to forces that produce a semidiurnal tide, so lunar semidiurnal tides prevail there (Fig. 10-2A). The Pacific Ocean basin is large enough to respond to both diurnal and semidiurnal periods; hence, the tides along the Pacific shores reflect a mixture of diurnal and semidiurnal components and are called *mixed tides* (Fig. 10-2B). Tides that are nearly diurnal are rare, but they do occur in such places as Viet Nam, Manila, and parts of the Gulf of Mexico (Fig. 10-2C).

Table 10–1   The Most Important Constituents of the Tide-Generating Force (Constituent Tides)

	Symbol	Period in solar hours	Amplitude $M_2 = 100$	Description
Semidiurnal tides	M_2	12.42	100.00	Main lunar (semidiurnal) constituent
	S_2	12.00	46.6	Main solar (semidiurnal) constituent
	N_2	12.66	19.1	Lunar constituent due to monthly variation in moon's distance
	K_2	11.97	12.7	Solilunar constituent due to changes in declinations of sun and moon throughout their orbital cycles
Diurnal tides	K_1	23.93	58.4	Solilunar constituent
	O_1	25.82	41.5	Main lunar (diurnal) constituent
	P_1	24.07	19.3	Main solar (diurnal) constituent
Long-period tides	M_f	327.86	17.2	Moon's fortnightly constituent

(After A. Defant, *Ebb and Flow: The Tides of Earth, Air, and Water.* Ann Arbor: The University of Michigan Press, 1958.)

Table 10–2   Some Tidal Constants in the Atlantic

Place	Lat.	Long.	Amplitude in cm				Phase in degrees			
			M_2	S_2	K_1	O	M_2	S_2	K_1	O
St. John's (Newfoundland)	47°34'N	52°41'W	35.7	14.6	7.6	7.0	210	254	108	77
New York (Sandy Hook)	40°28'	74°01'	65.4	13.8	9.7	5.2	218	245	101	99
St. George (Bermuda)	32°22'	64°42'	35.5	8.2	6.4	5.2	231	257	124	128
Port of Spain (Trinidad)	10°39'N	61°31'	25.2	8.0	8.3	6.7	119	139	187	178
Pernambuco	8°04'S	34°53'	76.3	27.8	3.1	5.1	125	148	64	142
Rio de Janeiro	22°54'	43°10'	32.6	17.2	6.4	11.1	87	97	148	87
Buenos Aires	34°36'	58°22'	30.5	5.2	9.2	15.4	168	248	14	202
Moltke Harbor (S. Georgia)	54°31'	36°0'	22.6	11.7	5.2	10.2	213	236	52	18
Capetown	33°54'S	15°25'	48.6	20.5	5.4	1.6	45	88	127	243
Freetown	8°30'N	13°14'	97.7	32.5	9.8	2.5	201	234	334	249
Puerto Lux (Las Palmas)	28°9'	25°25'	76.0	28.0	7.0	5.0	356	19	21	264
Ponta Delgada (Azores)	37°44'	25°40'	49.1	17.9	4.4	2.5	12	32	41	292
Lisbon	33°42'	9°8'	118.3	40.9	7.4	6.5	60	88	51	310
Brest	48°23'	4°29'	296.1	75.3	6.3	6.8	99	139	69	324
Londonderry	55°0'N	7°19'W	78.6	30.1	8.2	7.8	218	244	181	38

(After A. Defant, *Ebb and Flow: The Tides of the Earth, Air, and Water.* Ann Arbor: The University of Michigan Press, 1958.)

The tides that affect a particular location on a coast are predicted by obtaining a long record of the tide-height fluctuations from the area. This record is analyzed to reveal: (1) the dominant tidal constituents, (2) their amplitude, and (3) their phase (i.e., their timing with respect to one another). In other words, the actual record is broken into many partial tides. The partial tides repeat themselves continually, so the tide can be predicted by adding the partial tides expected in the future. Examples of some constants that describe common partial tides are given in Table 10-2. The definitions of the symbols and their periodicities are in Table 10-1. Note, for example, that the M_2 constituent at St. George is one-half the amplitude of that at Pernambuco, whereas the K_1 constituent is twice as great. This fact illustrates the influence that coastal areas have upon the tides.

A tidal curve for Lisbon, Portugal, is obtained by plotting tidal constants from Table 10-2 and then combining the individual curves (Fig. 10-14). A more graphic example is given in Fig. 10-15. Here, an observed tidal record is broken into 15 partial tides. This illustration also shows the influence that meteorological conditions have upon the tide.

The technique just described is incorporated in the operation of a tide-producing machine, a mechanical device used to predict and simulate tides in hydraulic models. The machine shown in Fig. 10-16 simulates the tides in a large hydraulic model of Puget Sound, Washington. It incorporates six cams, each representing a tidal constituent important in that location. Each cam rotates at a rate determined by the periodicity of the tidal constituent it represents. The phase and amplitude of each cam is adjusted to account for the relative importance of the constituent it represents. All six cams are connected to a large plunger by means of a taut wire. As each cam turns, it displaces the wire and causes the plunger to move vertically. The amount of vertical

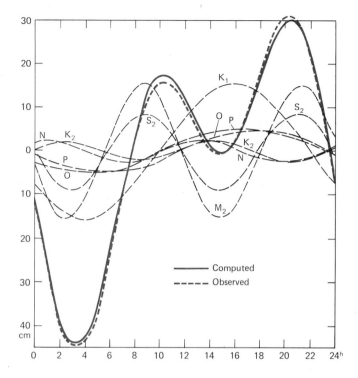

Figure 10-14 Comparison between the computed and observed tides at Pula (January 6, 1909). The thin curves represent the 7 main constituent tides, the thick curve shows their resultant, and the thick broken curve the observed tide. (After Defant, 1958, by permission of the University of Michigan Press)

movement of the plunger is the sum of all cam displacements. The plunger displaces water in the model and causes simulated tides. The model shown in Fig. 10-16 completes a diurnal cycle in approximately 50 sec.

The tide reference level is different at various places. On the U.S. East Coast *mean low water* represents the *chart datum* to which tide heights are compared. In the Indian Ocean, *indian spring low water* is used; it is the average level of the low-water spring tides. The datum used in Fig. 10-17 is *mean lower low water*, the average of the lower of the two low tides that occur each day.

Scientists formerly did calculations for tide tables on tide-prediction machines. The machine shown in Fig. 10-16 is a small one designed for a model. To predict tides for a general use throughout the world, machines had to be capable of handling over 70 tidal constituents. These machines, once set up, could predict a year's tide by operating for a couple of days. Now, however, large high-speed digital computers have replaced tide-prediction machines.

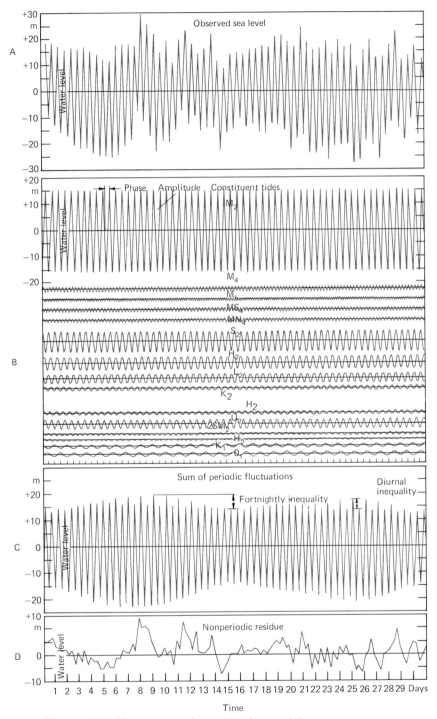

Figure 10-15 Harmonic analysis: (A) observed fluctuations in water level; (B) harmonic constituents; (C) sum of harmonic constituents; (D) nonperiodic residue due to wind and pressure. (From Defant, 1958, by permission of the University of Michigan Press)

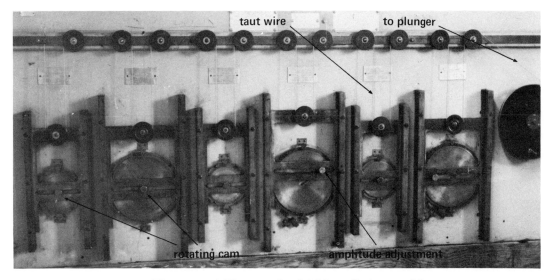

Figure 10-16 Photograph of tidal prediction machine.

10.5 *Types of Tides*

In a bay, the incoming progressive wave can be reflected at the head of the bay in such a way that the outgoing crest meets the next incoming trough at the mouth. A node forms at the mouth and an antinode forms at the head (Fig. 10-18A); the water tilts up, then down, in a manner called a *standing wave.* Every basin of water on earth, by virtue of its size and shape, has the potential of maintaining a standing wave. Standing-wave tides are produced when the period of natural oscillation of the basin is approximately equal to the tidal period and when frictional effects in the basin do not dampen the oscillation to any great extent. Resonance causes the tidal range to be amplified to a value limited only by friction. This is the case in the Bay of Fundy. The length and depth of this estuary are such that the natural period of oscillation is about equal to the semidiurnal tide in the Atlantic Ocean basin. At the mouth of the bay, there is small vertical movement (3½ m), but at the head of the bay, the maximum tidal range is over 15.4 m.

It is possible to distinguish whether the tide in an inlet or basin is a progressive tide or a standing-wave tide. A progressive tide rises the same amount but at different times along an inlet. A standing-wave tide, however, rises different amounts but simultaneously at all points along the inlet (Fig. 10-18B). Often, tidal behavior in an area is a combination of progressive and standing waves. Moreover, atmospheric effects such as storms at sea and local winds may tend to modify or obscure the pattern of the tide in any given location.

April

Day	Time h.m.	Height ft	m	Day	Time h.m.	Height ft	m
1 TU	0042	12.4	3.8	16 W	0043	14.9	4.5
	0647	-0.1	0.0		0701	-3.1	-0.9
	1301	11.9	3.6		1327	13.2	4.0
	1859	0.4	0.1		1911	-0.3	-0.1
2 W	0109	12.6	3.8	17 TH	0125	14.8	4.5
	0721	-0.3	-0.1		0746	-3.0	-0.9
	1333	11.6	3.5		1413	12.6	3.8
	1927	0.9	0.3		1954	0.7	0.2
3 TH	0138	12.5	3.8	18 F	0204	14.3	4.4
	0754	-0.3	-0.1		0833	-2.3	-0.7
	1407	11.2	3.4		1503	11.7	3.6
	1957	1.6	0.5		2041	1.9	0.6
4 F	0205	12.4	3.8	19 SA	0247	13.4	4.1
	0831	-0.1	0.0		0922	-1.3	-0.4
	1444	10.6	3.2		1558	10.8	3.3
	2033	2.4	0.7		2129	3.0	0.9
5 SA	0231	12.1	3.7	20 SU	0333	12.2	3.7
	0911	0.3	0.1		1014	-0.1	0.0
	1527	9.8	3.0		1707	9.9	3.0
	2111	3.2	1.0		2225	4.1	1.2
6 SU	0305	11.6	3.5	21 M	0433	11.0	3.4
	0956	0.8	0.2		1113	1.0	0.3
	1622	9.1	2.8		1823	9.5	2.9
	2156	4.0	1.2		2328	4.9	1.5
7 M	0348	11.0	3.4	22 TU	0550	10.0	3.0
	1051	1.3	0.4		1220	1.9	0.6
	1742	8.7	2.7		1935	9.5	2.9
	2252	4.6	1.4				
8 TU	0506	10.5	3.2	23 W	0051	5.0	1.5
	1157	1.6	0.5		0713	9.6	2.9
	1905	8.8	2.7		1337	2.3	0.7
					2037	9.9	3.0
9 W	0006	4.9	1.5	24 TH	0222	4.5	1.4
	0639	10.3	3.1		0824	9.6	2.9
	1313	1.5	0.5		1448	2.1	0.6
	2014	9.5	2.9		2122	10.3	3.1
10 TH	0136	4.4	1.3	25 F	0330	3.4	1.0
	0757	10.8	3.3		0921	9.9	3.0
	1429	0.9	0.3		1538	1.8	0.5
	2109	10.5	3.2		2202	10.8	3.3
11 F	0254	3.2	1.0	26 SA	0413	2.2	0.7
	0904	11.5	3.5		1010	10.3	3.1
	1530	0.1	0.0		1619	1.4	0.4
	2159	11.6	3.5		2234	11.3	3.4
12 SA	0354	1.4	0.4	27 SU	0448	1.2	0.4
	1003	12.3	3.7		1052	10.6	3.2
	1621	-0.7	-0.2		1652	1.2	0.4
	2244	12.7	3.9		2303	11.8	3.6
13 SU	0445	-0.3	-0.1	28 M	0521	0.2	0.1
	1058	13.0	4.0		1132	10.9	3.3
	1704	-1.2	-0.4		1724	1.1	0.3
	2324	13.7	4.2		2333	12.3	3.7
14 M	0531	-1.7	-0.5	29 TU	0553	-0.5	-0.2
	1151	13.4	4.1		1209	11.2	3.4
	1746	-1.3	-0.4		1755	1.1	0.3
15 TU	0004	14.5	4.4	30 W	0004	12.6	3.8
	0617	-2.7	-0.8		0625	-1.0	-0.3
	1239	13.5	4.1		1244	11.3	3.4
	1828	-1.0	-0.3		1827	1.4	0.4

May

Day	Time h.m.	Height ft	m	Day	Time h.m.	Height ft	m
1 TH	0033	12.8	3.9	16 F	0058	14.5	4.4
	0657	-1.3	-0.4		0729	-3.2	-1.0
	1319	11.2	3.4		1404	12.0	3.7
	1859	1.8	0.5		1934	1.8	0.5
2 F	0103	12.9	3.9	17 SA	0139	13.9	4.2
	0732	-1.3	-0.4		0814	-2.5	-0.8
	1358	10.9	3.3		1452	11.5	3.5
	1934	2.3	0.7		2018	2.6	0.8
3 SA	0133	12.7	3.9	18 SU	0221	13.0	4.0
	0810	-1.1	-0.3		0900	-1.6	-0.5
	1436	10.5	3.2		1542	10.8	3.3
	2013	2.9	0.9		2111	3.4	1.0
4 SU	0205	12.4	3.8	19 M	0307	11.9	3.6
	0852	-0.7	-0.2		0950	-0.5	-0.2
	1522	10.1	3.1		1641	10.2	3.1
	2055	3.5	1.1		2204	4.1	1.2
5 M	0242	11.8	3.6	20 TU	0400	10.7	3.3
	0937	-0.2	-0.1		1041	0.6	0.2
	1617	9.6	2.9		1742	9.9	3.0
	2145	4.0	1.2		2304	4.5	1.4
6 TU	0332	11.1	3.4	21 W	0505	9.6	2.9
	1030	0.3	0.1		1135	1.5	0.5
	1727	9.4	2.9		1846	9.8	3.0
	2245	4.3	1.3				
7 W	0445	10.4	3.2	22 TH	0013	4.6	1.4
	1131	0.7	0.2		0627	9.0	2.7
	1839	9.7	3.0		1236	2.2	0.7
	2355	4.3	1.3		1941	10.0	3.0
8 TH	0617	10.1	3.1	23 F	0133	4.1	1.2
	1238	1.0	0.3		0737	8.8	2.7
	1941	10.3	3.1		1342	2.5	0.8
					2027	10.3	3.1
9 F	0116	3.6	1.1	24 SA	0245	3.2	1.0
	0736	10.2	3.1		0840	8.9	2.7
	1347	0.9	0.3		1441	2.5	0.8
	2034	11.2	3.4		2106	10.8	3.3
10 SA	0235	2.2	0.7	25 SU	0338	2.1	0.6
	0845	10.7	3.3		0933	9.2	2.8
	1454	0.6	0.2		1530	2.4	0.7
	2122	12.3	3.7		2141	11.3	3.4
11 SU	0337	0.5	0.2	26 M	0417	0.9	0.3
	0946	11.3	3.4		1021	9.5	2.9
	1547	0.3	0.1		1610	2.2	0.7
	2207	13.2	4.0		2216	11.9	3.6
12 M	0429	-1.1	-0.3	27 TU	0452	-0.1	0.0
	1044	11.8	3.6		1108	10.0	3.0
	1636	0.1	0.0		1647	2.1	0.6
	2252	14.0	4.3		2252	12.4	3.8
13 TU	0515	-2.4	-0.7	28 W	0527	-0.9	-0.3
	1138	12.2	3.7		1148	10.3	3.1
	1721	0.1	0.0		1722	2.1	0.6
	2335	14.6	4.5		2327	12.8	3.9
14 W	0601	-3.3	-1.0	29 TH	0602	-1.5	-0.5
	1229	12.4	3.8		1230	10.6	3.2
	1806	0.4	0.1		1758	2.2	0.7
15 TH	0017	14.8	4.5	30 F	0003	13.0	4.0
	0643	-3.5	-1.1		0638	-1.9	-0.6
	1319	12.3	3.7		1309	10.8	3.3
	1848	1.0	0.3		1834	2.4	0.7
				31 SA	0038	13.1	4.0
					0713	-2.0	-0.6
					1349	10.9	3.3
					1915	2.7	0.8

June

Day	Time h.m.	Height ft	m	Day	Time h.m.	Height ft	m
1 SU	0114	13.0	4.0	16 M	0202	12.7	3.9
	0755	-1.9	-0.6		0839	-1.6	-0.5
	1431	10.7	3.3		1520	11.0	3.4
	1957	3.0	0.9		2049	3.3	1.0
2 M	0152	12.7	3.9	17 TU	0244	11.7	3.6
	0837	-1.6	-0.5		0921	-0.7	-0.2
	1513	10.6	3.2		1604	10.6	3.2
	2042	3.3	1.0		2139	3.6	1.1
3 TU	0234	12.1	3.7	18 W	0327	10.6	3.2
	0924	-1.2	-0.4		1004	0.2	0.1
	1608	10.4	3.2		1654	10.2	3.1
	2135	3.5	1.1		2233	3.9	1.2
4 W	0326	11.4	3.5	19 TH	0425	9.6	2.9
	1012	-0.6	-0.2		1051	1.1	0.3
	1707	10.4	3.2		1749	10.0	3.0
	2235	3.5	1.1		2328	4.0	1.2
5 TH	0433	10.5	3.2	20 F	0531	8.7	2.7
	1106	0.0	0.0		1139	2.0	0.6
	1807	10.6	3.2		1839	10.1	3.1
	2342	3.2	1.0				
6 F	0558	9.9	3.0	21 SA	0034	3.7	1.1
	1204	0.6	0.2		0645	8.2	2.5
	1905	11.2	3.4		1232	2.6	0.8
					1926	10.3	3.1
7 SA	0057	2.6	0.8	22 SU	0146	3.1	0.9
	0718	9.7	3.0		0750	8.1	2.5
	1309	1.1	0.3		1332	3.1	0.9
	1958	11.9	3.6		2011	10.7	3.3
8 SU	0213	1.4	0.4	23 M	0252	2.2	0.7
	0829	9.9	3.0		0853	8.3	2.5
	1415	1.4	0.4		1432	3.3	1.0
	2049	12.7	3.9		2053	11.2	3.4
9 M	0319	0.0	0.0	24 TU	0341	1.1	0.3
	0933	10.2	3.1		0949	8.7	2.7
	1518	1.5	0.5		1525	3.2	1.0
	2137	13.4	4.1		2133	11.8	3.6
10 TU	0413	-1.4	-0.4	25 W	0423	0.1	0.0
	1036	10.7	3.3		1039	9.2	2.8
	1610	1.5	0.5		1611	3.1	0.9
	2223	13.9	4.2		2215	12.3	3.7
11 W	0500	-2.5	-0.8	26 TH	0502	-0.9	-0.3
	1132	11.2	3.4		1127	9.8	3.0
	1700	1.5	0.5		1653	2.9	0.9
	2309	14.3	4.4		2257	12.8	3.9
12 TH	0546	-3.1	-0.9	27 F	0540	-1.7	-0.5
	1222	11.5	3.5		1213	10.4	3.2
	1745	1.7	0.5		1735	2.6	0.8
	2353	14.3	4.4		2337	13.3	4.1
13 F	0630	-3.2	-1.0	28 SA	0618	-2.2	-0.7
	1309	11.7	3.6		1252	10.8	3.3
	1830	1.9	0.6		1815	2.5	0.8
14 SA	0039	14.0	4.3	29 SU	0019	13.5	4.1
	0712	-3.0	-0.9		0657	-2.5	-0.8
	1354	11.6	3.5		1334	11.1	3.4
	1915	2.3	0.7		1857	2.4	0.7
15 SU	0120	13.5	4.1	30 M	0101	13.5	4.1
	0756	-2.4	-0.7		0738	-2.6	-0.8
	1438	11.4	3.5		1415	11.3	3.4
	2001	2.8	0.9		1942	2.3	0.7

Time meridian 150°W. 0000 is midnight. 1200 is noon.
Heights are referred to mean lower low water which is the chart datum of soundings.

FIG 10-17

Figure 10-17 Example of a tide table published by the U.S. Department of Commerce. The station experiences a mixed tide with a rather large tidal range.

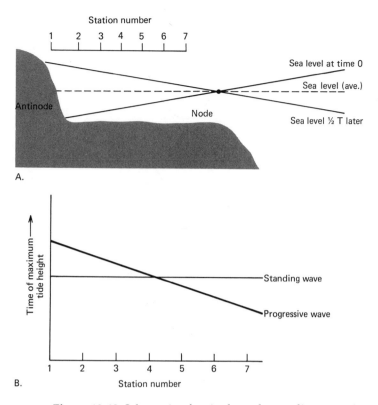

Figure 10-18 Schematic of a single-node standing wave in a coastal embayment (A); and the relation between the time of maximum tide height and position in an embayment for progressive and standing waves (B).

The natural period of oscillation is important because it determines the oscillation frequencies that can be sustained in a basin. Since the Atlantic Ocean basin responds to semidiurnal constituents, diurnal periods are not present. Conversely, the Pacific Ocean basin responds to both semidiurnal and diurnal periods; hence, mixed tides are common there. This phenomenon occurs to some extent in every irregularity in the world oceans. It explains why the contribution of each tidal constituent varies from place to place.

10.6 Tidal Currents

Progressive Tides

The rise and fall of sea level associated with the tides imparts other important motions to the water. In the open ocean, tidal currents follow paths that approximate the water-particle movements of shallow-water progressive waves. These paths are highly elliptical or flattened orbits with maximum horizontal velocity under the crest and trough. Tidal currents of this type are

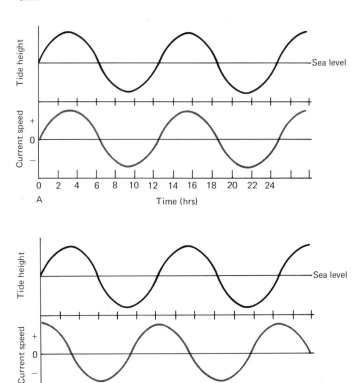

Figure 10-19 Relation between the height and current speed for a progressive wave tide (A); and a standing wave tide (B).

maximum during times of both high and low water and are minimum when sea level is midway between these extremes. Figure 10-19 shows the relationship between water level and tidal current during the passage of a progressive tide.

An estimate of tidal currents can be obtained by calculating the maximum horizontal orbital velocity associated with shallow-water progressive waves if the water depth and tidal amplitude are known. Some calculations of typical cases are shown in Table 10-3.

Table 10-3 indicates that tidal currents are swifter in shallower water. Tidal amplitudes are larger in shallower water, so a 62 cm per sec estimate for currents along the continental shelf (100 m depth) is approximately correct. Tidal current velocities are the same from the sea surface to near the bottom, where the velocities decrease because friction retards the flow.

Table 10–3 Estimates of Maximum Tidal Currents of Semidiurnal Tides (Calculated from Shallow-Water Progressive-Wave Orbital Velocities)

Depth	Tidal amplitude of 1 m	Tidal amplitude of 2 m
100 m	31.3 cm/sec*	62.6 cm/sec
500 m	14.0 cm/sec	28.0 cm/sec
2,000 m	7.0 cm/sec	14.0 cm/sec
4,000 m	4.9 cm/sec	9.8 cm/sec

*50 cm/sec = about 1 knot = about 1 nautical mile per hour.

Standing-Wave Tides

The sequence of tidal currents associated with standing-wave tides is illustrated in Fig. 10-19B. Notice that maximum current speeds occur at mean tide level and that current speeds are nearly zero at maximum flood and ebb, just the opposite of the case for progressive tides. If the tides are semidiurnal, maximum current occurs approximately 3 hours before high or low water.

Rotational Effects

The rotation of the earth causes an apparent deflection of tidal currents. In the northern hemisphere, the deflection is to the right, or clockwise. In the southern hemisphere, it is counterclockwise. These rotational motions are developed best in approximately equidimensional basins of the major oceans. Figure 10-20A shows the rotary systems thought to exist in the Atlantic Ocean basin. The cotidal lines on this figure represent the geographical positions of the tidal crest at hourly intervals over a 12-hour semidiurnal period. The point where cotidal lines merge is an *amphidromic point,* a place where no tidal fluctuation of sea level exists. The tidal range is zero at an amphidromic point; it increases with distance from that point in an approximately regular manner. Figure 10-20B illustrates the motion of the water surface in an amphidromic tidal system.

The positions of amphidromic points and cotidal lines in the deep sea are inferred from tidal measurements made at nearshore sites on continents and oceanic islands. The results of the measurements are then extrapolated into the deep sea. Direct measurement in the deep sea would greatly improve the oceanographer's understanding of oceanic tides.

Nearshore Tides

Tides in nearshore regions greatly differ from those assumed to exist in the deep sea. Because of the diverse shapes and sizes of bays, sounds, and straits, tides and tidal currents vary greatly. The strongest tidal currents exist where the tide must enter a bay through a constricted entrance. If the bay behind the

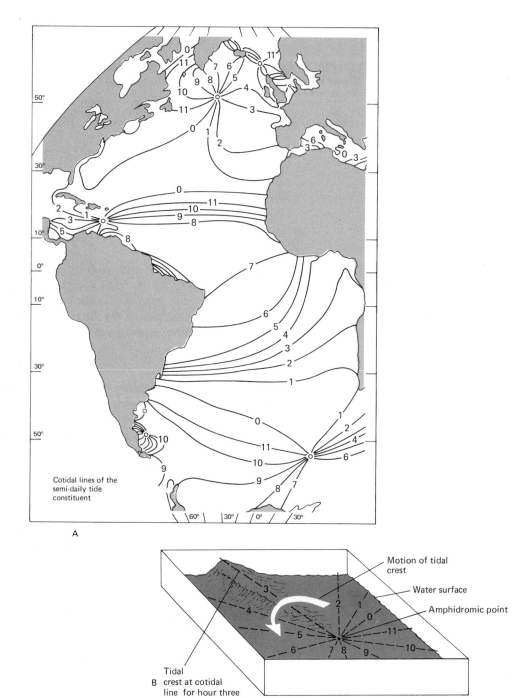

Figure 10-20 (A) Cotidal lines of semidaily tide constituent of the Atlantic Ocean Basin; (B) Motion of the water surface in a schematic amphidromic tidal system in the northern hemisphere.

constriction is large and has a significant tidal range, then the flood and ebb currents through the entrance must be large. San Francisco Bay is such an example; tidal currents of 300 cm per sec have been measured during spring tides.

Tidal currents are also high where channels connect different bodies of water. Strong hydraulic currents arise if the water level fluctuations in the two basins are out of phase. One example is Akutan Pass in the Aleutian Islands where tidal currents of 450 cm per sec have been recorded. Currents exceeding 300 cm per sec have been measured in the Bungo Strait entrance to the Sea of Japan.

Tidal Bores

In some tidal rivers, the incoming tidal wave becomes steepened into a wall of turbulent water called a *tidal bore*. The exact cause of tidal bores is not known, However, they have a critical relationship to the characteristics of the

Figure 10-21 The Severn bore rushing up the river at Stonehead, Gloucester, England.

incoming tidal wave, slope and shape of the channel, mean channel depth, and river flow. Few rivers develop well-defined tidal bores, although spectacular examples of bores exist. For instance, the Tsientang River bore in mainland China is 3.7 m high and surges upriver at 800 cm per sec. The bore of the Amazon River reaches 5 m and rushes upstream at 600 cm per sec for a distance of 480 km. Figure 10-21 shows the tidal bore of the Severn River in England.

10.7   *Measuring the Tides*

It was mentioned in Sec. 10.4 that, in order to predict the tides in a given place, one must first measure them and analyze them for certain tidal constants. For this reason, tidal stations are located in thousands of coastal areas around the world. There are many types of tidal measuring devices; in this section, one of the more simple types will be discussed. Another type is mentioned in the discussion of oceanographic instruments in Chap. 16.

A self-registering tide gauge is one that can be set in a coastal region to operate continuously with minimal upkeep or maintenance. The gauge is located on a pier or sea wall. It consists of a tube or reservoir that has a very small opening to the sea (Fig. 10-22). The size of the opening relative to the cross section of the tube is critical in order to restrict the flow of water. If a surface wave with a 4-sec period passes, the flow of water through the orifice during that time must be so slight that the level in the reservoir does not change appreciably. In other words, the restricted opening acts as a filter that eliminates shorter period waves from the tide record. Inside the reservoir there is a float that is connected mechanically to a stylus. The stylus places a continuous mark on a turning drum, thus making a record of the tidal variations.

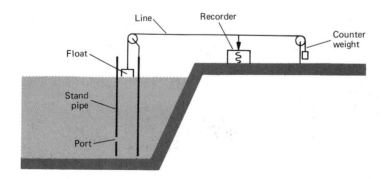

Figure 10-22 A simple tide recorder.

10.8 *The Tides as a Source of Power*

Under the right conditions it is possible to use the tides as a means of generating electrical power. For this application, the tidal range must be greater than 3 m, and the water must flow into a rather large basin through a narrow constriction. Because of these constraints, there are relatively few areas in the world that can support a tidal generating plant. Some of these are the Rance estuary off the coast of Brittany, Passamaquoddy Bay in the Bay of Fundy, the San Jose and Deseado rivers in Argentina, Cook Inlet in Alaska, the Severn estuary in England, and Penzhinskaya Bay in Siberia.

The tidal generating facility of the French government in the Rance estuary exploits a maximum tidal range of 11.3 m. The basin into which the water flows has an area of 20 sq km. A dam 710 m long has been built across the entrance to the bay, and two-way turbines have been placed so that power is generated on both ebb and flood tides. The facility has been in partial operation since 1960 and will ultimately produce 565 million kw hr annually. This amount is equivalent to the energy produced by the combustion of ½ million tons of coal. It could support the electrical needs of an industrialized city with a population of 75,000 persons.

reading list

CHRISTOPHER, P., H. RUSSEL, AND D. H. MACMILLAN, *Waves and Tides.* London: Hutchinson's Scientific & Technical Publications, 1952. 348p.

DARWIN, G. H., *The Tides and Kindred Phenomena in the Solar System.* San Francisco, Calif.: W. H. Freeman & Company, Publishers, 1962. 378p.

DEFANT, A., *Ebb and Flow: The Tides of Earth, Air and Water.* Ann Arbor: The University of Michigan Press, 1958. 121p.

NICHOLSON, T. D., "The Tides," *Natural History,* LXVIII, No. 6 (June-July 1959), 326–333.

WARBURG, H. E., *Tides and Tidal Streams.* New York: Cambridge University Press, 1922. 95p.

inshore oceanography 11

At the coastal zone of the world ocean, air, water, and solid earth meet; and there is endless interaction among the geological, biological, meteorological, and oceanic processes. Each of these environmental processes affects the nature of a coastal region to some degree. Consequently, a study of the processes at work in a coastal sector can help us to understand the origin, relative age, and history of that coast.

11.1 *The Open Coast*

Oceanic Influence

The diverse influences of ocean waters upon coastal features are related to both the physical attributes of seawater (i.e., waves, currents, and turbulence) and to its chemical properties (i.e., solubility and concentration). The effect of ocean waves is the most important, because the configuration of a coastal area and the offshore floor of the sea is largely the result of wave action. For this reason, the properties of shoaling waves are emphasized in this section.

Nearshore circulation. As waves carry energy toward shore, they encounter shallow water and their speed of propagation decreases. If the direction of wave attack is not perpendicular to the shoreline, the shoreward part of a wave slows more than the seaward portion and *refraction* occurs (Fig. 11-1). Figure

Figure 11-1 A large ocean swell refracts against a complex coastline. (Photograph courtesy Barbee Scheibner)

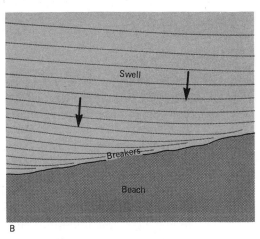

A   B

Figure 11-2 Photo (A) and line drawing (B) of wave refraction just seaward of the surf zone. The direction of longshore currents is from right to left along the beach.

11-2 shows how the process of refraction causes wave crests to align themselves parallel to the shoreline. However, this alignment is only a tendency. Wave crests seldom become completely parallel to the shore except where the beach has a long, gentle offshore profile.

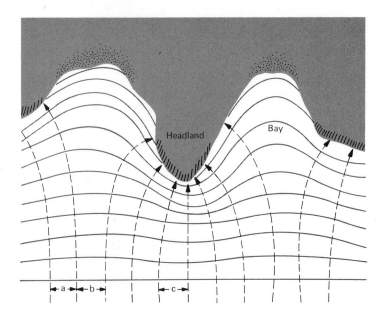

Figure 11-3 Schematic diagram of·refraction on an irregular coast.
Waves are approaching parallel to the coastal trend. Solid lines
represent wave crests. Dashed lines are wave orthogonals. (After A. N.
Strahler, 1963)

The behavior of waves in expending their energy on a beach can be illustrated by the use of *orthogonals*. These are imaginary lines drawn in such a way
that they divide the crest of an unrefracted wave into equal segments of length
and energy. Orthogonals are always perpendicular to wave crests and thus
show the direction of wave propagation (Fig. 11-3). At the same time, orthogonals indicate the distribution of energy in a wave train; the amount of energy
contained between any pair of orthogonals is assumed to be constant regardless
of refraction. Where waves attack an irregular coastline, a point of land refracts
the waves so that energy is focused on it; an embayment has the opposite effect.
In Fig. 11-3, the amount of energy moving onshore is the same for sections A,
B, and C. However, this energy is spread over a longer stretch of beach at B
and a shorter stretch of beach at C; consequently, the energy per unit length
of coastline is increased in section C and decreased in section B. The net effect
is that wave erosion is greater on the headlands. Given enough time, erosion
tends to straighten an irregular coastline, regardless of the direction of wave
attack.

As a wave approaches shore, the orbital velocity at the wave crest continually
increases, whereas the propagation speed decreases. Eventually, the crest
"overruns" the trough, and the wave breaks. Theoretical considerations as
well as field observations indicate that breaking occurs when either of two

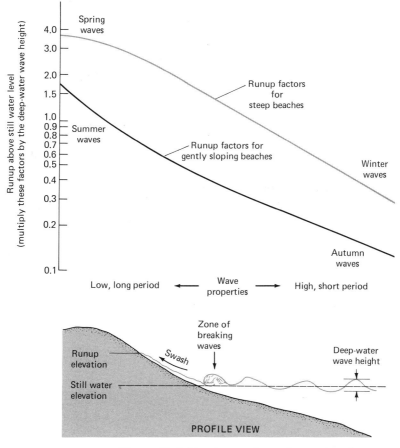

Figure 11-4 The runup of swash on a beach.

conditions are met: (1) the water depth becomes less than 1.28 times the wave height, or (2) the wave steepness (H/L) surpasses 1/7, the steepness that governs waves that break in deep water at sea.

After a wave breaks, the water particle motion becomes intensely turbulent, and energy approaches the beach in a wave of translation rather than oscillation.* The mass of turbulent water that moves upon the beach is called *swash* (see Fig. 11-4B). Swash runs up the beach to elevations above the stillwater level. Low, long-period waves, typical of summer, drive swash to *runup* elevations that are about 1½ times the height of deep-water waves. High winter waves characterized by short periods produce swash that reaches an elevation above stillwater level that is only 50 percent of the deep-water wave height. The magnitude of uprush of swash depends upon the steepness of the beach as well as wave height and period. The runup

---

*Depending on the way in which breaking occurs, the oscillatory characteristics of a wave are often maintained to the extent that the wave may reform and break several times as it approaches the beach. Each succeeding breaker is smaller than the previous one.

elevations on a steep beach are about three times as high as the runup elevations on a low-sloping beach. These relationships are demonstrated by the curves in Fig. 11-4.

After the broken wave expends its kinetic energy of translation on the beach it runs back down the beach under the influence of gravity. This water motion is termed *backwash*. Backwash removes the water from the beach and causes it to oppose the oncoming waves. In so doing, the oncoming waves are steepened and break a bit sooner.

The transport of water inside the breaker zone is in the direction the waves were traveling just prior to breaking. In Fig. 11-5, the transport is resolved to

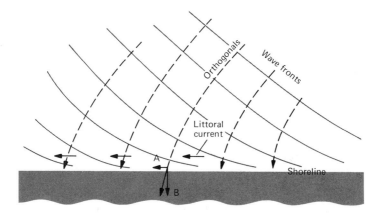

Figure 11-5 Direction of littoral currents resulting from waves breaking at an angle to the shore.

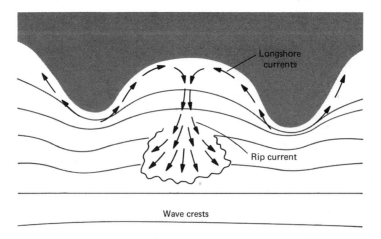

Figure 11-6 Net movement of water in an embayment causes rip currents to form.

show a component onto the beach (B) and a component along the beach (A). The upbeach transport (swash) is balanced by backwash, whereas the transport of water along the beach forms a *longshore,* or *littoral, current.* The quantity of water transported by a littoral current is related to the character of the approaching waves and the angle of approach. The larger the waves or the greater the angle of approach, the stronger the longshore current.

On an irregular shoreline the net movement of water is from headlands toward embayments as determined from the orthogonals in Fig. 11-3. As a result there is a *convergence* of longshore currents at the mouth of a bay where water accumulates (Fig. 11-6). This accumulation can cause a narrow, swift current, called a *rip current,* to move seaward from the convergence zone (Fig. 11-7).

This example shows only one way in which rip currents may originate. Actually, they are associated with any situation where water accumulates in the surf zone until the excess water flows seaward. Several factors can cause such accumulation: converging longshore currents; a physical obstruction to longshore currents, such as a rock groin (a barrier, illustrated in Fig. 11-19), breakwater, or headland; or just the continuous addition of water from breakers approaching parallel to the beach. Rip currents can be recognized in several ways: discoloration due to suspended sand, premature steepening of the approaching waves and the seaward displacement of the breaker line, or the accumulation of foam at the head of the rip. A small cusp of sand may also occur on the beach where the convergence or obstruction occurs.

Figure 11-7 Photograph of rip currents in an embayment.

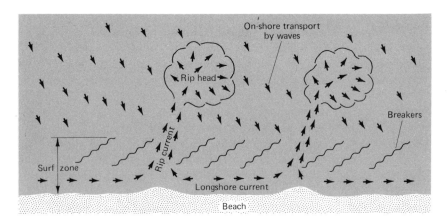

Figure 11-8 Schematic diagram of the nearshore circulation pattern on a straight beach. (From F. P. Shepard, *Submarine Geology,* 2nd edition, Harper & Row, New York, 1963)

Some rip currents extend as far as 1,000 m offshore, are 30 m in width where they flow through the surf, and travel up to 1 m per sec. These currents carry sand as well as excess water from the beach. Because of their velocity, they often erode shallow channels through the surf zone.

The well-developed rip current system exhibits a circulation pattern as shown in Fig. 11-8. Rip currents may be semipermanent features or may last only a few hours or a few days. They are probably the greatest single cause of drownings on a beach. A swimmer caught in a rip current (also called an *undertow*) can avoid being swept out to sea if he or she swims parallel to the shore rather than trying to swim against the direction of the current; the latter recourse only enhances the possibility of exhaustion.

To summarize, the effect of waves approaching an irregular coastline is the formation of circulation patterns related to the direction of wave approach and the shape of the coastline. Water is pushed onshore by the waves and flows offshore as rip currents. Littoral currents occur within the surf zone and move from areas of relatively high energy (headlands) to areas of low energy (embayments).

Nearshore sediment transport.   The nearshore circulation system is very effective in moving sand. Waves provide the energy to erode the coastline and temporarily suspend sedimentary particles, while the longshore currents transport the sediment along the coast. The process of suspension and movement of sediment in the surf zone is called *longshore,* or *littoral, drift.* Laboratory and field studies have shown empirically that the sand transported as littoral drift can be related to the rate that wave energy is expended on the beach (Fig. 11-9).

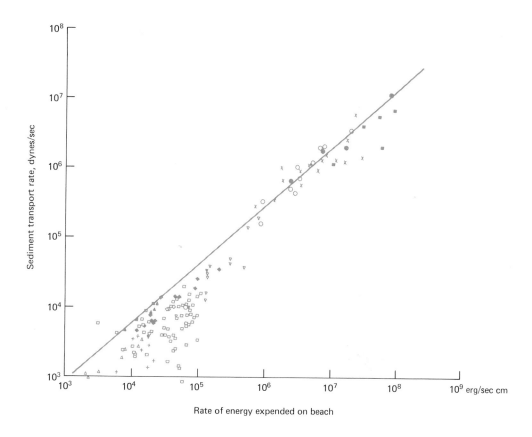

Figure 11-9 The relationship between the rate of transport of sediment along a beach (expressed as an immersed weight transport ratio) and the wave power (rate of wave energy expended) affecting the shoreline. The various symbols represent different sets of measurement data. The line represents an approximate trend in the data. (After Komar and Inman, 1970, *Journal of Geophysical Research*, Vol. 75, No. 3)

Moving water transports sand according to its *competency,* or the size of the material that can be moved by a given current, and according to its *capacity,* which is the quantity of material that the flow is capable of moving. With increasing current speed, both competency and capacity increase. Hence, large waves are usually associated with higher rates of littoral drift and move coarser sediment than do small waves.

In general, beaches on stormy coasts (e.g., in high temperate latitudes or polar regions) are steep, narrow, and consist of coarse sand, pebbles, or cobbles (Fig. 11-10). Protected beaches and those located in many tropical areas, where winds and waves have low energy, frequently are broad, have gentle slopes, and are composed of medium to fine sand (Fig. 11-10). Similarly, around headlands, wave energy is high; in embayments, waves are smaller.

A

B

Figure 11-10 A steep rock beach (A) and flat sandy beach (B) illustrate the association of beach slope with sediment size. (B courtesy Clifford E. Moon)

Bays, therefore, have sandy beaches, whereas the coasts along headlands are rocky or consist of quite coarse material (Fig. 11-11).

In the swash–backwash zone, sand is transported up the beach face with the swash and moves directly downslope during backwash. Figure 11-12 shows how this motion results in a net drifting of sand along the beach. This *beach drift* is generally parallel to the direction of longshore drift but is highly irregular. Note that the direction of these two modes of sediment movement (beach drift and longshore drift) is dependent upon the direction of wave attack. If the direction of wave attack is resolved into components parallel and perpendicular to the direction of the beach, the direction of the parallel component indicates the direction of sediment drift (see Fig. 11-4), and its length indicates the relative strength of the current.

The two processes, beach drift and littoral drift, transport beach materials from river mouths and eroding headlands to their ultimate destinations in embayments or, via submarine valleys and canyons that intercept littoral drift, to the sea floor lying below depths affected by wave activity.

The sands, gravels, and coarser materials on the beaches have formed gradually throughout geologic time. Indeed, some sands have existed as such for centuries. In other cases, sand has gone through several cycles of incorporation in sedimentary rocks (sandstones), erosion, transportation to the beach, and movement in the littoral zone. In a geological sense, involvement in such

Figure 11-11 The sediment size in an embayment decreases from rocks on the exposed headland where wave energy is high to sand at the back of the bay where energy is low.

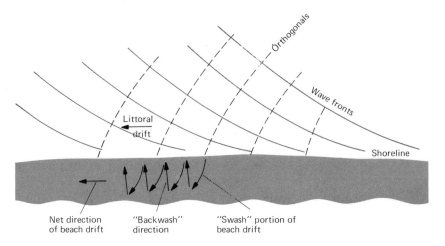

Figure 11-12 Sediment movement along the beach occurs in the surf zone as littoral drift and on the beach face as beach drift.

cycles is transitory, as are the beaches we enjoy today. Compared to the quantity of sand that has been made throughout geologic time, the amounts being introduced today are relatively small. Therefore, the net removal of sand to below the limit of wave activity must proceed at a relatively small rate; otherwise, the coasts along the world ocean would be barren rock cliffs and wave cut platforms except near the mouths of large rivers.

The beach profile.   Direct observations of beaches establish that sand transport in the littoral zone is primarily along the shore. Where prevailing winds and semipermanent storm centers cause waves to attack the coast chiefly from one direction, there is a natural tendency for the beach to adjust itself to the average waves and the rate of sediment supply. The distribution of wave energy will cause the beach either to *prograde* (build out) locally or to recede so that eventually a dynamic equilibrium is attained. This equilibrium often reflects some sort of annual average wave condition. However, the sediment in a sector can vary: it can be eroded in winter and deposited during the summer, because the nature of the waves changes seasonally. Figure 11-13 shows a beach profile as it changes through the year. From April to September, the beach is prograding, whereas it retreats during the winter season (September to March in the northern hemisphere).

Laboratory studies and measurements on beaches show that short-period steep waves from local winter storms occurring close to shore have increased capacity and tend to keep sand suspended. Under these conditions, rip currents move sand from the beach and deposit it in the seaward part of the littoral zone. During the summer, the beach is attacked by long swells of low steepness that arrive from distant storms. These waves influence the floor of

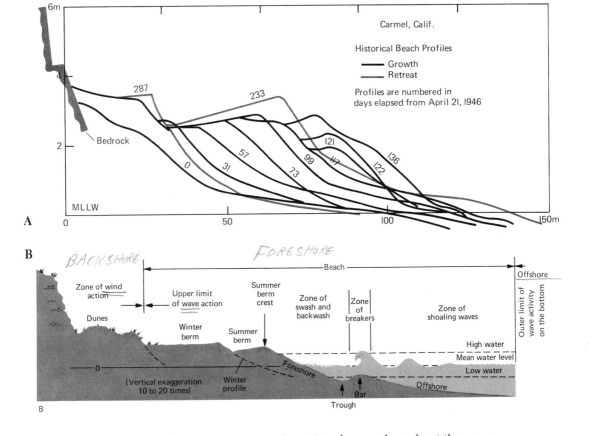

Figure 11-13 The beach configuration changes throughout the year as a function of wave conditions (A). The characteristic elements of a beach profile are shown (B). (A after Office of Naval Research, 1957; B after A. N. Strahler, 1963)

the sea at the seaward extreme of the littoral zone so they gradually return sand shoreward and repair beach erosion of the previous winter. A winter beach profile is recognizable by a steep face, relatively coarse sediment, and a sea cliff or winter berm. A summer beach profile is characterized by finer sediments, less steep beach face, and smaller berm. Sometimes certain portions of the winter profile (i.e., the winter berm or some offshore bars) remain as remanent features because the following summer's waves might not be capable of affecting them (Fig. 11-13B).

We can often determine the state of the sediment and the short-term processes acting on a beach sector by examining certain features of a beach. Its configuration in profile and plan, distribution of grain sizes of beach sediments, and types of vegetation at the shore indicate whether a beach is being eroded or accreted.

In addition, a beach's features reveal the types of waves acting on it. The

291

Figure 11-14 Grasses growing on the beach help to stabilize the sand and promote further deposition.

slope of the beach and the height of the berm are determined by the energy in the swash of the waves. An energetic swash will carry sand to the top of the beach berm and deposit it there, thus steepening the face of the beach. If the energy of the waves increases suddenly, a sea cliff quickly forms because of the increased rate of erosion. Under prolonged attack, however, a smooth slope eventually results. If waves are so energetic that the swash overtops the berm, the beach will build upward in response. If this action occurs infrequently, coastal winds may erode the berm and build a dune field behind the beach. When conditions remain relatively constant for several years, certain types of vegetation, crawing plants, and beach grasses (Fig. 11-14) will become established and stabilize the beach in that configuration.

The distribution of various types of sand on a beach reflects the prevailing regimen of waves. Extremely coarse and heavy materials tend to remain where the strongest waves deposit them, usually along the highest berm. Extremely fine and light materials tend to persist in suspension and so are removed downcoast and eventually seaward. Variations in the normal wave patterns are shown vividly where dark, heavy minerals are present in minor quantities in a light-colored sand. The heavy minerals remain after the differential erosion of the light sand; in this way, lenses and stringers of heavy materials become segregated. In some instances the heavy minerals become so concentrated by

Figure 11-15 Sedimentary particles are sorted by wave action according to size and density, producing layers or bands paralleling the beach. Examples of sorting are seen by bands of shell fragments (A) or layering of dark high density minerals (B). The dark layers in (B) are approximately 1 to 3 mm thick.

Figure 11-16 View of a large model of a beach. A wave generator is at
the near side of the water tank. The men in the background are
standing on the model beach that is being tested.

beach processes that *economic* mineral deposits, called *beach placers*, are
formed. Sometimes layers or zones of concentrated shell fragments are separated by the same process (Fig. 11-15). These layers often are exposed in sea
cliffs that form when steeper waves begin to attack the shore.

Nearshore deposition and erosion.   Scientists do not completely understand how
sand movement onshore and offshore responds to wave conditions. Much of
what we know about this complex mechanism comes from studies of beach
models in wave tanks where scaled experiments are conducted. An example of
a physical beach model is shown in Fig. 11-16. Although natural beaches do
not always corroborate observations of beach behavior in models, at least some
broad generalizations can be drawn. Empirical measurements on natural
beaches are generally not satisfactory because the generalizations derived
usually apply only to a single location.

The movement of sand along the coast is the result of littoral drift acting in
discrete coastal segments called *littoral cells.* A littoral cell is a segment of coast

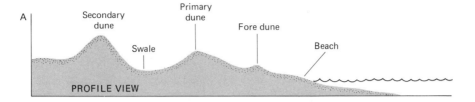

Figure 11-17 A typical dune field profile (A) and (B) coastal sand dunes represent a depository of excess beach sand. (After South Australian Coast Protection Board)

lying between points where the uniform littoral transfer of sand along the coast is interrupted. Such interruptions are caused at points that are either sources of littoral sand or points where sand is removed from the littoral zone. Locally, the currents move sand from promontories toward embayments. Regionally, the drift tendency is in the direction of the longshore component due to the prevailing wind waves. Most littoral sand is introduced at the mouths of streams. Sand is lost as it is carried by steep, high waves into deep water or submarine canyons, or as it is removed to dunes by onshore winds (if rainfall is not excessive) as seen in Fig. 11-17. A negligibly small amount of sand is lost by attrition from colliding grains. The long-term effect of all these factors is a straightening of an irregular coastline.

Whenever either a longshore current is interrupted or the waves that provide the energy to maintain the longshore current are interrupted, the capacity of

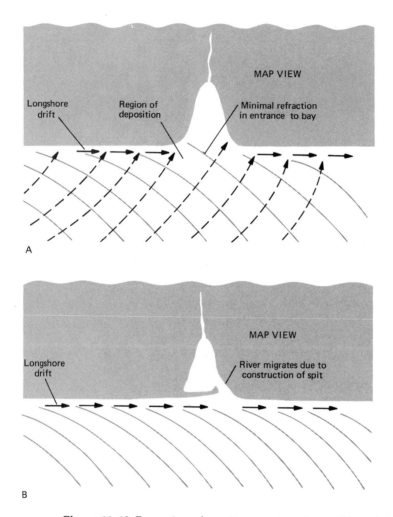

Figure 11-18 Formation of a spit across an estuary. The spit builds into
the estuary because of wave refraction into the mouth of the bay: (A)
inition situation; (B) well-developed spit.

the water flow to transport sediment is decreased, and deposition occurs.
Figure 11-18 shows how an embayment interrupting a straight coast alters the
wave refraction in such a way that deposition of littoral drift occurs, causing
the formation of a spit or small point of sand across the mouth of the bay (Fig.
11-19). In cases where the embayment has a vigorously flowing river at its
head, the estuary will never become completely sealed. However, the river
may be forced to migrate because of fluctuation in the dynamic equilibrium
between sediment deposition from littoral drift and sediment erosion by

Figure 11-19 A sandy spit built across a small tidal embayment due to longshore sand transport from right to left.

outflowing river water (Fig. 11-20). Often the way in which a spit has been built indicates the direction of sediment drift that tends to persist in that area. If we extend this reasoning, sometimes we can infer correctly the direction of the prevailing winds or waves.

When an offshore island or barrier interrupts the waves approaching the shore, the energy that maintains the longshore current is diminished in the beach sector behind the barrier. The sediment transport capacity of the longshore current decreases and sediment is deposited behind the island. If the deposition is such that the island becomes attached to the coastline by a sand deposit, then the resulting coastal feature is called a *tied island* or *tombolo* (Fig. 11-21).

Frequently, the natural tendency of littoral processes is not desirable. Coastal installations are jeopardized if excessive erosion occurs where they are built or if they are built on an unstable beach, where wide variations in accretion and erosion take place yearly or over a few years. Artificial installations also may cause undesirable changes in the shoreline. Damming of coastal rivers for

Figure 11-20 Littoral drift tends to close the river mouth of this small river. The river is forced to migrate to the right in order to reach the sea.

flood control and power generation traps sand in upland reservoirs, depriving the beaches down the coast that normally were nourished by the sand from that river's mouth. Such removal of sand supply results in continued beach erosion over long stretches of shoreline. Coastal installations, such as harbors and breakwaters, might interrupt the littoral drift to an extent that causes changes in the configuration of the coastline. In all these cases it is desirable to stabilize the beach to prevent excessive erosion or accretion. In practice, it is more important to control erosion than accretion, for losses of sand during a prolonged period tend to be permanent.

Techniques for controlling beach erosion involve such procedures as retarding the littoral drift rate, trapping sand or otherwise diverting sand from the heads of submarine canyons, building jetties and breakwaters to protect segments of beaches exposed to concentrated wave attack, or bringing in sand to nourish eroding beaches.

Figure 11-22A illustrates the effects of placing a barrier across the nearshore zone in order to protect and even cause accumulation of sand on the beach. This figure shows a groin, or barrier, constructed to extend from the beach out into the breaker zone. To be totally effective, the groin must extend from the

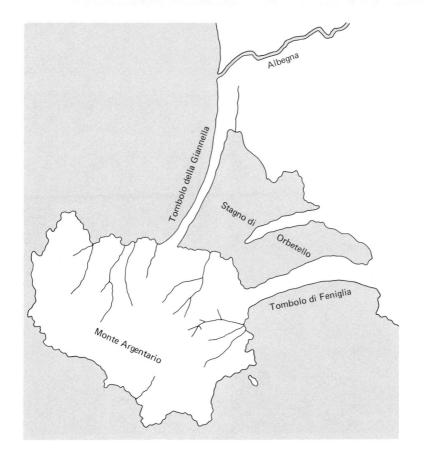

Figure 11-21 A double tombolo at Monte Argentario, Italy (A); and in Puget Sound, Washington (B). (A from Johnson, 1919)

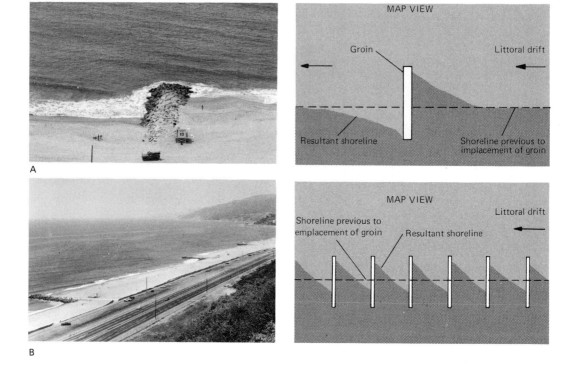

Figure 11-22 Photograph and line drawing of (A) nearshore refraction and sedimentation around a single groin; (B) sedimentation associated with a series of groins.

bottom of the surf zone to high tide level. When a groin is installed it interrupts the littoral drift and sand accumulates (deposition) on its updrift side. As a consequence sand is removed (erosion) on its downdrift side. Usually the quantity of sand deposited on the updrift side is equal to the quantity of material eroded from the downdrift side. Figure 11-22B shows the effects of a series of groins.

Deposition of littoral drift also occurs when the waves that provide the energy to move sand are interrupted. A simple breakwater parallel to shore may decrease wave activity along a beach. If wave energy decreases, littoral drift also decreases, causing deposition of sand. This condition is shown in Fig. 11-23 and is similar to the illustration of the offshore island and tombolo shown in Fig. 11-21 except that the barrier is artificial. Depending on the dimensions of the offshore breakwater, its distance from shore, and the littoral drift rate, the zone of accretion in Fig. 11-23 may or may not eventually connect with the offshore breakwater.

Deposition and erosion are major considerations associated with construc-

Figure 11-23 Sand accumulation behind an offshore breakwater.

tion and maintenance of harbors. Several examples of simple harbor designs are illustrated in Fig. 11-24. Note that both a zone of accretion and a zone of erosion are associated with the breakwater. Generally, sand is dredged or pumped from the site of deposition to the zone of erosion. Although the cost is considerable, the procedure maintains the harbor entrance and minimizes damage by erosion. The harbor in Fig. 11-25 was formed by the construction of a jetty that interrupted the regional littoral drift and formed a wide beach upcoast (foreground of photo). A breakwater, added later at the end of the jetty, directed littoral transport of sand to its far end where deposition formed a spit. The spit's growth threatens to obstruct the harbor and its entrance, so a dredge must operate throughout the year to remove sand from the spit area and pump it down the coast to nourish the beaches there. In this way, the dredge carries out a "sand bypassing" operation to keep the harbor open and to reduce the effects of erosion down the coast.

Fluctuations in Sea Level

Sea-level changes have a considerable influence on coastal processes and on beaches. Often a large tidal range is associated with broad beaches and extensive salt marshes. Wave energy is greatly diminished by friction over the broad intertidal platform, and coastal erosion is intermittent. The strength of tidal currents is associated with tidal range. In coastal areas exposed to both

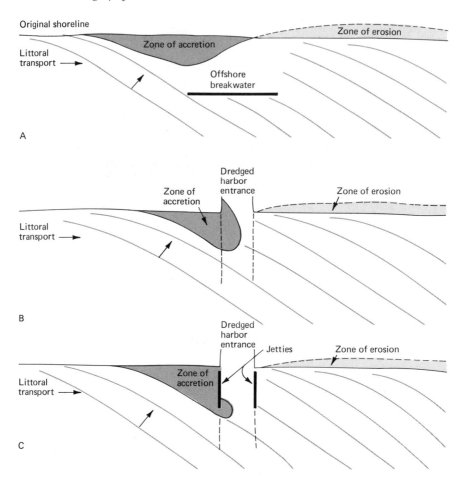

Figure 11-24 Deposition of sediment associated with the interruption of longshore currents in the nearshore zone.

large waves and a large tidal range, erosive processes can be significant in the nearshore zone.

Changes in sea level have occurred in past geologic time as a result of vertical movements of the land and changes in the volume of water in the ocean basins, The land can move either up or down and submerge or raise coastal areas. Such movements can be related to faulting, folding, and tilting, or to isostatic adjustments of the crust when heavy loads of ice, sediment, or lava are added or removed. For example, crustal subsidence generally occurs in the vicinity of large deltas; crustal rebound follows a period of glaciation.

Coasts that have been influenced by recent earth movements are recognized in New Zealand, New Guinea, Japan, California, and around the Mediterra-

Figure 11-25 Aerial view of the harbor at Santa Barbara, California.

nean Sea. Isostatic movements from the melting of continental glaciers are recognized in Scandinavia and Canada.

The continental glaciers of the Pleistocene epoch removed significant volumes of water from the ocean basins. Geological evidence from the land has led scientists to conclude that the Pleistocene epoch was characterized by alternate advances and retreats of the ice of continental glaciers. Sea-level fluctuations accompanied these oscillations in ice formation.

Calculations of the volume of water frozen in glaciers during the last glacial stage indicate that the sealevel must have been lowered by 110 to 130 m. These calculations are corroborated by fathograms of submerged shorelines and by beach sands dredged from depths to 130 m throughout the world.

The ice of the last glacial stage began to melt about 20,000 years ago. Since then, glacial melt water has elevated sea level approximately 120 m (Fig. 11-26) to produce the Holocene marine transgressions that submerged the estuaries, embayments, and coastal regions of the world. However, most coastal features seen today are modified by the effects of erosion, deposition, and biologic growth that have occurred in the past few thousand years.

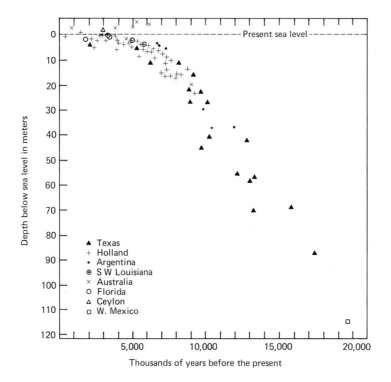

Figure 11-26 Estimates of the Holocene marine transgression during the past 20,000 years. The trend of the sea level rise is clear; the scatter of the data points is due in part to motion of the land produced by tectonism. (Courtesy F. P. Shepard)

Geologic Influence

The degree that erosion affects a coastal zone depends, to a large extent, on the differences in hardness and durability of rocks. Variations in the character or structure of coastal rocks exposed to waves and seawater are reflected in differential physical or chemical erosion.

The hardness or durability of a rock can be measured by (1) its degree of induration, or ability to withstand constant wave attack; (2) its chemical resistance to the solvent properties of seawater; (3) its resistance to attack by repeated wetting and drying; and (4) its resistance to attack by freezing and thawing. On exposed coasts where wave forces are great, the harder rocks stand as rocky promontories after the softer ones are removed (Fig. 11-27), or they form bold cliffs surrounded by shore platforms (Fig. 11-28). The shore platform is cut as deeply as waves can erode. The depth of a shore platform is controlled by the nature of wave attack, the tide range, and the degree of crustal motion raising or lowering the coast. The durability of rocks exposed

Figure 11-27 Resistant rock formations may control the erosion patterns and thus the coastal configuration. Here, more resistant strata remain as stacks and headlands after the softer rock has been eroded by wave action. (Photograph courtesy Joe S. Creager)

Figure 11-28 Shore platforms formed by wave action on massive basalt promontories.

to identical oceanic conditions can be compared in Figs. 11-29 and 11-30.

These figures show adjacent coastal regions on the Mornington peninsula near Melbourne, Australia. One coast is composed of an ancient dune field that has been cemented with calcium carbonate. These rocks are relatively weak, and stacks extend a distance offshore, indicating a kilometer of coastline retreat since the Holocene marine transgression. Several miles away, the coastal rocks are massive and durable basalts. These basalts are exposed to the same

Figure 11-29 Numerous offshore stacks give evidence of rapid retreat of the coast due to marine erosion.

Figure 11-30 When rock formations are more durable, cliff erosion proceeds more slowly. Here, the horizontal flow planes of the lava flows control the orientation of the shore platform.

Figure 11-31 The orientation of bedding planes in coastal formations can influence the erosion patterns. Here the dipping strata cause a serrated shore platform and beach cliff. Average thickness of layers is approximately 15 cm. (Photograph courtesy Joe S. Creager)

Figure 11-32 Aerial view of a fringing reef shows how coral growth extends the coast and supplies sand for adjacent beaches. (Photograph courtesy Joe S. Creager)

waves as is the sandstone, but cliff erosion is only about one-tenth as pronounced. Note that the horizontal bedding planes between successive lava flows in Fig. 11-30 also control the level and inclination (in this case, horizontal) of the shore platform. Gently dipping coastal formations often impress this "signature" on the shore platform. Figure 11-31 shows an example of inclined slopes and benches of the shore platform. Also evident are the effects of differences in the resistance to erosion of alternating layers of rocks.

Biologic Influence

Certain organisms living in the coastal zone likewise influence the genesis, shape, and structure of coastal landforms. Noteworthy examples are the colonies of reef-building calcareous organisms on exposed coasts and the marsh grasses and mangroves in protected waters.

Reef corals and calcareous algae flourish in tropical regions of the world (as described in Chap. 2). These organisms produce massive platforms that can extend seaward for 180 km. Buccoo Reef on Tobago Island in the West Indies is an example of a fringing reef that not only actively extends to the coast seaward but also provides carbonate sand for the island's beaches (Fig. 11-32).

Coastal erosion can be caused by biological processes. Some marine organisms living in the surf zone can dissolve or abrade the rock mass to which they cling. Certain mollusks and echinoderms actually carve holes in the rock to provide a shelter from waves. In some areas, the feeding activity of snails wears away the sea cliffs (Fig. 11-33). In fact, scientists generally agree that, under favorable conditions, the biochemical degradation of limestone in the shore zone surpasses the effects of purely physical and chemical processes.

Coastal vegetation plays a primary role in both stabilizing and building up the shore environment. Several forms of grass grow on sand dunes and cliffs exposed to wind and salt spray (Fig. 11-14). These grasses strengthen the beach's resistance to erosion and cause further deposition by trapping wind-blown sand. Grasses have been introduced into coastal areas for the specific purpose of stabilizing drifting coastal sand.

For example, marine grasses, such as *Zostera* (eel grass), act as stabilizers of subtidal mud and sand flats. Other salt-tolerant plants, such as the marsh grass, *Salicornia,* colonize the margins of protected marine waters. In tropical estuaries, varieties of the mangrove, a treelike shrub, are rooted in the tidal zone. All these plants inhabit intertidal mud banks and cause the drainage from them to follow definite channels. They promote deposition of mud by decreasing the speed of currents along the shore. Inevitably, accretion of mud follows the spread of these plants into a bay or lagoon (Fig. 11-34).

11.2 *The Estuarine Environment*

People have always lived close to estuaries, that is, at the mouths of rivers, because these bodies of water are sources of large quantities of food, are bordered by sites suitable for industrial activity, and provide transportation for commerce. Furthermore, estuaries are used to provide an easy means of waste disposal. It has been only recently that people have realized the

Figure 11-33 In browsing the rock for alga, snails carve small pits into this sandstone which accounts for significant coastal erosion.

Figure 11-34 Various forms of salt-tolerant grasses cause deposition of sediment and thus extend protected coasts seaward. (Photograph courtesy Larry Lewis)

vulnerability of river mouths and, indeed, the entire watersheds of rivers.

Prior to the mid-nineteenth century, abuses of the estuarine environment were limited to silt erosion from agriculture, overgrazing, and deforestation. Since the Industrial Revolution, cities, factories, and great transportation facilities have centered around the protected water of coastal embayments. Today, seven out of the ten largest metropolitan areas of the world have grown up around estuaries. It has been estimated that one-third of the population of the United States lives or works adjacent to its major estuaries. As a result, many coastal bodies of water are suffering from the contaminating effects of industrial and human waste products. An understanding of estuarine processes, therefore, is critical if the population is to use these natural bodies of water without causing them irreversible damage.

Types of Estuaries

An estuary has been defined as a semienclosed coastal body of water that has a free connection with the open sea and within which seawater is measurably diluted with freshwater derived from land drainage. From a geomorphological standpoint, estuaries can be divided into the following four types: (1) coastal plain estuaries, or drowned river valleys, (2) fiords, (3) bar-built estuaries, and (4) estuaries produced by tectonic processes. Each of these types has certain attributes associated with its geography, geometry, catchment basin, bathymetry, and offshore oceanic characteristics.

Coastal plain estuaries. The rise in sea level during the Holocene marine transgression caused extensive flooding of lowland areas throughout the world. On broad coastal plains, seawater extended up Pleistocene river valleys to form what are called *coastal plain estuaries.* The shorelines of such drowned river valleys follow the drainage patterns of the lower reaches of the rivers (Fig. 11-35).

Water circulation in a coastal plain estuary is driven by river flow and tidal currents. The river flow carries freshwater seaward at the surface, while oscillatory tidal currents move seawater in and out of the estuary at its bottom. A zone of shearing usually exists at the interface between freshwater and seawater because river flow and tidal flow velocities seldom equal each other. Mixing is induced at the interface by shearing-induced turbulence and possibly by breaking internal waves that move along the pycnocline that develops. Seawater is mixed into the river water all along the estuary so the salinity of the surface layer ranges from virtually 0 ‰ upriver to oceanic values at the river mouth. Estuarine mixing is shown diagrammatically in Fig. 11-36.

The degree of vertical mixing and the nature of circulation in an estuary are related to the ratio between the amount of seawater transported inward during the flood tidal cycle (the *tidal prism*) and the quantity of river flow. A *stratified* estuary is one in which the river flow greatly exceeds the tidal prism. Vertical

Figure 11-35 The rising sea level of the Holocene marine transgression caused seawater to fill the lower portions of existing river valleys.

PROFILE VIEW

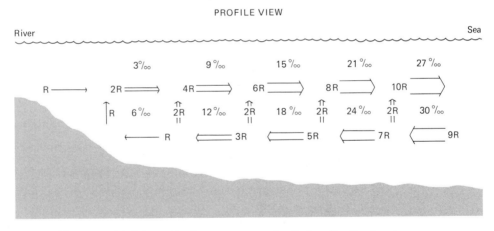

Figure 11-36 Schematic flow pattern and salinity distribution (parts per thousand) in a partially mixed estuary. Volume rate of flow is expressed in terms of the volume rate of river R. (After Schubel, 1971)

mixing is restricted, and the interface between fresh and salt water is characterized by a sharp pycnocline. The Mississippi River estuary is an example of a stratified estuary (Fig. 11-37A).

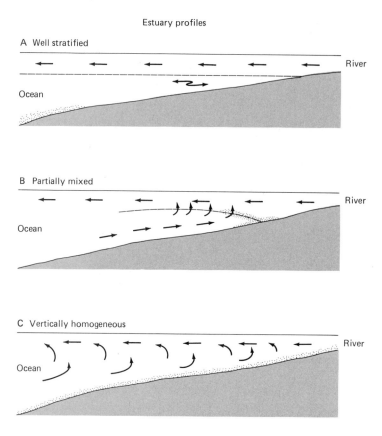

Figure 11-37 Examples of estuarine mixing types. The dashed line represents the approximate position of the pycnocline when it is well defined. Stippling represents zones of sediment accumulation.

When the river flow is about equal to the tidal prism the estuary is classed as *partially mixed*. Substantial vertical mixing occurs in a partially mixed estuary and a horizontal surface salinity gradient, a less pronounced pycnocline, and well-developed inflow in the bottom layer (Fig. 11-37B) are typical.

When the tidal prism exceeds river flow, extensive vertical mixing occurs and the estuary is considered as *vertically homogeneous*. This type of estuary is characterized by small vertical density gradients and a uniform increase in salinity in a seaward direction (Fig. 11-37). Stratified (river-dominated) and homogeneous (tide-dominated) estuaries represent the ends of a continuous spectrum of possible circulation patterns. In most estuaries the circulation is of the partially mixed type. Where river flow changes significantly between seasons, the estuarine circulation changes accordingly. As a result, an estuary may be stratified during the river's flood stage, partially mixed during average flows, and vertically homogeneous during periods of low runoff.

Sedimentation within an estuary is controlled by the water circulation pattern. Fine sediment (clay) particles that are dispersed in river water tend to cluster in aggregates when introduced into seawater. This process, called *flocculation*, occurs in water whose salinity is as low as 8 ‰.

Simplified sedimentation patterns associated with estuarine circulation are illustrated in Fig. 11-37. In stratified estuaries sediments tend to remain in the surface water and are carried seaward to be deposited in entrance bars and on the adjacent inner continental shelf. In partially mixed estuaries flocculated sediments sink rapidly and tend to accumulate in the turbulent mixing zone and at the base of the salt wedge. This accumulation is enhanced as particles from the surface layer settle to the bottom and are transported upstream in the saline bottom layer. Sediment particles are also carried into the estuary from the ocean by this circulation pattern (Fig. 11-37). Sediment deposition in vertically homogeneous estuaries tends to be spread out over the floor of the estuary rather than concentrated in specific regions. Actual sedimentation patterns in estuaries are usually considerably more complex than illustrated here.

A knowledge of circulation and associated sedimentation in estuaries is important for many reasons. Dredging and river diversion in estuaries can change the circulation type with concomitant changes in the shoaling by sedimentation. Also, the design of waste discharge systems for municipalities and industries depends strongly upon circulation. For example, waste materials discharged near the bottom of a partially mixed estuary would migrate upstream rather than be dispersed quickly by mixing processes.

Fiords.   Fiords are inlets in the coastal reaches of formerly glaciated valleys. They occur at latitudes above 38°, usually on the western sides of continents or large islands where Pleistocene glaciers carved their way to the sea. We find them, therefore, in Greenland, Norway, western Siberia, Scotland, Newfoundland, Labrador, Baffin Island, British Columbia, Chile, and New Zealand.

Fiords are characterized by steep walls, a U-shaped cross section, and a sill carved in rock or built of glacial drift deposited near the seaward entrance (Fig. 11-38). Many fiords have almost vertical walls; they are some of the few places in the world where beaches do not exist (Fig. 11-39). Because the sill and the narrow mouth restrict the entrance, the circulation of water within a fiord is often unique, being controlled by its geometry.

An example of the circulation within a relatively deep-silled fiord is shown in Fig. 11-40. Most fiords exist in temperate and polar regions where the runoff of freshwater is large. We find, consequently, the estuarine features shown in Fig. 11-40A. Biological productivity in mixed estuaries of this sort is potentially high because mixing and runoff add nutrients to the surface water layers.

Figure 11-38 A steep, narrow fiord-type estuary carved by glaciers and subsequently drowned during the Holocene marine transgression. The peaks rise for over 2,500 m while maximum depth in this fiord exceeds 350 m.

However, cold water temperature might inhibit reproduction and consequently limit productivity in fiords.

Many fiords have shallow sills and great depth (300 to 400 m). These basins tend to become stagnant, because tidal mixing is not sufficient to recirculate deep-water layers. Bottom water becomes *anoxic* when the rate of oxygen consumption during breakdown of organic detritus settling from the surface layers exceeds the rate of oxygen replenishment (Fig. 11-40B). Anoxic water, although rich in the nutrients produced in the decomposition process, is devoid of organisms other than anaerobic bacteria. Although it is not a fiord, the Black Sea provides an illustration of this phenomenon.

The dense bottom water in an anoxic basin can be replaced with oxygenated seawater. Occasionally, when either the runoff of freshwater becomes very low or upwelling brings uncommonly dense water above the sill depth, the body of anoxic water is displaced and kills many marine organisms as it circulates outward. After such an episode of overturning, the process of oxygen depletion in the basin repeats itself.

Bar-built estuaries.   On broad, gently sloping continental shelves, sand carried by wave action accumulates in offshore bars aligned parallel to the coast. These bars become barrier islands as they are built upward and shoreward by storm

Figure 11-39 The walls of some fiords are vertical. Water depth at the place where this photo is taken exceeds 350 m.

waves that move sand from offshore areas and from sediment sources upcoast. The barrier islands enclose coastal water and form shallow estuaries (Fig. 11-41).

Bar-built estuaries are found on lowland coasts throughout the world. The eastern and gulf coasts of the United States have many good examples. There are several types of circulation and mixing processes within these estuaries. The lower valley of the river that discharges into such an estuary exhibits the characteristics of a salt–wedge estuary. The main part of the bar-built estuary is shallow, with restricted entrances between the barrier islands. As a result, the influence of tides (except within the entrance channels) is minimized. Wind, on the other hand, is an important source of energy for mixing and circulation.

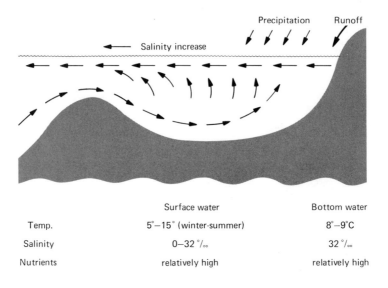

	Surface water	Bottom water
Temp.	5°–15° (winter-summer)	8°–9°C
Salinity	0–32 °/₀₀	32 °/₀₀
Nutrients	relatively high	relatively high

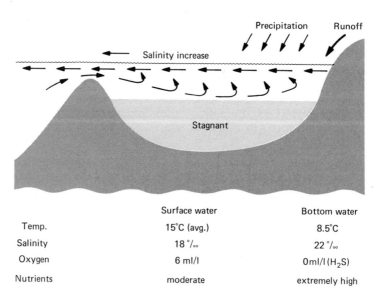

	Surface water	Bottom water
Temp.	15°C (avg.)	8.5°C
Salinity	18 °/₀₀	22 °/₀₀
Oxygen	6 ml/l	0 ml/l (H_2S)
Nutrients	moderate	extremely high

Figure 11-40 (A) Circulation and water characteristics in Puget Sound, Washington, a basin characterized by excess precipitation and strong mixing. (B) Idealized sketch of the Black Sea, a stagnant basin. The surface layer extends to approximately 200 m.

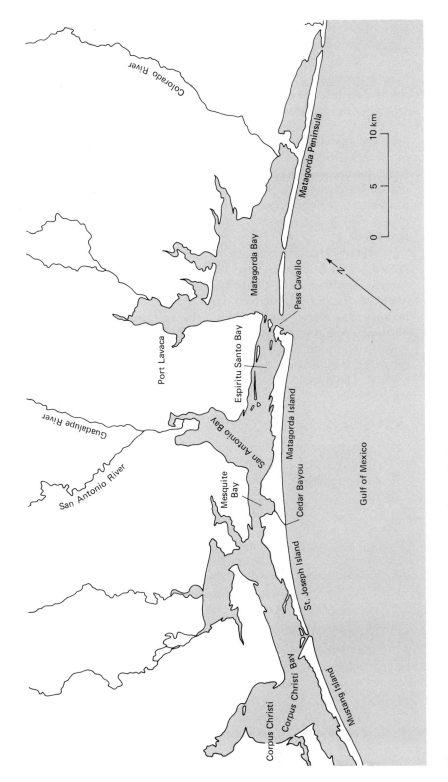

Figure 11-41 The central Texas coast consists of complex bar-built estuaries.

317

In dry climates where river flow fluctuates dramatically with rainfall, the salinity within the estuary can vary from essentially fresh during high runoff to highly saline (greater than 40 ‰) when net evaporation is excessive.

Estuaries produced by tectonic processes.   In some coastal areas, earth movement by faulting, folding, or local subsidence produces marine basins that receive river discharges. The entrances to these tectonically produced estuaries are often restricted (as in San Francisco Bay). Hence, the circulation and mixing processes can be dominated by either river or tidal flows. In areas having an excess supply of freshwater, the circulation can follow the examples shown in Fig. 11-40.

In regions characterized by net evaporation, the circulation might be reversed, as illustrated in Fig. 11-42. Here, seawater enters the basin on the surface, becomes more dense because of evaporation, sinks, and flows out at depth. Biological productivity within an estuary of this sort is relatively low, because the water comes from oceanic surface water already depleted in nutrients. Some nutrients are introduced into the estuary by runoff, but not in sufficient quantities to promote phytoplankton growth. Estuaries and larger restricted basins that exhibit a surface inflow of water are found in arid regions. The upper Gulf of California, the Red Sea, and the Mediterranean Sea are examples.

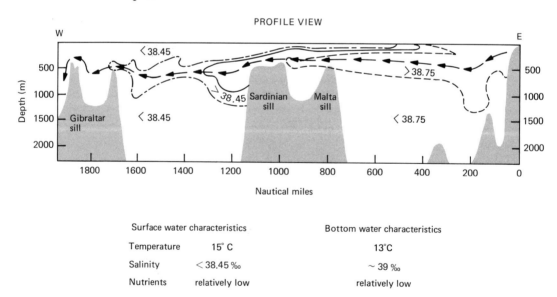

Figure 11-42 Circulation and approximate water characteristics in the Mediterranean Sea, a large basin characterized by net evaporation. The longitudinal section of salinity represents the summer condition. The arrows indicate the flow of water.

reading list

BIRD, E. C. F., *Coasts*. Canberra: Australian National University Press, 1968. 246p.

COASTAL ENGINEERING RESEARCH CENTER, *Shore Protection Manual*. Washington, D.C.: Dept. of the Army Corps of Engineers, Government Printing Office, 1973. 3 volumes.

KING, C. A. M., *Beaches and Coasts*. London: Edward Arnold Ltd., Publishers, 1960. 403p.

KOMAR, P. D., *Beach Processes and Sedimentation*. Englewood Cliffs, N.J.: Prentice-Hall, Inc., 1976. 429p.

LAUFF, G. H., ED., *Estuaries*. Washington, D.C.: American Association for the Advancement of Science, Publication 83, 1967. 656p.

classification and description of marine organisms

12

Before discussing the principles of biological oceanography, we shall describe the kinds of life found in the sea. It will be necessary to use a classification scheme in order to organize the description of marine organisms because of their great diversity. For example, over 30,000 specific types of unicellular organisms exist in the world, while one of the more diverse groups, the *Phylum Arthropoda*, contains more than 800,000 species. A classification scheme is a necessary tool for maintaining a systematic treatment of the numerous forms of life.

12.1 Taxonomic Classification

The organisms living in the sea have been studied for centuries. Early observers recognized gross differences between plants and animals, so all life was classified in either of two kingdoms. The study of the kingdoms became formalized as the respective sciences of botany and zoology. For the more complex or highly organized life forms, the simple division between plants and animals appears adequate, but for some one-celled organisms this division is not sufficient. For example, certain marine organisms have both animal characteristics of motility and plant characteristics of photosynthetic pigments. The study of bacteria adds further confusion, because some are pigmented and others are not, some photosynthesize and others do not. Indeed, certain viruses may behave like crystalline materials rather than like living organisms.

Table 12–1   Taxonomic Classification for Several Organisms

Basic taxonomic subdivisions	Examples			
	Giant kelp	*Purple sea urchin*	*Blue whale*	*Song sparrow*
Kingdom	Plantae	Animalia	Animalia	Animalia
Phylum/division	Phaeophyta	Echinodermata	Chordata	Chordata
Class	Phaeophycae	Echinoidea	Mammalia	Aves
Order	Laminariales	Echinoida	Mysticeti	Passeriformes
Family	Sessoniaceae	Strongylocentrotidae	Palienopteridae	Fringillidae
Genus*	*Macrocystis*	*Strongylocentrotus*	*Balaenoplera*	*Melospiza*
Species*	*M. pyrifera*	*S. purpuratus*	*B. musculus*	*M. melodia*

*Note the convention of capitalization and italics for genus and species names.

Studies in cellular biology have provided a basis for another classification of life forms. The organization of the nuclear parts of the cell suggests the separation of *prokaryotes,* organisms consisting of a single cell that does not possess a nucleus (e.g., bacteria and blue green algae), from the *eukaryotes,* or all forms of life having definite membrane-bound nuclei. Eucaryotes can be classified according to whether their structure is unicellular or multicellular. Such a variety of form and function must be considered if we are to classify and name the approximately 1.5 million different life forms that have been identified on our planet. For this purpose it is convenient to construct a hierarchy of categories in the form of a pyramid. At the top of the pyramid is the most basic division—the kingdom. The foundation or base of the pyramid is the *species.* The kingdom represents the most general group while species relates to individual organisms. Intermediate levels or *taxa* are defined on the basis of comparative anatomy, physiology, or other diagnostic characteristics of organisms. These intermediate levels include phylum, class, order, family, genus, and species. A functional definition of a species is a group of individual organisms that freely interbreed and produce fertile offspring. Thus, species share a common gene pool that can mutate, form subspecies, races, or breeds, and ultimately can evolve into a different species if it can survive changes in the environment. The taxonomic subdivisions are shown in Table 12-1. Some examples of common organisms are also included. This system of identification is called the Linnaean system of nomenclature, after the Swedish botanist Linnaeus who developed it in the eighteenth century. The headings are listed with the most general group first (phylum) and the degree of specialization increasing downward. The phylum represents a broad group of organisms having common features, whereas the species represents the smallest commonly used subdivision.

The purposes of a taxonomic classification are many. A primary goal is to develop a means of grouping organisms into natural units. Another goal is to place groups in a natural sequence that defines a genealogical, or *phylogenetic,*

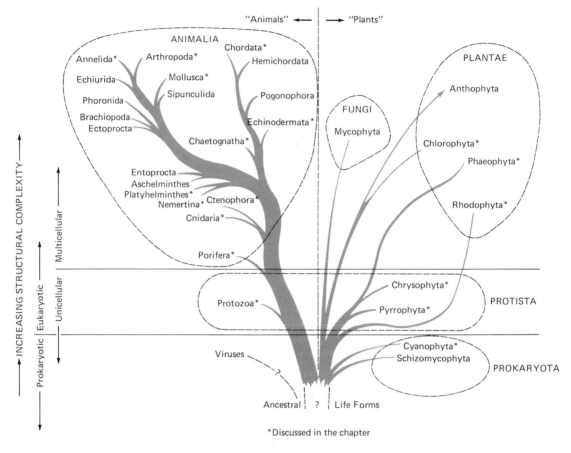

INCREASING STRUCTURAL COMPLEXITY →

Prokaryotic | Eukaryotic

Unicellular | Multicellular

"Animals" ← | → "Plants"

ANIMALIA

Annelida*
Echiurida
Phoronida
Brachiopoda
Ectoprocta
Arthropoda*
Mollusca*
Sipunculida
Chordata*
Hemichordata
Pogonophora
Echinodermata*
Chaetognatha*
Entoprocta
Aschelminthes
Platyhelminthes*
Nemertina* Ctenophora*
Cnidaria*
Porifera*

FUNGI
Mycophyta

PLANTAE
Anthophyta
Chlorophyta*
Phaeophyta*
Rhodophyta*

Chrysophyta*
Protozoa*
Pyrrophyta*
PROTISTA

Viruses
?
Cyanophyta*
Schizomycophyta
PROKARYOTA

Ancestral ¦ ? ¦ Life Forms

*Discussed in the chapter

Figure 12-1 A "phylogenetic tree," illustrating probable evolutionary relationships of the major groups of marine organisms. Each phylum and division is listed at the tips of the "branches." Kingdoms are outlined with dashed lines. (Adapted from James L. Sumich, *Biology of Marine Life*, 2nd ed., © 1976, 1980, William C. Brown Publishers, Dubuque, Iowa, reprinted by permission)

tree of life. An additional goal is to try to trace evolutionary trends in the genealogical tree. The last and most important goal, and our immediate task in this chapter is simply giving every organism an identifying name.

The taxonomic classification developed over the past two centuries has addressed all of the above goals. This is illustrated schematically by the phylogenetic tree shown in Fig. 12-1 which places five identifiable kingdoms into perspective with regard to cell structure and plant and animal characteristics. Figure 12-1 also includes the phyla that are represented significantly in the marine environment and suggests some general evolutionary trends.

For the purpose of this text it is not necessary to discuss marine organisms with respect to five kingdoms. Rather, the basic plant and animal kingdoms will be used with the understanding that, for other purposes, organisms may be better grouped as shown in Fig. 12-1.

12.2 *Plants in the Ocean*

The plants in the marine environment are diverse in their morphological characteristics and living habits. The major marine plants and some of their group characteristics are summarized in Table 12-2. The characteristics are generalizations, however, and notewworthy variations within the groups are discussed in the following sections.

The Algae

By far the most important plants in the ocean are the algae (Plate I). These organisms have a very primitive structure and contain no roots, flowers, stems, or leaves. Marine algae inhabit all portions of the world ocean that receive direct solar energy. For instance, algal forms abound on rocks high in the intertidal zone, and as microscopic plankton they drift throughout the surface waters of the world ocean. Their role in the economy of the sea is critical and will be discussed in detail in Chaps. 13 and 14.

The primary classification of algae is usually based on the color of the organism, although the color seldom indicates the family or genus to which the plant belongs. These more specific classifications are determined by life history and, to some extent, by anatomical structure and type of food reserves.

Chrysophyta.   This division is characterized as single-celled, eukaryotic plants that occur primarily as plankton. Most plants in this division have either mineralized cell walls or internal skeletons which are composed of silica or calcium carbonate. Some species have *flagella*, or whiplike appendages, that provide them with a limited degree of mobility.

Diatoms (Class Bacillariphyceae) are the most abundant of the phytoplankton in the world ocean. They are small, one-celled plants that occur as individual cells, in loose chains, or in loose aggregates.

The plant cell is enclosed in a small "shell" or *frustule* composed of silica. Diatom frustules vary in size from 15 μm to 1 mm and are perforated by many pores often arranged in geometric patterns. The perforations aid in the transfer of fluids and nutrients between the plant cell and the surrounding seawater. The shapes of diatoms are quite varied; they include circular or pillbox, triangular, and modified square shapes (Plate I).

Diatoms reproduce by cell division, as do many algae, and in some cases one half of the diatom population reproduces every 24 hours. Usually, the diatom reproduces in such a way that one circular pillbox separates, and two

Table 12–2   Major Plant Divisions in the Marine Environment

Phylum or division	Method of reproduction	Dominant habit	Approx. no. living marine species	Remarks	
Algae					
Chrysophyta		Planktonic			
diatoms			5,000		
golden brown algae			130	Unicellular microscopic often flagellated	
coccolithophores			200		
silicoflagellates			?		
Pyrrophyta dinoflagellates		Planktonic	1,000	Unicellular or colonial flagellated microscopic	
Cyanophyta blue green algae	Cell division	Benthic	150	Unicellular nonflagellated prokaryotic microscopic	
Rhodophyta red algae		Benthic	4,000	Multicellular macroscopic	
Phaeophyta brown algae		Benthic	1,500	Multicellular macroscopic	Known as the "seaweeds"
Chlorophyta green algae		Benthic	100	Multicellular microscopic to macroscopic	
Flowering plants					
Anthophyta sea grasses	Seeds and vegetative reproduction	Benthic	45	Macroscopic multicellular	
Other					
Mycophyta fungi	Cell division	Benthic	300	Microscopic multicellular nonphotosynthetic or variable	
lichens		Benthic	15		
Schizomycophyta bacteria	Cell division	Planktonic and benthic	180	Unicellular prokaryotic mostly flagellated microscopic	Most are not photosynthetic; some bacteria photosynthesize

pillboxes result (Fig. 12-2). Because this form of reproduction leads to increasingly smaller individuals, it cannot continue indefinitely. After a number of cell divisions, an auxospore is formed within which a cell, separated from its tiny shell, may grow and form a full-sized frustule. Resting spores also can be formed; these spores allow the cell to survive unfavorable environmental conditions. Diatoms survive only by remaining in the upper sunlight regions of the world ocean. Consequently, these plants are adapted to spend their lives

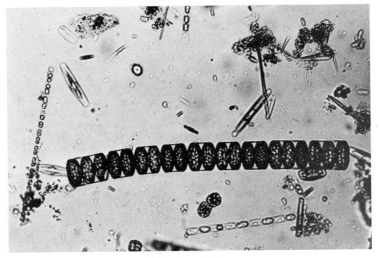

(A) Various diatoms, magnification 400 ×.

(B) Highly magnified view of a diatom frustule, magnification 8000 ×.

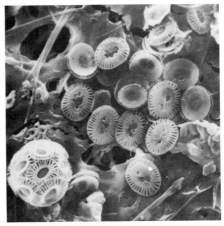

(C) Highly magnified view of a coccolithophore and separate plates, magnification 4600 ×.

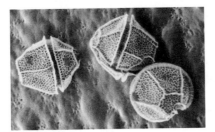

(D) The Dinoflagellate *Gonyaulax*, responsible for *Red Tides*, magnification 250 ×.

Plate I Characteristic forms of planktonic marine algae. (Photograph A courtesy Bernard Nist; B and C courtesy U.S. Department of Interior, Geological Survey EROS Program; D courtesy Kent Cambridge Scientific)

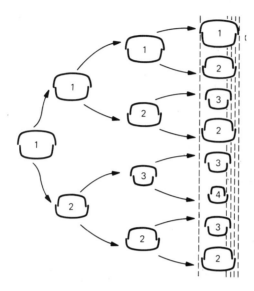

Figure 12-2 Reproduction in diatoms. Diminution of size resulting from cell division in three generations. (After Sverdrup, Johnson, and Fleming, 1942)

near the ocean surface (see Chap. 14). However, benthic (bottom-dwelling) forms do exist in shallow water, and some forms live attached to other plants and animals.

Golden Brown Algae (Class Chrysophyceae) are classified on the basis of the number and length of flagella or whiplike appendages. Most chrysophyceae are found in freshwater.

Coccolithophores (Class Chrysophyceae) are among the smallest phytoplankton in the open ocean (Plate I). They possess two flagella and are weakly motile. The soft parts of these single-celled organisms are covered with small calcite plates called coccoliths. These plates separate from the cell when the organism dies and accumulate on the sea floor as a biological component of marine sediment. Coccoliths were originally observed in geological strata of the Cretaceous age. They were discovered from the deep-sea oozes collected during the Atlantic Cable survey of 1858. Their association with marine algae was recognized in the latter part of the nineteenth century.

Silicoflagellates (Class Chrysophyceae) have internal skeletons composed of silica that are very ornate in shape. Silicoflagellates were first recognized as fossil skeletons in marine sediments and later were recognized to be flagellated plants with photosynthetic pigments that relate them to the chrysophyta.

Pyrrophyta. This division of planktonic organisms is known as *dinoflagellates.* They are unicellular and have two flagella that provide weak motility. As a group, the dinoflagellates include both photosynthetic forms of plantlike characteristics and *heterotrophic* forms of animallike characteristics that obtain energy from dissolved organic compounds or ingested organic particulate matter.

Most dinoflagellate cells are enclosed by a heavy cellulose wall composed of platelike parts (Plate I). Reproduction occurs by cell division (similar to the diatom) that can be very rapid under ideal conditions. Dense concentrations of cells discolor the water to red or brown hues. This condition is known as a *red tide*. Some species of dinoflagellates produce toxins that when produced in high concentrations cause mortality to other forms of marine life.

Cyanophyta.   This division represents the blue green algae; microscopic procaryotes that occur in large concentrations both in the marine and freshwater environments. They are common in freshwater where they form large mats and surface scum having a bad odor. In temperate climates blue green algae form dark zones encrusting rocks above the high tide level (Fig. 12-6). The Red Sea derives its name from a planktonic (drifting) form of this type of alga that is reddish in color. This organism is classified as a blue green alga on the basis of its anatomical structure. Blue green algae reproduce by division of single cells into two smaller individuals. After growth, the smaller individuals continue to divide. The cells of the blue green algae are not nucleated, which fact suggests that they are extremely primitive plants.

Benthic plants: the seaweeds.   Nearly all of the marine plant divisions include benthic forms, but the majority of the benthic plants in the world ocean are the macroscopic, attached plants that are known as *seaweed*. These marine algae are quite large and exhibit structural specializations that adapt them to nearshore and coastal environments. The seaweeds have representatives in the plant divisions *Chlorophyta* (green algae), *Phaeophyta* (brown algae), and the *Rhodophyta* (red algae). These divisions are classified on the basis of the photosynthetic pigments they contain.

Chlorophyta (green algae) are *sessile* (attached) plants that inhabit rocky shores. Their forms are often bright green and consist of very thin, broad leaves that are usually less than 0.5 m in length. Examples are sea lettuce *(Ulva)*, which occurs in the temperate regions (Plate II) and *Halimeda*, a calcium carbonate-secreting plant that grows in abundance in tropical regions and forms part of the flora of coral reefs (Fig. 14-3). These algae reproduce by spores that are simple in structure and may or may not have the power of spontaneous movement. Spores produced at different seasons of the year eventually become free from the parent plant. Provided that they find an attachment place within a reasonable amount of time, they then develop into new plants.

Phaeophyta (brown algae) include kelp, the largest marine plants in the world ocean (over 80 m long). Kelp includes diverse plants, but they all have certain common characteristic structural features (Fig. 12-3A). Mature forms of kelp consist of a *blade* or leafy structure; a *stipe*, or a stemlike organ; and a *holdfast* which is an anchoring device that attaches the plant to the sea floor.

(A) Green algae *(Ulva)*, about half natural size.

(B) Brown algae *(Nereocystis)*, about ¹/₂₅ natural size.

(C) Red algae, about half natural size.

(D) Red algae, about ¼ natural size.

(E) Encrusting algae, about twice natural size.

Plate II Characteristic forms of attached marine algae. (A, C, D, and E courtesy Bernard Nist; B courtesy Peter B. Taylor)

A number of the larger forms also have *pneumatocysts* which are gas-filled floats located at the upper part of the stipe. These floats keep the blades floating at the more sunlit regions of the surface. Kelp occur in forests along rocky coasts and headlands in temperate latitudes. These kelp beds are associated with a characteristic assemblage of fish and invertebrates, and to an extent protect the coastline from wave action.

The coastal or nearshore environment is swept by severe wave action and currents, so the success of the brown algae to a large extent depends on their attachment to the sea floor. Some forms attach themselves to the bottom by a complex network of branched appendages that penetrate sand or mud with rootlike filaments. Others attach to the outsides of rocks, pebbles, or shells by a holdfast (Fig. 12-3).

The brown algae are very diverse in their size and structure. Examples of some common temperate forms are shown in Fig. 12-3B. These examples illustrate the various types of stipes, pneumatocysts, and blades that occur. All of these plants often coexist in kelp forests. The genus *Egregia* flourishes at the inner or shallow boundary (approximately 6 m depth), while the bull kelp *Pelagophycus* occurs at the deeper limit (40 m). *Macrocystis* and *Nereocystis* grow throughout the kelp forest, and *Laminaria* and *Pterygophora* occur as undergrowth.

Sargassum (gulfweed) is also a brown alga, but it is much smaller than kelp. It grows in the Caribbean Sea but during storms it breaks off and is swept into the center of the North Atlantic current gyre, giving the Sargasso Sea its name. A few species lead a pelagic life. The loose masses and tangles of floating seaweed segments are only several centimeters long. They float freely for a time and then sink when their floats are lost. It is estimated that between 4

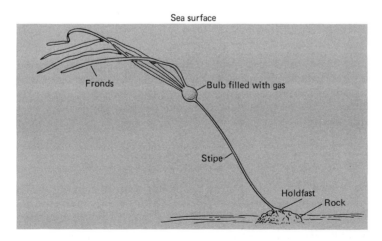

Figure 12-3A The gross structure of the brown algae *Nereocystis*.

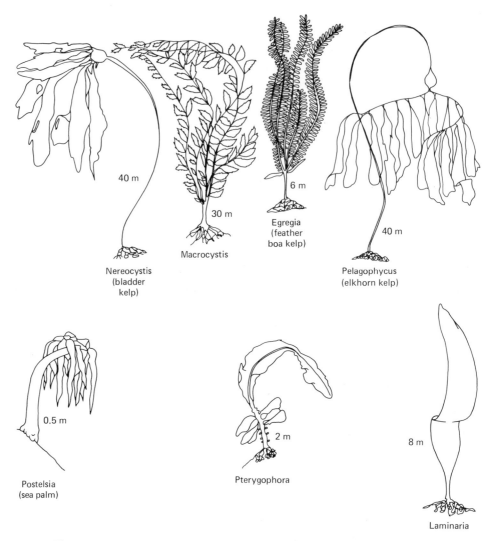

Figure 12-3B Some large forms of brown algae (kelp) from temperate latitudes. Lengths of each form are shown on each drawing. (Adapted from James L. Sumich, *Biology of Marine Life,* 2nd ed., © 1976, 1980, William C. Brown Publishers, Dubuque, Iowa, reprinted by permission)

and 11×10^6 tons of sargassum weed float in the Sargasso Sea at any given moment.

Rhodophyta (red algae) are generally smaller than brown algae. They are also capable of living under very low light conditions and are known to occur at depths to 200 m. Red algae are sedentary forms and may look like crumpled red paper (Plate II). Colors range from rose red to deep purple-red or almost black. A variety called *Lithothamnion* secretes calcium carbonate in its cell walls and is a principal organism in cementing carbonate reefs. Another form is a source of agar. Others are used for extracting minerals and for fertilizers. These algae are distributed widely in intertidal and subtidal regions of the world ocean.

Many of the seaweeds are edible and have been used by humankind for both food and medicinal purposes from early times. Actually, the commercial use of seaweed goes far beyond its nutritive and medicinal uses, and a seaweed harvesting industry flourishes in many parts of the world. In this industry, commercial harvesters are used to cut kelp about 3 ft below the surface and lift it into a barge to be returned to the processing plant (Fig. 12-4). Some of the modern uses of seaweeds are:

Fertilizer

Agar—substitute for gelatine; antidrying agent in foods; preservative for meat and fish; waterproofing in paper and cloth; substrate for bacterial cultures for hospitals and medical research.

Algin—thickener for foods (e.g., ice cream); suspending medium for paints, polishes, pigments; emulsifier for water-base paints; cosmetics.

Figure 12-4 Kelp-processing vessel.

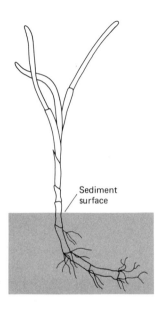

Figure 12-5 (A) The eel grass *Zostera* on an intertidal sand flat. The strands are about 1 m long. (Photograph courtesy Peter B. Taylor) (B) Root and leaf configuration relative to the sandy substrate. (Adapted from James L. Sumich, *Biology of Marine Life*, 2nd ed., © 1976, 1980, William C. Brown Publishers, Dubuque, Iowa, reprinted by permission)

Figure 12-6 Mangroves are common flowering plants that colonize the edge of the sea in tropical latitudes.

Flowering Plants

Anthophyta. Marine flowering plants have true roots or rhizomes, leaves and stems, and produce seeds. These plants, called *halophytes,* actually evolved on land and, having developed mechanisms for accommodating the higher levels of salts in seawater, invaded the shallow water of the sea. Common marine anthophyta include forms that are submerged to depths of 20 m. Examples are eel grass or *Zostera* (Fig. 12-5) and surf grass or *Phyllospadix*. Other marine anthophyta include the salt marsh plants in tidal flats, embayments, and estuaries and mangroves in tropical regions (Fig. 12-6).

Marine flowering plants may reproduce vegetatively, drop seeds into the surrounding sediment, or produce fruit which may float for great distances before the seeds are discharged.

Fungi

Fungi *(Mycophyta)* are simple multicelled plants that do not carry on photosynthesis and that subsist on ingestion of dead or living organic matter. Marine fungi are found on pilings, driftwood, timbers, and other organisms. They are most abundant in shallow waters, but specimens have been collected from depths greater than 3,000 m. Fungus parasitism is known to occur and is thought to be responsible for the death of large marine algae populations. Infectious fungi also cause severe mortality in invertebrates (sponges, oysters, crabs) and fish (herring, mackerel, flounder).

Bacteria

Bacteria (Schizomycophyta) are single-celled prokaryotic organisms that are found in all parts of the marine environment. Most of the marine bacteria possess a whiplike flagellum that provides them with limited movement. The concentration of bacteria varies widely, with cell counts as high as 400,000 per ml in coastal waters and marine sediments and as low as 40 cells per ml in open ocean waters. They are vitally important to the marine ecosystem and play key roles in the processes of remineralizing of nutrients from organic matter, consumption of oxygen, and *diagenesis* (changes in sedimentary deposits). They are a source of food for many microscopic organisms. The importance of bacteria in the world ocean is demonstrated in Chaps. 4, 13, 14, and 15.

12.3 Animals in the Ocean

Representatives of all major animal groups, except amphibians, are found in the world ocean. In fact, many animal groups are exclusively marine. This variety of animal life is much greater than on land or in freshwater. The variety depends, however, upon latitude; there is more variety in the tropical ocean than in the polar seas. Most of the animal forms are small; the average marine organism is smaller than a mosquito. In the following discussion, only those forms particularly relevant to oceanography are included.

Phylum Protozoa

Protozoa are small organisms that perform all their life processes in a single cell. Planktonic (drifting) and benthic (bottom-dwelling) forms inhabit all parts of the world ocean. Of particular importance are those protozoa that secrete or build shells, which are called *tests*. Tests show a wide diversity in structure and are composed of calcium carbonate ($CaCO_3$), silica (SiO_2), or detrital material cemented with calcium carbonate. The organisms extend their protoplasms outside of their tests in order to surround organic food particles to be digested within the cell. The dinoflagellates and other motile algae are sometimes included with this group of organisms in the Protista kingdom.

Order Foraminifera is a group of protozoans that is both benthic and planktonic. However, the benthic forms are not prevalent in the open ocean areas. The planktonic genus *Globigerina*, for example, abounds in the warmer or subtropical surface waters of the open ocean and can live at higher latitudes. It secretes a calcium carbonate test consisting of one or more spherical chambers (Plate III). Upon death or reproduction, these chambers sink to the sea floor and become a recognizable portion of the sediments.

Order Radiolaria is an important group of planktonic protozoans that secrete a silica test (Plate III). These tests are extremely intricate and varied in their form and structure. Radiolaria are distributed throughout the Arctic, Antarctic, and tropical surface regions of the world ocean and contribute significantly to the sediment at the sea floor.

Phylum Porifera

The Porifera, or sponges, are clusters of cells of several types that have loose organization. This assemblage of cells is supported by an internal skeleton which may be a mass of fibrous protein. called *spongin,* or a complex network of needle-shaped spicules oriented at random throughout the body or intermingled with the fibers of spongin. Spongin is the material forming the common bath sponge; sponge spicules are needlelike secretions composed of siliceous or calcareous compounds (Fig. 12-7).

Sponges live at all depths and are generally attached to firm substrates, such as pilings, rocks, or shells. Sponges are filter feeders and use their body structure as a filter mechanism. Flagella on each cell in the organism circulate water through the body wall into an internal cavity via the variety of pores, holes, and channels that characterize the sponge. The water is expelled through larger holes or *oscula* (Fig. 12-7). Food particles are extracted in this filtering process and digested by the digestion cells of the organism.

(A) Various Radiolaria tests, magnification 100 ×.

Plate III Characteristic forms of planktonic protozoa. (Photograph A courtesy Kent Cambridge Scientific; B courtesy Y. R. Nayudu; C courtesy U.S. Department of Interior, Geological Survey EROS Program)

(B) Foraminifera tests, magnification 45 ×.

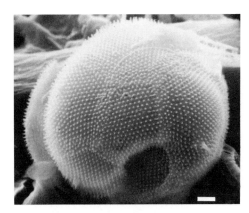

(C) Highly magnified view of a *Globigerina*, magnification 7000 ×.

Phylum Coelenterata (or Cnidaria)

The Coelenterata (Plate IV) are fairly simple organisms that consist of a protoplasm-lined gut having an opening at one end ringed with tentacles. Coelenterates may be either stationary (polyp) or planktonic (medusa). The stationary polyp form is a common tide pool inhabitant; examples are sea anemones and hydroids. Jellyfish are an example of the medusa form. This phylum contains three major classes. Class Hydrozoa includes the hydroid

A

B

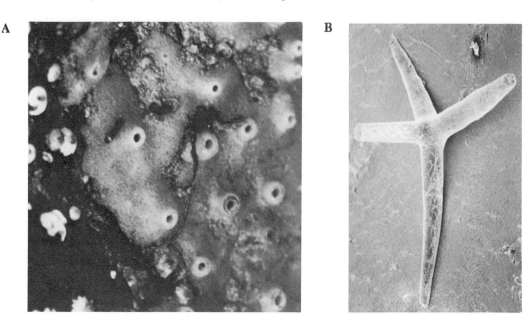

Figure 12-7 (A) A colony of sponges, magnification about 4×; (B) a sponge spicule approximately 1 mm long. (Photograph A courtesy Bernard Nist; B courtesy Kent Cambridge Scientific)

polyps and some medusae, little jellyfish about 2 cm in diameter. Class Scyphozoa contains the true jellyfish, free swimming medusae that inhabit all parts of the world ocean. They sometimes attain a diameter of 2 m with tentacles extending 30 m below the umbrella. The Anthozoa is the largest class; it includes the sea anemones and corals. All members of the Coelenterata are carnivores and possess stinging cells called *nematocysts* in their tentacles. A nematocyst looks like a small bladder filled with a coiled, hollow needle, tipped with barbs. When a trigger at one end of the needle is touched, the needle fills with water and distends itself from the cell, thus injecting anything nearby with a poisonous secretion. In tropical seas and along the eastern coast of the United States, a jellyfish known as *Physalia* (Portuguese man-of-war) is a nuisance to swimmers, because it can inflict severe pain to those who touch its tentacles. In the tropics, a jellyfish called the sea wasp inflicts a sting that may be fatal.

Reproduction of many species of coelenterates is accomplished by an alternation of two forms of generation. Polyps can reproduce themselves by budding, forming additional polyps, or by producing small medusae which in turn produce eggs that, after becoming fertilized, become free-swimming larvae that subsequently develop into polyps. In the Class Scyphozoa the medusae stage dominates and polyp production is very reduced or missing.

(A) Small hydroid polyp.

(B) Medusa.

(C) Sea anemones in a tide pool. One exposed specimen has its tentacles retracted.

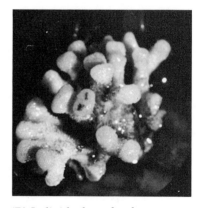

(D) Individual coral polyps.

(E) Typical coral colony comprising a coral reef.

Plate IV Characteristic coelenterates about natural size. (Photographs A, B, and D courtesy Bernard Nist; E, courtesy Peter B. Taylor)

337

A

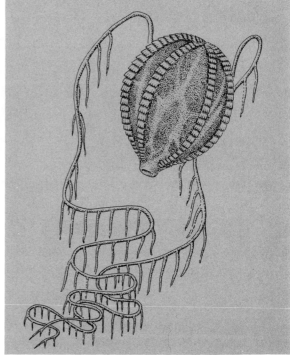

B

Figure 12-8 Photograph (A) and line drawing (B) of a comb jelly. The body is approximately 1.5 cm long. (Photograph courtesy Bernard Nist)

In the Class Anthozoa the polyp form dominates and the medusae generation does not occur.

Phylum Ctenophora

Ctenophora are marine organisms that attain diameters of only a few centimeters. They have a general body plan similar to that of the Coelenterata. Most of these organisms are planktonic, and all of them are bioluminescent—that is, they are able to emit light from photo cells in the body. This luminescence is often seen at night in the wake of a ship. Ctenophora have eight rows of comblike appendages used as paddles while swimming. They also have two long tentacles that contain sticky cells used in capturing prey. Some members of this group are called comb jellies, sea walnuts, or sea gooseberries in accordance with their appearance (Fig. 12-8). A very beautiful member of the Ctenophora, Venus' girdle, is ribbon-shaped and appears iridescent in the proper light.

Phylum Platyhelminthes

This division is made up of the flat worms. Some of these organisms are leaflike in shape, less than 10 cm in length, and are often attractively colored (Plate V). They live on the bottom of the ocean among rocks or crevices and burrow into the mud. Movement is by means of hairs *(cilia)* that cover the body of the organism and allow it to move along the bottom.

Phylum Ectoprocta

The outstanding members of this group of animals are the *Bryozoa*. These are small, colonial animals that secrete a tubular case of calcium carbonate or a horny material from which they extend their tentacles. The tentacles are situated around the central mouth and are ciliated so they can sweep in food particles. The animals form encrustations on rocks, seaweed, or any other solid surface in the sea.

Phylum Mollusca

The molluscs are a very abundant group of marine organisms and very obvious because of their diversity and habitation throughout all parts of the world ocean. This phylum includes chitons, snails, pelecypods (clams, oysters, and mussels), octopus, and squids (Plate VI). These organisms are characterized by soft bodies, development of the head, and a central region that consists of a muscular foot for crawling, burrowing, or swimming. They have a circulatory system with a heart and lungs, a well-developed digestive tract, and a rasping area around the mouth *(radula)* that consists of rows of small chitinous teeth used for obtaining food. The body is covered by a layer of tissue called a *mantle* which secretes a calcareous shell of one or more pieces. Reproduction occurs by the laying of fertilized eggs in gelatinous masses or clusters which are usually attached to some object in the water. Some of the molluscan groups are *hermaphroditic* and others have separate sexes.

Class Amphineura includes the chitons that inhabit tide pools and rocky coastlines. These organisms have soft bodies with eight separate plates of shell material over their backs. They feed by scraping algae off rocks.

Class Gastropoda includes the snails and slugs found on land, in freshwater, and in the sea. Gastropods are generally benthic as adults and, by using a large "foot," can creep along the sea floor. In some species, the foot has evolved into a swimming organ, and these gastropods are wholly planktonic. A notable example is the *pteropod* that is frequently found in tropical ocean waters. The calcareous portions of the pteropod shells contribute to marine sediments in areas where these organisms are abundant.

Class Pelecypoda (or Lamellibranchia) is made up of clams, oysters, and mussels. These are bivalve organisms; that is, they have two calcium carbonate shells that are fastened together along a hinge line. Pelecypods are filter

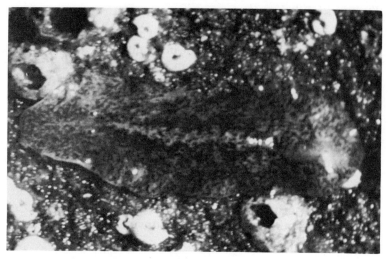

(A) A flatworm well camouflaged on a tide-pool rock, about four times natural size.

(B) A polychaete worm with tentacles exposed, about twice natural size.

Plate V Characteristic marine worms. (Photographs courtesy Bernard Nist)

(A) Chiton, natural size.

(B) Limpet, about twice natural size.

(C) Pecten, natural size.

(D) Nudibranch, about twice natural size.

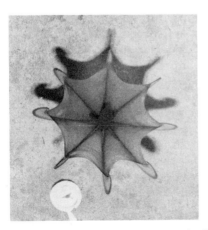

(E) A benthic octopod photographed at a depth of 4000 m, about 1/20 natural size.

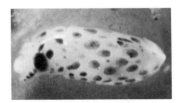

(F) Juvenile squid, about natural size.

Plate VI Characteristic forms of molluscs. (Photographs A, B, C, D, and F courtesy Bernard Nist; E courtesy U.S. Naval Research Laboratory)

341

feeders. As adults, they are benthic, living attached to rocks and pilings or burrowing beneath rocks, pilings, and sediments on the sea bottom.

Class Cephalopoda includes the octopus, squid, and chambered nautilus. These organisms have a parrotlike chewing beak, tentacles with suckers for catching prey, and a water-jet propulsion apparatus. The squids have remarkably developed eyes and are very fast swimmers. They swim tentacle-first and when startled will propel themselves backward rapidly by squirting water from an opening in their bodies. Cephalopods can attain a length of 16 m.

Phylum Annelida

This phylum includes the various kinds of segmented worms (Plate V). The largest class is *Polychaeta,* whose members resemble the common earthworm, although many have bristly fans or tentacles and build tubes that stand up, giving the appearance of a flower. These organisms are mainly benthic. The planktonic forms have rows of paddlelike appendages down their sides for swimming.

Phylum Arthropoda

Arthropods are joint-legged organisms. Terrestrial examples are insects, spiders, and scorpions. In the oceans, the various arthropods are well developed, diverse, and extremely numerous (Plate VII). Taxonomically, the marine forms belong to the Class *Crustacea,* which has a number of subdivisions. Only a few of the more important oceanic groups of crustaceans are discussed here.

Subclass Cirripedia includes the barnacles found in all benthic environments. Barnacles live inside calcareous enclosures that are attached to rocks, pilings, or on floating materials such as ships, turtles, whales, logs, and net floats. Some forms build their own floats and drift as plankton. These organisms resemble crustaceans only during their larvae stages when they closely resemble copepod larvae. Barnacle larvae must settle on a suitable surface in order to complete their adult growth; hence, they are dependent on the presence of solid objects.

Subclass Copepoda contains some very small organisms, about 2 mm in length, which make up the bulk of the zooplankton in the world ocean. They are probably the most numerous of all multicelled animals. These organisms are characterized by a jointed outer carapace or exoskeleton, composed of chitin, and two long bristly antennae located near the mouth. Copepods are important because of their position in the food chain. As grazers of phytoplankton, they convert the tiny plants of the ocean into animal matter that is used subsequently by still larger animals. They feed on phytoplankton by trapping them in numerous bristles on their large appendages. The bristles form a basketlike apparatus near the mouth that filters water and collects phytoplankton as the copepod swims.

(A) Acorn barnacle dormant.

(B) Goose barnacle with feet in feeding position.

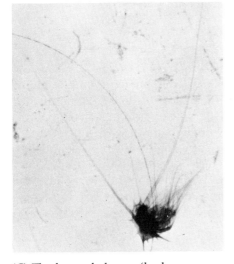

(C) The barnacle larvae (body diameter 2 mm).

(D) Crab.

(E) Shrimp.

(F) The copepod *Calanus* (length approximately 2mm).

(G) *Euphausia pacifica* (length approximately 3 cm).

Plate VII Characteristic forms of arthropods about natural size (except as noted). (Photographs A, B, D, and E courtesy Bernard Nist; C courtesy Dora P. Henry)

Order Euphausiacea is made up of shrimplike organisms that attain a length of between 1 and 5 cm and have luminescent spots along their sides. These organisms are abundant as plankton and are also found at, or near the sea floor. Euphausids, frequently called krill, are the principal food for filtering-type whales, such as the baleen whale.

Order Decapoda includes several subgroups. These are lobsters, crabs, hermit crabs, shrimps, and prawns. Most of the adult decapods are benthic and provide a source of food for humans.

Phylum Echinodermata

Echinoderms are spiny-skinned organisms that are exclusively marine and are generally bottom dwellers (Plate VIII). Commonly known examples are the starfish (or sea star), brittle star, sea urchin, and sand dollar. Some of these organisms are filter feeders (sea cucumbers), but most eat algae (sea urchins) or clams (starfish). They all have radial symmetry, usually with five parts in the shape of a star. These organisms are very highly developed and have independent digestive, respiratory, and nerve systems. They also have a unique *water vascular system* which is a hydraulic pumping system that operates the numerous *tube feet* on the exoskeleton as sensory and locomotive organs.

Phylum Chaetognatha

This phylum contains the arrow worms, which are exclusively marine planktonic organisms (Fig. 12-9). They are voracious eaters and feed largely on copepods that are captured with the bristles surrounding the mouth. These organisms are apparently very sensitive to the chemical characteristics of the water because arrow worms in one water mass are distinctively different from those of another. This permits their use in tracing water masses.

Phylum Chordata

Chordates are animals that have, at some time in their development, gill slits and a cartilaginous skeletal rod known as a *notochord* (Plate IX). Although there are several subphyla, only two are significant in the world ocean. The lower chordates in Subphylum Urochordata, or Tunicata, have no backbone and are exclusively marine organisms (Plate IX A).

Some are benthic filter feeders (sea squirts or tunicates), and others are planktonic *(Oikopleura)*. Oikopleura builds a fragile gelatinous body and moves through water by whipping its tail. As it moves, it filters water through a screen within its body. When this screen becomes full of captured material, it eats the filter, leaves its gelatinous body, and builds a new one.

The vertebrate chordates, those organisms with a vertebral column support-

(A) Starfish, about ⅕ natural size.

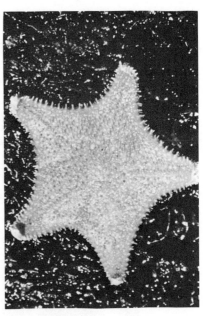

(B) Starfish, about ⅕ natural size.

(C) Sea urchin, about ⅓ natural size.

(D) Sea cucumber, about ½ natural size.

Plate VIII Characteristic forms of echinoderms. (Photographs courtesy Bernard Nist)

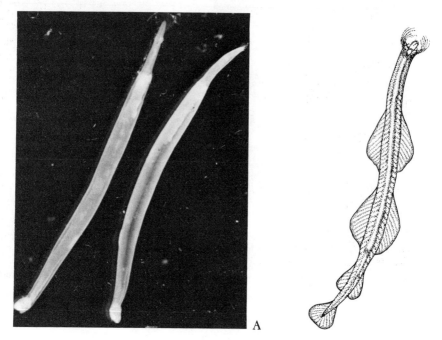

A   B

Figure 12-9 (A) Photograph and (B) sketch of the arrow worm *Sagitta* (body length approximately 2 cm).

ing the body, are the Subphylum Vertebrata which is made up of several important and familiar subgroups or classes.

Class Chondrichthyes consists of primitive fishes (sharks and rays) that have a skeleton composed of cartilage. These organisms grow very large. The whale shark is the largest of all fishes and attains a length of over 20 m.

Class Osteichthyes contains true fishes that have a bony skeleton. They are generally streamlined, carnivorous, and live throughout the marine environment. Fishes show exceptional degrees of development, depending on their habitat in the ocean. In fact, they serve as an excellent example of environmental adaptation as discussed in Chap. 14.

Class Reptilia includes sea turtles and some air-breathing snakes found only in surface waters. Sea snakes 2 m long inhabit tropical and semitropical waters and are very poisonous. Sea turtles often attain weights exceeding 400 kg and return to the land to lay their eggs during certain seasons of the year (Plate IX B).

Class Aves includes a number of birds that are dependent upon the sea for food—for example, penguins, pelicans, and gulls. Some birds, such as the albatross, petrel, and auk, return to land only for nesting.

(A) Tunicate, about ½ natural size.

(B) Green sea turtle, about ¹/₁₀ natural size.

(C) Porpoise and killer whale.

(D) Jaw and teeth of a killer whale, a man's hand provides the scale.

(E) Part of a whale baleen, about ¹/₁₀ natural size.

Plate IX Characteristic forms of chordates. (Photographs B and C courtesy Bernard Nist; E courtesy F. Raco, Brooks Institute)

Class Mammalia includes a number of mammals that are also closely associated with the ocean. Polar bears, sea otters, seals, walruses, sea lions, and sea cows are more adapted for life in a marine environment than life on land.

Whales and porpoises (Plate IX C) are exclusively marine mammals and carry out their total life history at sea including the birth of their young. Two basic types of whales exist: the toothed whales (order Odontoceti) and the baleen or whalebone whales (order Mysticeti). Toothed whales include dolphins and porpoises and the sperm whales which may reach 18 m and weigh 53,000 kg (58 t). This group also includes killer whales, narwhales, and beaked whales.

Baleen (whalebone) whales have a series of long, frayed plates hanging in their mouths (Plate IX E). The plates filter large volumes of water in order to capture plankton. The baleen whales include the pilot whale, or blackfish, that reaches 5½ m in length and the blue whale, which is the largest known mammal ever to inhabit the planet. The blue whale attains a length of over 30 m and a weight of about 100,000 kg. Some other species in this group are the gray whale, bowhead whale, fin whale, and the right whale.

Whales tend to migrate great distances over an annual cycle. They spend their summers at high-latitude feeding grounds, and as winter approaches they migrate to warmer waters to breed and give birth. The California gray whale migrates from north of the Bering Straits to Mexico, a round trip distance of 18,000 km covered over an 8-month period. Whales can sustain a speed of 5 knots, and have great diving capability to evade predators and catch food. Blue whales have been known to dive to depths of 1.8 km (1 mile) and remained submerged for as long as an hour.

reading list

BUCHSBAUM, R., *Animals without Backbones* (rev. ed.). Chicago: University of Chicago Press, 1948 405p.

DAWSON, E. Y., *How to Know the Seaweeds.* Dubuque, Iowa: Wm. C. Brown, 1956. 197p.

————, *Marine Botany; An Introduction.* New York: Holt, Rinehart & Winston, 1966. 371p.

GARDENER, M. S., *The Biology of Invertebrates.* New York: McGraw-Hill, 1972. 954p.

HERALD, E. S., *Living Fishes of the World.* Garden City, New York: Doubleday, 1961. 303p.

NICOL, A. C., *The Biology of Marine Animals.* New York: Interscience, 1960. 707p.

SUMICH, J. L., *An Introduction to the Biology of Marine Life.* Dubuque, Iowa: Wm. C. Brown, 1976. 348p.

ZOBELL, C. E., *Marine Microbiology.* Waltham, Mass.: Chronica Botanica Co., 1946. 240p.

introduction to biological oceanography 13

13.1 *Development of Life in the Sea*

Life probably began in the sea. The diversity and the antiquity of marine organisms support this conclusion. Major subdivisions of both plant and animal kingdoms have many representatives in the world ocean. In fact, five of the animal phyla are exclusively marine, and only 6 percent of the invertebrates are exclusively nonmarine.

The oldest known evidence of marine life is bacteriumlike fossils from sediments in Swaziland. They are 3.5 billion years old and were living a billion years or so after our solar system formed. Fossil evidence suggests that anaerobic prokaryotes 3 billion years old that could photosynthesize but did not generate oxygen were among the first to evolve. By about 2 billion years ago a diversity of fossil types developed. Next, the blue green algae and the oxygen-releasing photosynthesis mechanism evolved. Only then did oxygen begin to accumulate in the earth's atmosphere. Eukaryotic algae and higher plants developed about 1.1 billion years ago. Evolution of eukaryotes proceeded rapidly, and multicellular animals (metazoans) appeared in the fossil record prior to 700 million years ago.

Marine invertebrates thrived 400 to 500 million years ago and continue to do so. Some forms, such as the brachiopod, *lingula*, (a marine mollusklike organism), have changed little over time, whereas many other organisms have experienced continuous evolution (Fig. 13-1). Fish appeared in the sea during the early Paleozoic era, and amphibians invaded the land in the late Paleozoic

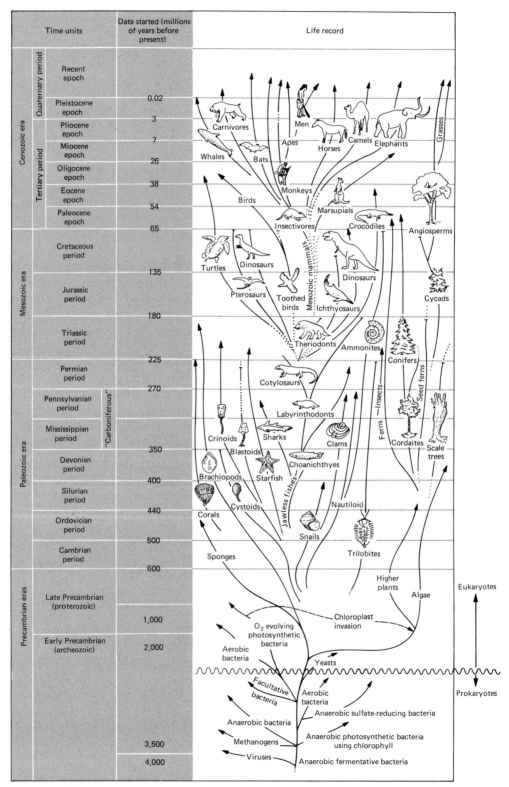

Time units			Date started (millions of years before present)	Life record

Carnivores

Men

Apes

Horses

Camels

Elephants

Grasses

Whales

Bats

Monkeys

Birds

Marsupials

Crocodiles

Angiosperms

Insectivores

Turtles

Dinosaurs

Pterosaurs

Toothed birds

Mesozoic mammals

Dinosaurs

Ichthyosaurs

Cycads

Theriodonts

Ammonites

Conifers

Cotylosaurs

Labyrinthodonts

Insects

Seed ferns

Crinoids

Sharks

Clams

Cordaites

Scale trees

Blastoids

Choanichthyes

Ferns

Brachiopods

Starfish

Jawless fishes

Cystoids

Nautiloid

Corals

Snails

Sponges

Trilobites

Higher plants

Algae

Eukaryotes

Chloroplast invasion

O_2 evolving photosynthetic bacteria

Aerobic bacteria

Yeasts

Prokaryotes

Facultative bacteria

Aerobic bacteria

Anaerobic bacteria

Anaerobic sulfate-reducing bacteria

Anaerobic photosynthetic bacteria using chlorophyll

Methanogens

Viruses

Anaerobic fermentative bacteria

Figure 13-1 Geologic time chart. Ascending lines indicate the range in time of most of the chief groups of marine animals and plants. If the line ends in a crossbar, this denotes the time of extinction; if it ends in a dart, the group is still living. (After Dunbar, *Historical Geology,* 1949, John Wiley & Sons, New York)

(300 million years ago). Mammals evolved on land about 225 million years ago; as a group, they reached an extreme development during the Cenozoic era (from 65 million years ago to the present). Some mammals, such as the whale and the porpoise, have evolved back into the sea.

The influence of the environment upon the development of life in the sea is reflected in the chemistry of body fluids in many marine animals. The concentrations of major ions in seawater are similar to those in the body fluids of many marine invertebrates. This observation supports the idea that seawater developed its salinity early in its history (see Chap. 4) and that the composition of seawater is fundamental to the metabolic processes of primitive organisms.

13.2 *Life Requirements of Marine Organisms*

The requirements for life in marine organisms are generally similar to those of terrestrial forms; however, significant differences do exist. Representing evolutionary responses to the environment, these differences are noticeable in the morphology and physiology of various groups of organisms. Some important life requirements and a short discussion of how organisms respond to these needs are listed below.

The body fluids and vital organs of marine organisms are separated from seawater by a boundary membrane. In single-celled organisms this membrane may be a lining on the inner side of the cell wall structure, or in multicelled organisms the boundary membrane may take a variety of forms, such as the skin of a fish, the cuticular covering of a copepod, or the carapace of a crab. This outer covering protects the organism, provides a degree of structural support, and generally isolates it from the surrounding water.

Marine organisms are primarily composed of water (80 to 98 percent), and their intra- and extracellular fluids must have the proper composition to maintain the biochemical processes necessary for life. Thus, some form of *ionic regulation* of body fluids is necessary. Ionic regulation requires that a continual exchange of seawater constituents occurs between the body fluids of an organism and the surrounding seawater in order to maintain the necessary conditions within the organism. The exchange of constituents across the boundary membrane facilitates the dilution requirements for enzyme systems to operate the metabolic processes efficiently, the ionic balance necessary for body functions, buoyancy adjustments, nutritional needs, and the removal of waste materials. Important constituents that are exchanged include water, major ions, nutrient ions, some trace elements, and waste products from body tissue.

The degree to which an organism can regulate the composition of body fluids is one measure of the organism's tolerance for environmental change and the range of marine environments that the organism can inhabit. For example, the body fluids of most sponges, Coelenterates, and echinoderms are very close to the concentration of "normal" seawater, and these organisms have little or no capability for ionic regulation. This means that these organisms are very restricted in the habitats they colonize and they cannot adjust to changes in environmental conditions. At the other extreme, certain fishes have a very high degree of ionic regulation and can swim freely throughout much of the world ocean. For example, the body fluids of most bony fishes are about 18 ‰. These body fluids are never at equilibrium with the surrounding seawater and the organism continually expends energy to carry out its ionic regulation processes. Some examples of the ratios of major cations in the body fluids of representative molluscs, annelids, arthropods, fish, and echinoderms are given in Table 13-1 to illustrate the degree of ionic regulation relative to seawater.

Table 13-1   Ratios of Major Cations in the Body Fluids of Representative Molluscs, Annelids, and Crustaceans, and Also of Seawater

	Na^+		K^+		Ca^+		Mg^+
Mollusca							
Mytilus (mussel)	41	:	1	:	1	:	5
Sepia (squid)	48	:	2	:	1	:	5
Annelida							
Arenicola (polychaete)	46	:	1	:	1	:	5
Pheretima (polychaete)	14	:	6	:	1	:	1
Arthropoda							
Cancer (crab)	46	:	1	:	1	:	2
Homarus (lobster)	50	:	1	:	2	:	1
Fish, average	1.9	:	7.4	:	1	:	0.7
Echinodermata							
Echinus (sea urchin)	25.6	:	1	:	1	:	3.1
Seawater	25.9	:	1	:	1	:	3.1

(After M. S. Gardener, *The Biology of Invertebrates*. New York, N.Y.: McGraw-Hill, Inc., 1972, 954p, and H. V. Sverdrup, M. W. Johnson, and R. H. Fleming, *The Oceans*. Englewood Cliffs, N.J.: Prentice-Hall, Inc., 1942, 1087p)

The mechanisms by which marine organisms regulate body fluids are varied depending on the degree of regulation required. All marine organisms transfer some substances across their boundary membranes by osmosis. Boundary membranes are found to be selectively permeable, allowing only the passage of smaller-sized molecules, such as water and some solutes. These substances diffuse through the membrane in the direction of the gradient, that is, toward the region of lower concentration. Thus, as waste molecules build up within a simple organism they diffuse out of the cell or body toward seawater, while other constituents may diffuse into the body.

Other mechanisms of ionic regulation are exhibited by fish and higher invertebrates. A salmon is an example of an organism that must survive both freshwater and marine habitats while it maintains its body fluids at some intermediate salinity. While at sea the salmon takes in seawater through its mouth, loses excess salts through its gills and urine, and regulates its water content by osmosis through its skin. In freshwater the salmon does not drink; it absorbs salts through the gills, regulates water content by osmosis through its skin, and excretes large volumes of very dilute urine. Another mechanism of regulation is found in crabs living in an environment of excess salts. Internal salinity is maintained by depositing the excess salts resulting from their metabolism in their carapaces, or outer cover. These animals shed their carapaces as they grow, thus disposing of the excess salts.

Plants adjust ionic balances by *osmoregulation* of the water content of their tissues by active transport of nutrient ions and wastes across their cell walls using molecular transfer, by storage of salt in tissues and by excretion of salt via salt glands, as well as other mechanisms.

Sunlight

As discussed in Chap. 6, the quality and quantity of sunlight penetrating the sea diminishes rapidly with depth depending on wavelength and the amount of dissolved chemical substances and suspended organic and inorganic particulate matter in the water. Some examples of light penetration for various types of seawater are shown in Fig. 13-2.

From the biological point of view, the decrease of radiant energy with depth is of vital importance because it limits the depth to which photosynthesis can occur. As a general rule, the average level of sunlight that a plant cell receives must exceed about 1 percent of the typical surface radiation in order for plant photosynthesis to exceed respiration (net growth). The depth at which photosynthesis equals plant respiration is called the *compensation depth* and is plotted in Fig. 13-2. The compensation depth is also approximated as twice the depth of disappearance of a Secchi disk (see Table 15-2). These estimates show that the compensation depth varies from 8 m for turbid coastal water to a maximum of 80–100 m for clear oceanic water. This depth can also be considered as the approximate lower limit of the *photic zone* in the sea; a marine plant must spend most of its time above this level in order to flourish.

Marine plants respond to this phenomenon in several ways. Attached plants (e.g., kelp) can live in coastal regions where they are within the photic zone or can extend their leaves toward the surface to obtain radiant energy. Away from coastal regions, marine plants must develop a particular structure and

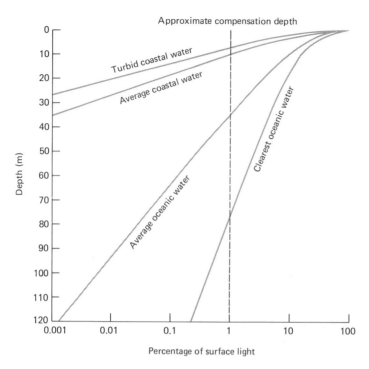

Figure 13-2 Relative penetration of radiant energy at different depths and in different types of water with the sun at zenith and with a clear sky. The approximate condition for the compensation depth is also included. Note logarithmic scale. (After Sverdrup et al., 1942)

mode of living. They are planktonic, microscopic in size, and exhibit a variety of shapes, many of which are adaptations that permit the organism to spend a sufficient part of its life cycle within the photic zone by retarding its rate of sinking.

Response to light is a very complex phenomenon. Some marine animals respond to light by avoiding it; some are attracted to it. Other organisms exhibit daily movements suggesting that they seek an optimum light intensity. Some of these adaptations will be discussed in the next chapter.

Heat

The high heat capacity of water imparts a great degree of stability to the temperature of the sea. In contrast to the terrestrial environment, daily and seasonal temperature fluctuations are subdued and do not extend deeply into the sea. For example, the seasonal variation of temperature in the North Atlantic Ocean is minimal below a depth of 200 m (Fig. 13-3). Such temperature stability assures that marine organisms of the open ocean do not experience extreme temperature variations. Accordingly, most marine organisms do not

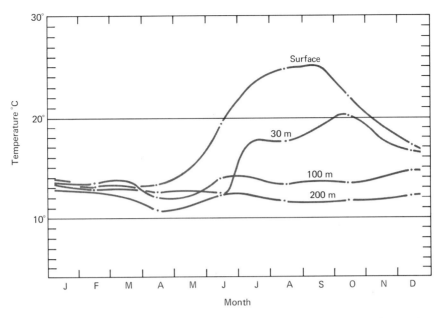

Figure 13-3 Annual variation in temperature with depth in the North Atlantic. (Data from Walford and Wicklund, American Geographical Society, 1968)

possess physiological temperature-regulating mechanisms. This means that their body temperatures are controlled by temperature variations occurring in the marine environment. Exceptions to this are the marine mammals and birds which are "warm blooded" and control their internal temperature at some optimum level.

The rates at which many physiological functions operate are strongly controlled by temperature. As a general rule a 10°C increase in temperature causes the metabolic rate in marine organisms to approximately double. This can be observed in the growth rate of algae, and the feeding and oxygen consumption rates of various zooplankton. Thus water temperature is one of the key factors in controlling the metabolic rates of most marine organisms. Water temperature determines the habitat in which many marine organisms can survive depending on their ability to withstand temperature fluctuations. Since marine mammals regulate their internal temperatures, they are less restricted on the basis of water temperature.

Oxygen and Carbon Dioxide

Dissolved oxygen and carbon dioxide are abundant throughout the sea except in closed basins where circulation is restricted and possibly at the oxygen minimum layer. These gases are important to life in the sea. Plants require CO_2 for photosynthesis, whereas both plants and animals consume O_2

during respiration, the process that organisms use to oxidize matter and obtain the energy for life. Both photosynthesis and respiration are discussed in detail in Chap. 14. In this section, we only consider how animals and plants obtain O_2 and release CO_2.

Living cells obtain energy by the oxidation of organic molecules that are either absorbed directly or provided by ancillary digestive and circulatory systems. The breakdown of food molecules occurs within the cell, which means that there must be a mechanism for transferring oxygen from the surrounding environment into the organisms and for removing carbon dioxide, the waste product of metabolism.

In the sea, organisms exchange gases in several ways. Ultimately, the transfer of dissolved substances depends on diffusion of molecules from a region of high chemical concentration to a region of low concentration. In the simplest case, diffusive exchange between the cell and its surroundings occurs directly across the cell wall. This type of exchange occurs in plants and animals having a low degree of organization (i.e., protozoans, sponges, coelenterates, and flatworms). Complex marine animals have special organs—gills in fishes and lungs in mammals—for diffusive exchange.

Gills are membranes that contain many blood vessels. When water moves past the surface of the membrane, gases are exchanged between the water on one side of this membrane and the blood vessels on the other side. Oxygen absorbed by the blood is circulated to the cells; carbon dioxide produced within the body cells diffuses into the blood and is carried to the gills where it diffuses into the water. This method of exchange is a three-step process: diffusion, circulation, and diffusion. It is used by fishes, crustaceans, molluscs, and some worms.

The higher animals in the sea (marine mammals) have lungs for breathing air from the sea surface. Lungs are a complex system of membrane and blood vessels that provide an efficient means of transferring gases from the air into the blood.

Food

All forms of life require food substances to form their tissue and to provide a source of energy for their life processes. A variety of food exists in the sea. Marine organisms, therefore, use many kinds of food and have several means of acquiring nutrition.

The simplest organisms in the sea, the *autotrophs,* are self-nourishing and produce their own food from H_2O, CO_2, and radiant energy. These organisms are the green plants and certain bacteria.

Heterotrophic organisms cannot synthesize food from inorganic nutrients but must eat other organisms or organic molecules. Heterotrophs include all animals, most bacteria, and some plants. Three types of heterotrophic nutrition are used by animals: *holozoic, saprozoic,* and *parasitic.*

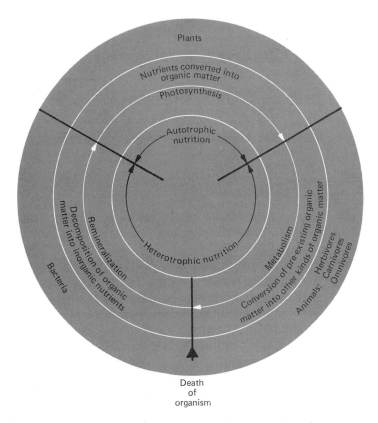

Figure 13-4 Comparison of types of nutrition, nutritional processes, and organisms using these processes.

The process of catching, eating, and digesting food particles is called holozoic nutrition. Holozoic organisms have developed sensory, nervous, and muscular organs to use in capturing food particles. They have also developed digestive systems to break food particles into useful nutrient chemicals. In animals, selective diets have evolved; consequently animals are grouped on the basis of this selectivity. *Herbivores* are animals that feed on plants; *carnivores* feed on animals; and *omnivores* feed on both plants and animals. The relationship between organisms and their feeding habits is shown in Fig. 13-4.

Saprozoic organisms cannot ingest particulate foods but rely on the direct absorption of organic molecules for nourishment. This process requires that these organisms live in an environment containing decomposed animal or plant matter. This form of nutrition is not common among the animal kingdom; it is restricted mainly to the protozoans (single-celled organisms).

Parasitic nutrition occurs when one organism lives on or within another organism and obtains its food at the expense of the host. Almost every animal

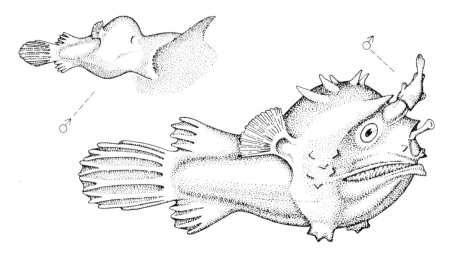

Figure 13-5 A female angler fish *(Photocorynus spiniceps)* with a
degenerate male fused to her body. The female nourishes the male and
he in turn fertilizes her eggs. A luminous fishing organ can also be
seen on the front of the female's head. (After Sverdrup, Johnson, and
Fleming, 1942)

is the host for one parasite or more. Some parasites cause little or no injury to
the host; this relationship is called *commensalism*. Other parasites, however,
do great harm by destroying cells, removing nutrients, or producing toxic
waste products. Some parasites provide a benefit to the host in one respect
and a disadvantage in others. One example is the deep-sea angler fish, which
is a sexual parasite (Fig. 13-5). The male fish is permanently attached to the
female; fertilization of eggs is assured at the expense of nourishment from the
female's bloodstream.

Support

The protoplasm of most animals must be protected from the environment by
a covering or a structure that supports the organs and muscle tissue (i.e., a
skeleton). Because the density of protoplasm of marine animals is close to that
of seawater, the necessity of extensive structural body parts is minimized, and
many forms have meager skeletons or none at all. Examples are the jellyfish,
squid, and octopus. Even the skeleton of a whale would not be adequate to
support its body weight in air.

On the other hand, massive skeletal structures are needed by organisms
living in the rigors of the littoral environment where wave action and strong
currents would quickly damage animal protoplasm. Consequently, thick external shells, or exoskeletons, protect littoral species of clams, snails, and crabs.

Animals that swim need strong muscles attached to a flexible support. Fishes have endoskeletons inside their bodies and protective scales (or skin) outside. This arrangement of support and protective structures provides an optimum degree of mobility for these animals.

Protection from Enemies

Most of the sea is a place without shelter. It is true that there are areas for concealment in the rocks, mud, and seaweeds at the margins of the sea, but most organisms live in open water and therefore are unprotected.

Concealment through protective coloration or transparency helps some of the small invertebrates escape predators. However, organisms, such as the copepods, anchovies, and the larvae of most marine organisms, cannot outsmart, outswim, or avoid predators, so their survival depends upon their rate of reproduction. Such organisms produce tremendous numbers of offspring, few of which need to survive in order to propagate the species. For example, codfish can produce 5,000,000 eggs at a time, even though only one pair of eggs has to reach maturity in order to replace the parents. If several pairs survived, the eventual production of cod would be overwhelming were it not for the fact that a larger population of predators would be supported. The balance between predator and prey is maintained in such a way that the survival of the species of prey is assured.

There is a premium on simplicity and diversity in the sea. Generally, marine forms are both morphologically and physiologically simpler than their terrestrial counterparts. Furthermore, there is a tendency for primitive marine species to be preserved once they have evolved, probably because the marine environment has remained so uniform during most of its history. Hence, marine life has both great simplicity and great diversity.

13.3 Classification of Marine Environments

Many, but certainly not all, of the individual marine environments recognized by oceanographers are illustrated in Fig. 13-6. We shall consider only the major environments; the others are included for reference. The environments shown in this figure are defined by unique chemical and physical properties and geographic configurations. Since marine organisms respond to these conditions, classification of environments is meaningful in a biological sense. When individual environments are defined from a biological point of view, they are called *biotic* units. Two such biotic units are recognized as the *photic* (lighted) and *aphotic* (dark) regions of the ocean. The boundary line is placed at about 100 m, which is the limit of 1 percent light penetration in clear ocean water (Fig. 13-2). The photic zone is an important biotic unit, for it is there that plants, the ultimate source of food for all organisms, combine sunlight, CO_2, and nutrients to produce organic matter.

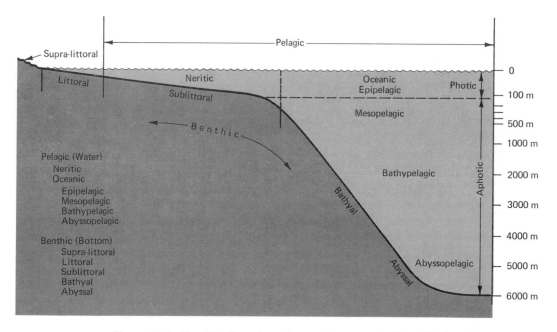

Figure 13-6 Classification of marine environments. (After Hedgpeth and Ladd, 1957)

Pelagic Environment

The term *pelagic* refers to the water of the world ocean. The pelagic environment is divided into provinces both horizontally and vertically. The *neritic province* is the water over the continental shelf, and the *oceanic province* includes all water seaward of the shelf break. The neritic and oceanic provinces are divided vertically into a photic zone and an aphotic zone. The boundary between the two corresponds to the approximate depth of light penetration and to the depth at the outer edge of the continental shelf.

Environmental conditions in the oceanic and in the neritic provinces differ even though they overlap. In the open ocean, physical conditions—particularly temperature and salinity—do not vary a great deal. Light penetration is also greater in the oceanic than in the neritic provinces (Fig. 13-2). The neritic province receives a greater continental influence than does the oceanic province. River runoff causes water on the continental shelf to have lower salinity and greater seasonal variation in both temperature and salinity. There is a large supply of nutrients from land; furthermore, nutrients are regenerated on the seabed and are welled up from depth in the neritic province. These factors make this area highly productive of plants and animals. Most of the world's fisheries, therefore, are on the continental shelf. The abundance of marine life in the neritic province is as striking as the paucity of life in the subtropical open ocean.

Benthic Environment

This type of environment is found at the bottom of the world ocean regardless of depth. It is divided into the *supralittoral, littoral, sublittoral,* and *deep-sea* regions (Fig. 13-6).

The supralittoral environment is that area of the beach above the extreme high water line. This region is rarely submerged; however, it is subject to sea spray and the influence of large storm waves.

The littoral environment is in the intertidal region. This environment is extremely variable. In high latitudes, for instance, temperatures could be subzero in winter (with the occurrence of ice) and 40°C during warm summer periods. The salinity in tide pools ranges from zero to greater than 40 ‰, depending on the degree of exposure, evaporation, runoff, and tidal range. Vigorous water movements characterize the littoral province. The intertidal zone is continually pounded by waves and swept by currents. Materials at the bottom—rocks, sand, or mud—sometimes change seasonally. Many beaches that are sandy in the summer become rocky during the winter when large waves transport the beach sand to offshore regions.

The sublittoral environment extends from below the tidal zone to approximately the outer edge of the continental shelf. This environment is the transition between the shore and the deep sea. For example, the benthic region of the inner shelf can have daily temperature and salinity changes, but the outer portions vary seasonally. The bottom sediment of the sublittoral includes rock, coral, sand, or mud, depending on conditions of sedimentation (see Chap. 15 for a discussion of marine sediments).

The deep-sea benthic regions are characterized by extensive deposits of fine sediment, uniform conditions of temperature and salinity, no light, and extreme pressures. Seasons do not exist and the values of ambient temperature and salinity are related to the distribution of water masses (Chap. 9).

13.4 *Modes of Life in the Sea*

Contrary to the beliefs of early oceanographers, life is found throughout the marine environment and is as varied as the physical and chemical conditions that prevail. There are three important modes of life in the sea: planktonic, nektonic, and benthic. Marine organisms are classified within these modes according to their swimming abilities and habitat.

Plankton

Plankton are those organisms that drift passively with the ocean currents. Some organisms in this category can swim weakly, but they spend most or all of their lives subject to the motion of the waters that surround them.

Over 15,000 different organisms can be considered as plankton. Members of this group range in size from *nanoplankton*, plants smaller than 60 μ (60/1,000,000 m), to *megaloplankton*, such as large jellyfish whose diameters reach 2 m. Floating plants in the sea are called *phytoplankton;* floating animals are *zooplankton*. Many organisms drift only during their egg or larval stages (*meroplankton*), but others spend their entire lives adrift (*holoplankton*).

The existence of a meroplankton phase is an interesting and important aspect of marine life. The majority of marine animals, including fishes, begin as plankton. This mode of life affords them a mechanism of dispersal and survival in a changing environment. Because meroplankton are seasonal, the occurrence of a particular species depends upon its spawning habits. The planktonic larval period can last only a few hours (as in certain worms) or 4 or 5 months (as in sand crabs). The larvae of many species spend this time drifting; a few reach a place where they can attach themselves for their adult lives. Most of the meroplanktonic larvae do not survive: they become food for other marine organisms.

Nekton

This category includes adult squids, fishes, marine mammals (i.e., whales, seals, and porpoises), and larger crustaceans (shrimplike organisms). The difference between plankton and nekton is indistinct in certain cases. For example, the eggs and larvae of fish are planktonic, but fish become nektonic at an early stage in their lives.

The term *nekton* implies complete freedom of movement; indeed, nekton are found in all parts of the world ocean. However, certain organisms appear to be restricted to particular geographical locations and depths. There are, consequently, geographical limitations in the distribution of various fisheries throughout the world. For example, the commercially important cod inhabits northern waters of both the Atlantic and Pacific oceans. These fish migrate freely in these waters; however, they live near the bottom and are rarely caught in depths greater than 350 m. Hence, their habitat is limited in both a geographical and vertical sense.

The boundary that limits the distribution of a species need not be a physical barrier. It can be an environmental one, such as changes of temperature, salinity, oxygen supply, nutrient supply, character of the substrate, or any of many physical and chemical properties. Cod swim off the northeastern coast of the United States only as far south as the latitude where water temperature begins to rise above 30°C, the temperature of coagulation of cod albumen. The thermal boundary for cod coincides with the edge of the Gulf Stream off the southern United States. The distribution of other fishes in the world ocean may be controlled by different variables.

Many nekton seem capable of adjusting easily to rapidly changing physical conditions. Some, however, do not or cannot. For example, occasionally the warm equatorial countercurrent that flows toward the coast of Ecuador penetrates the coastal region as far south as Peru. The sudden influx of warm water (called "El Niño") causes great mortality to marine life and to birds that rely upon fish for food.

Benthos

Benthic organisms are plants and animals that are (1) *sessile*, or attached to the bottom (sponges, barnacles, corals, oysters, sea anenomes, seaweeds), (2) *vagile* and burrow into the substrate (clams, worms), (3) creep over the sea floor (starfish, crabs, lobsters, snails), or (4) spend much of their lives associated with the bottom (certain fishes).

The benthos of nearshore regions is characterized by the profusion and variety of organisms living there. In this environment, wave forces and tidal currents are extremely vigorous; hence, attached forms predominate. The littoral and sublittoral environments have extremely varied physical conditions, bottom types, and habitats, so it is not surprising that there is such a wide variety of littoral and sublittoral benthic organisms. In fact, nearly all major forms of the animal kingdom are represented in these regions.

A combination of several factors causes the abundance of life in the nearshore environment. Strong currents and associated vertical mixing, high nutrient supply from the land, and adequate sunlight reaching the bottom (permitting the growth of plants) are all important. Strong currents are particularly vital for carrying food to sessile organisms that are incapable of moving. Often food is so plentiful in this environment that animal populations are limited only by the scarcity of space or shelter. It is the luxuriant growth of plant material in the nearshore environment that causes such an abundance of animal life.

Like the nekton, littoral and sublittoral benthic organisms have a definite geographical distribution. Distinct fauna can be recognized in Arctic, tropical, and Antarctic regions. Some organisms, however, do occur in regions transcending the usual geographical boundaries. The geographical distribution of fauna appears to be controlled primarily by water temperature, but other oceanic factors are also important.

Within any beach or nearshore region, plants and animals tend to distribute themselves in zones that parallel the shore. The position along a beach that a given organism inhabits is a function of the tides (degree of exposure), substratum, currents, wave forces, temperature, salinity, light penetration, and biological conditions related to food, space, and competition. Near the upper limits of the intertidal zone physical factors, such as temperature, desiccation, salinity, and sunlight, tend to determine the distribution of organisms. Biological conditions, such as competition for space, predation, and grazing, tend to influence the distribution of organisms in the lower limits of the intertidal zone.

One scheme to describe the characteristic zones on a rocky shore is shown in Fig. 13-7. Each zone is defined by the presence or absence of certain

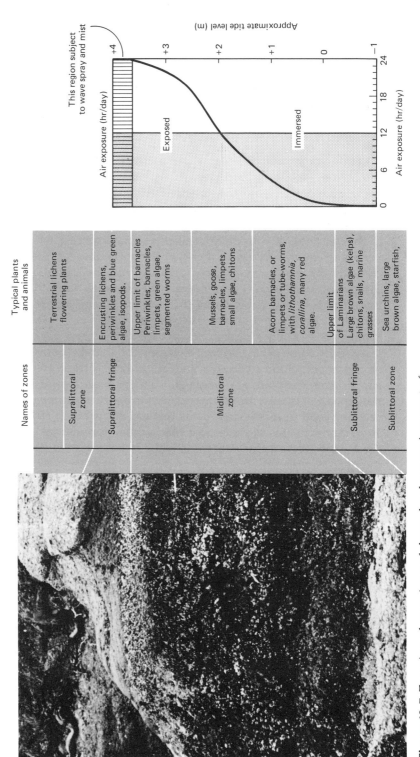

Names of zones	Typical plants and animals
Supralittoral zone	Terrestrial lichens flowering plants
Supralittoral fringe	Encrusting lichens, periwinkles and blue green algae, isopods.
Midlittoral zone	Upper limit of barnacles Periwinkles, barnacles, limpets, green algae, segmented worms Mussels, goose, barnacles, limpets, small algae, chitons Acorn barnacles, or limpets or tube-worms, with *lithothamnia*, *corallina*, many red algae.
Sublittoral fringe	Upper limit of Laminarians Large brown algae (kelps), chitons, snails, marine grasses
Sublittoral zone	Sea urchins, large brown algae, starfish,

Figure 13-7 Zonation of organisms of the rocky shore environment of Puget Sound, Washington. (Photograph courtesy Peter B. Taylor)

distinctive organisms and is strongly related to tidal conditions. Such classifications have been devised for rocky and sedimentary substrates of exposed
coasts, protected coasts, and estuaries.

Organisms living at the bottom, seaward of the sublittoral zone, are termed
deep-sea benthos. The number of deep-sea organisms decreases rapidly with
increasing depth. This decrease led early oceanographers to conclude that no
life existed below 700 m. This lifeless region was called the azoic zone. By
1860, however, life was found in the deep sea; since then, thousands of species
have been discovered at all depths.

Deep-sea benthic organisms are widely distributed because of the uniformity
of physical and substrate conditions. On the other hand, the scarcity of mates
limits dispersal. Also, there are environmental barriers that limit the migration
of organisms—for example, the Wyville Thompson Ridge that separates the
North Atlantic and the Norwegian seas. A temperature difference of only 4°C
across the ridge inhibits migration to the extent that only 11 percent of the
fauna are common to both sides.

reading list

BARRINGTON, E. J. W., *Invertebrate Structure and Function*. Boston: Houghton Mifflin
 Company, 1967, 549p.

MacGINITIE, G. E., AND N. MacGINITIE, *Natural History of Marine Animals*. New York:
 McGraw-Hill, 1949, 473p.

MEGLITSCH, P. A., *Invertebrate Zoology*. London: Oxford University Press, 1967. 961p.

RICKETTS, E. F., J. CALVIN, AND J. W. HEDGPETH, *Between Pacific Tides* (4th ed.).
 Stanford, Calif.: Stanford University Press, 1968. 614p.

SOUTHWARD, A. J., *Life on the Seashore*. Cambridge: Harvard University Press, 1965,
 153p.

YONGE, C. M., *The Seashore*. London: William Collins Publishers, Inc., 1949, 311p.

marine ecology
14

Marine ecology is the study of interrelationships among the organisms of the sea and the relation of these marine organisms to their environment. This definition is so broad that much of marine biology must be considered a part of marine *ecology.*

In this chapter, both aspects of marine ecology are presented. First, we discuss how marine organisms are adapted to environmental factors in the ocean. Second, we describe how the feeding habits of marine organisms show their interrelationships.

14.1 *Adaptations of Plant and Animal Groups to the Marine Environment*

Life has been found virtually everywhere in the sea. The myriad of species of marine organisms has survived because each species has become adapted to its environment. These adaptations involve all aspects of an organism's life, including its structure, reproductive processes, physiology, feeding habits, and movement. Each organism possesses many complex and subtle features that represent its evolutionary adaptations. A thorough discussion of so vast a subject is beyond the scope of this text, so we describe here only the broad classes of organisms in the sea. Examples are given of obvious adaptations that contribute to the success of the organisms in each group.

Phytoplankton

Marine plants, like all plants, require light. They flourish, therefore, only if they remain suspended in the photic zone long enough to grow and reproduce. The need to remain continually in the surface water of the ocean has led to several adaptations. Marine plants have little or no ability to swim. Their protoplasm is usually denser than seawater (1.02 to 1.06 g per cu cm), so they have developed ways to retard their sinking rate. These adaptations greatly influence the size, structure, and density of plants in the ocean today.

Size. The rate of sinking of an object is determined by its weight and its surface area. An object with a large surface area will settle through water more slowly than an object with the same weight but with a smaller surface area. The surface area relates to frictional retardation, and the volume is proportional to the weight of the object. An object with a large ratio between surface area and volume will sink more slowly than one equally dense but with a smaller ratio. The magnitude of the ratio is determined by size of an object; that is, the larger the volume of the object, the smaller the ratio, as shown by the following equation:

$$\text{Ratio} = \frac{\text{Area}}{\text{Volume}} = \frac{4\pi r^2}{(4\pi r^3/3)} = \frac{3}{r} \qquad [14\text{-}1]$$

Two equally dense spheres with radii of 1 mm and of 0.01 mm have ratios of 3 and 300, respectively. Thus, other factors being equal, the smaller the sphere, the slower the sinking rate.

The ratio between surface area and volume has one other important aspect. Phytoplankton obtain nutrition by passing nutrients through their surfaces. Thus, it is advantageous to have a large surface area relative to the quantity of protoplasm to be nourished (i.e., a large surface area–volume ratio).

Structure. Some of the phytoplankton have shapes and appendages that cause them to sink in nonstraight paths (Plate II). Disc-shaped diatoms, for example, sink in a zig-zag path; needle-shaped forms follow a wide circular path. In both cases, the organisms sink less rapidly than the theoretical sinking rate calculated on the basis of the mass of the organism.

Appendages or spines retard sinking by increasing the surface area of the organism. The spines on some dinoflagellates are asymmetrical in order to keep the organism oriented in such a way that its flagella can move it toward the surface.

The relative lengths of appendages can be related to water temperature. In warmer waters, where viscosity is low, appendages and spines are longer and more elaborate than in colder waters which have higher viscosity. This adaptation takes advantage of the retarding effect of viscosity upon the sinking rate of an object.

Density.   Phytoplankton adaptations to the marine environment include the constitution of the cell. Many species contain oil sacs that decrease their density. Accumulations of oil are also useful as food reservoirs while an organism awaits more favorable environmental conditions. Seasonal differences in density are observed in some species; that is, by accumulating oil, summer forms become less dense than their winter counterparts. This adjustment in density accompanies changes in water viscosity in such a way that the sinking rate does not increase. Also, density is adjusted by the exclusion of the heavier ions from the cell, thus decreasing its mass relative to the surrounding seawater.

Zooplankton

Many zooplankton species depend upon marine plants for food. Because they must remain close to the phytoplankton, many adaptations similar to those of the phytoplankton are observed. Zooplankton density is minimized by maintenance of a high-water content and by oil sacs in the body and eggs. The surface area–weight ratio is increased by small size and various appendages. The copepods, for example, possess bristles, plumes, spines, and antennae, all of which increase the body surface area and swimming ability (Fig. 14-1).

Mobility.   The zooplankton employ various means of locomotion. Copepods and euphausids swim by using muscular action. Ctenophores and marine worms have ciliary motion. Jellyfish move by jet action. Organisms can float by means of a buoyant froth, as does the barnacle, or by gas-filled floats, as in the jellyfish *Physalia.* The jellyfish *Velella* is nicknamed "by-the-wind-sailor" because of its characteristic sail (Fig. 14-2).

Daily migration.   An interesting environmental adaptation of pelagic organisms, especially the zooplankton, is the occurrence of daily vertical migrations. Investigations have shown that many of the pelagic zooplankton make daily journeys between the surface and deeper water. Although these organisms are classed as plankton, they are not completely passive, and they continually change their positions in the water column. Small plankton crustaceans can swim at rates of 16 m per hour; larger species are able to swim 95 m per hour.

The diagram in Fig. 14-3 traces the vertical distributions of the adult copepod *Calanus* throughout a 24-hour period. During the brightest part of the day, the vertical pattern of organisms is approximately diamond-shaped; the greatest

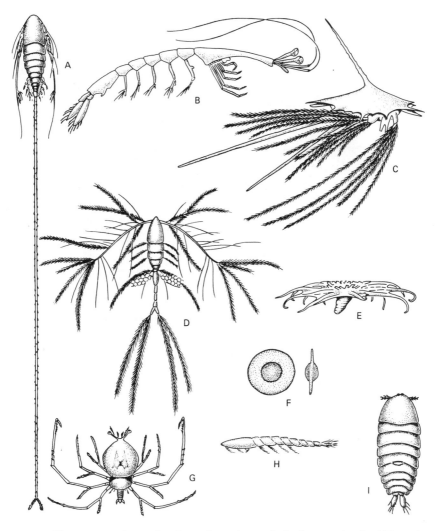

Figure 14-1 Some floating adaptations of plankton animals: (A) copepod *(Aegisthus)*; (B) decapod *(Lucifer)*; (C) barnacle nauplius; (D) copepod *(Oithona)*; (E) holothurian *(Pelagiothuria)*; (F) pelagic egg of copepod *(Tortanus)*; (G) phyllosoma larva of lobster; (H,I) copepod *(Sapphirina)*, side and dorsal views. (After Sverdrup, Johnson, and Fleming, 1942, by permission of Prentice-Hall, Inc.)

numbers occur at a depth of 15 m. The organisms begin migrating upward in late afternoon and become grouped at the surface. They are presumably feeding. Downward migration begins after midnight and is completed at noon, thus ending the daily cycle. The entire migration may extend over several hundred meters of depth. However, the vertical range shown in this figure is probably a more characteristic value.

Observations reveal that the greatest number of individuals are found at a

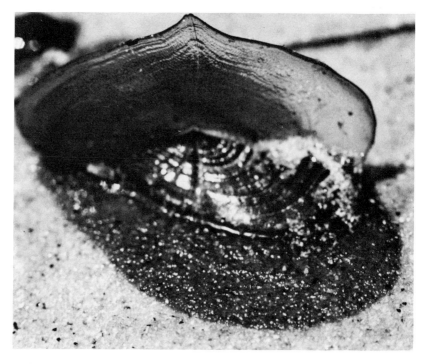

Figure 14-2 The jellyfish *Vellela sp.* floats at the sea surface and has a sail to provide a certain degree of mobility. Photograph approximately natural size. (Photograph courtesy Dora P. Henry)

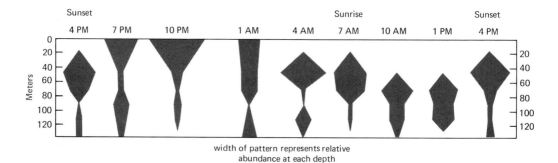

width of pattern represents relative
abundance at each depth

Figure 14-3 Vertical distribution of the adult female copepod, *Calanus finmarchicus* during a 24-hour interval. (After Nicholls, on the Biology of Calanus, which appeared in the *Journal of the Marine Biological Association*, 1933, by permission of the Cambridge University Press)

level where light and other factors are optimum. It is not known whether the light stimulates other responses (hunger or preference for a particular temperature). However, light appears to be the most important motivation; the depth of migration in winter and in summer differs as light penetration differs. In addition, the portion of the population found at a single level may consist of individuals of uniform age or sex, thus suggesting that there is a different migration pattern for each species, sex, and age. The net result is a more or less continuous, but uneven, pattern of vertical migration for the total population.

A seasonal migration pattern is also observed in certain species of the same copepod *Calanus*. At the onset of winter, they take on food reserves and sink to depths of 200 to 300 m to spend the winter months. An upward migration begins about February, and the organisms arrive in surface waters during the spring phytoplankton bloom. This cycle appears to be an adaptation to the scarcity of food (phytoplankton) at the ocean surface during winter.

Benthos

Littoral and inner sublittoral organisms. To succeed in this environment, an organism must be adapted for life under the most variable marine conditions. Temperature and salinity fluctuations of significant proportions occur on a seasonal basis. In shallow regions, such fluctuations also occur daily. The substratum may change from season to season. In addition, current and wave forces are extremely strong. Here, the problems are not food but the competition for shelter and space and the struggle against desiccation in the intertidal zone.

A prime requisite for organisms in this habitat is the physiological ability to withstand significant temperature and salinity variations. Some neritic (shallow-water) phytoplankton species form resting spores or dormant stages. This adaptation allows them to avoid adjusting to the rigors of the sublittoral environment. Other organisms have developed tolerances, becoming *eurythermal* and *euryhaline;* that is, they can withstand large temperature and salinity fluctuations.

Modifications in structure and mode of living are particularly noticeable in the organisms of the nearshore benthos. Sessile, or attached, forms predominate; they are flattened, massive, and streamlined to withstand strong currents and wave forces. These organisms must feed upon food suspended in the water. In the nearshore environment, therefore, filter feeding (straining organic particles from the water) is a highly successful adaptation, because strong currents assure a generous supply of suspended particulate matter and plankton.

The nearshore mobile forms are also sturdy and compact. Some organisms, such as sea urchins and pelecypods, can burrow into rocks; others, especially certain fish and mollusks, rely upon sucking discs to attain a degree of attachment. Barnacles attach themselves to surfaces by cementation. Mussels attach themselves with *byssus* threads that they secrete for this purpose. The mussel can detach and reattach its *byssus* threads to achieve limited locomotion. By using mucus as adhesive, certain worms cement sand grains into tubular shelters attached to rocks.

Feeding habits of these mobile organisms vary. Many, like pelecypods, are filter feeders. Others, such as some worms, sea urchins, pelecypods, and crustaceans, are deposit feeders that scavenge organic debris from rocks, sand, or mud. Predation by shore fish, crabs, birds, and starfish also occurs.

In the intertidal region, desiccation is a major problem, but there are a variety of ways for organisms to survive. Some position themselves at levels so that their exposure time coincides with their tolerance to drying. Other organisms bury themselves in the substrate or live in tide pools that retain some water at low tide. Many forms (i.e., barnacles, snails, small mussels) protect themselves from exposure by retracting into their shells. Littorinid snails form clusters to retain moisture (Fig. 14-4). Other organisms actually do dry out somewhat but replace this loss of water by absorbing more water during the next high tide. Sea urchins and sea anemones cover themselves with shell fragments while exposed (Plate IV C), although some sea anemones produce a mucous secretion that inhibits desiccation. Some forms of sessile algae and grasses form thick mats when exposed at low tide. The plants in the outer layer are sacrificial and protect the mat beneath from desiccation.

The brown algae that inhabit the inner sublittoral are especially well adapted to the rigors of the nearshore environment. To keep from being washed ashore by large waves, these plants attach themselves by a *holdfast* to rocks on the bottom. Large gas bladders float the fronds to the surface region where incident

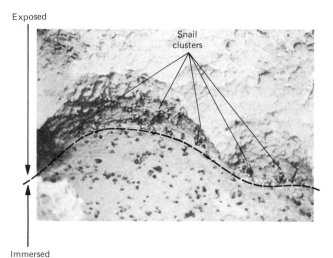

Exposed

Snail clusters

Immersed

Figure 14-4 When exposed at low tide the small *Littorinid* snails tend to cluster to retard desiccation. Those snails still underwater are dispersed while those exposed are clustered.

radiation is abundant (Fig. 12-2). These plants may grow to 80 m in length and produce thick kelp forests seaward of the surf zone in many coastal areas.

Deep-sea organisms.   There is extreme uniformity in the environment of the deep sea, so organisms have not adapted to (or have lost the ability to tolerate) wide differences in temperature and salinity. Consequently, animal and plant life in this region is *stenothermal* and *stenohaline.* An example of this lack of tolerance is the faunal assemblages on either side of the Wyville Thompson Ridge in the North Atlantic (noted in Chap. 13).

Organisms of the deep sea are not streamlined, and their skeletons are relatively frail. These characteristics reflect the lack of strong currents and wave forces in the environment. The absence of strong water motions and the low concentrations of suspended matter explain why deep-sea organisms are deposit feeders that must ingest large quantities of deep-sea sediment and digest whatever organic matter is available.

Nekton

Fishes.   Most fishes are predators that feed on highly mobile organisms. The most obvious adaptations of fishes are those that provide advantages in movement. Fishes have streamlined shapes, and some forms are covered with a slimy substance to decrease frictional resistance. Their muscles, nervous system, and sense of vision are extremely well developed. These adaptations permit fishes to expend minimal energy while hunting their prey. This ability is important, because the energy intake from food must exceed the energy used in obtaining food or the organism dies.

For protection from predators, fishes are camouflaged. They are generally blue or gray on top and light-colored underneath so that they blend with their backgrounds. Some fish, notably those in carbonate reef areas, are brighly colored and marked vividly to warn predators of their toxicity or bad taste. Others are poisonous or possess poisonous spines for protection. Surgeonfish, for example, possess sharp, knifelike bones on their sides near their tails. These bones extend when the fish is seized and serve as an effective defense weapon.

Whales.   Considered to be the most specialized of all marine mammals, whales exhibit some interesting adaptations. First, their large size and weight (100,000 kg) assures that they have few enemies. Second, several species of whales have developed a filtering mechanism made of baleen in their upper jaws and they feed on planktonic animals (Plate IX E). This adaptation is advantageous, because it does not require the expenditure of energy needed to chase fast-swimming fish. Third, whales have apparently descended from terrestrial mammals; but in the evolutionary transition, the hind legs were lost and the forelegs were modified into fins for steering during swimming. Finally, a thick layer of blubber insulates these warm-blooded animals from cold waters in the polar seas and at depths elsewhere.

Whales must breathe air at the sea surface; but they can dive to depths exceeding 1,000 m and can remain submerged for as long as an hour. This feat is made possible by the whale's ability to discontinue peripheral circulation during dives so that oxygenated blood is used only to maintain the vital organs.

The growth rate of young whales is unique in the animal kingdom. A newborn calf can be 7 m long and weigh 2,000 kg. Some species mature in 2 years. By then, the calf has increased its weight over 30,000 kg per year.

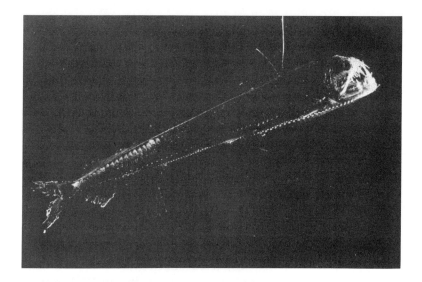

Figure 14-5A Full body and head views of the deep-sea fish *Chauliodus macouni*. Body length approximately 10 to 15 cm. (Courtesy Langton B. Quetin and Robin M. Ross)

 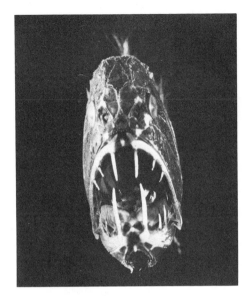

Figure 14-5B Full body and front views of the deep-sea fish *Anoplogaster cornuta*. Body length approximately 10 cm. (Photograph courtesy Langton B. Quetin and Robin M. Ross)

Bathypelagic organisms. The organisms living at depths greater than 1,000 m include crustaceans, chaetognaths, and fishes. Generally, the fishes are small (10 to 20 cm) and are colored black, black violet, or brownish. Life must be carried on in darkness, so these organisms possess many adaptations to assist them in food gathering, reproduction, and protection.

Food-procuring devices are the most evident. Some organisms have immense mouths in relation to their size, possess formidable teeth, and have elastic stomachs and abdominal walls. They can thus swallow organisms three times their size (Fig. 14-5) and enjoy a wide range in diet. In another case of adaptation, the angler fish carries its own luminous lure, which extends four times its body length, presumably for food gathering. Some lures are equipped with spines to decrease the chance of being eaten by other predators. Male angler fish that live in deep water (2,000 m) are dwarfed and are permanently attached to the females as parasites (Fig. 13-4). This bizarre adaptation assures the fertilization of eggs in an environment where the population is highly dispersed, and the search for a mate might require the expenditure of too much energy.

The eyes of bathypelagic organisms show several kinds of adaptation. Some near-bottom forms are blind or have degenerate eyes, but others have well-developed eyes. Some forms have enlarged eyes to receive the faint rays of light that reach mid-depths. For the same reason, other fishes show an increase in visual rods in the retina and even some degree of telescopic binocular vision.

Many forms of the bathypelagic fish are *bioluminescent* and have their sides lined with *photophores,* which are light-producing mechanisms. Although this mechanism is found in organisms at all depths, its advantages and uses are not definitely known. It might serve as a lure for prey, a warning for predators, a signal for the opposite sex at spawning time, or a signal for establishing territoriality among members of the same sex.

14.2   *The Marine Food Web*

The equilibrium in food energy in the ocean is visualized as a *food web,* which is a complex network of paths of food energy transfer. Each path is termed a *food chain.* Every major transfer of food energy defines a *trophic level* in the food chain. In the first level of the food web, plants manufacture organic matter. This level is called *primary production,* because solar energy and inorganic nutrients are combined into the organic matter that forms the ultimate source of food for all organisms in the sea.

The First Trophic Level

Plants complete the first step in the food web by converting inorganic nutrients into organic matter. Plants contain chlorophyll that allows them to use radiant energy from sunlight to combine carbon dioxide and water to produce carbohydrate (CH_2O) and oxygen. This process is called *photosynthesis* and is stated in Eq. 14-2. The reaction proceeds in the direction of the arrow.

$$CO_2 + H_2O \xrightarrow{\text{solar energy}} CH_2O + O_2 \qquad [14\text{-}2]$$

In this process, radiant energy from the sun is stored when low-energy inorganic compounds (CO_2 and H_2O) are converted into high-energy organic compounds (carbohydrates). Only plants can accomplish this primary production of organic matter.

All organisms obtain the energy to carry on life processes by oxidizing organic matter, a process called *respiration.* Respiration is the reverse of photosynthesis, and it proceeds according to the equation:

$$CH_2O + O_2 \longrightarrow CO_2 + H_2O + \text{energy as heat} \qquad [14\text{-}3]$$

Carbohydrate is oxidized to CO_2 and H_2O with a release of thermal energy equivalent to the amount required to produce the sugar. For example, when

180 g of carbohydrate are oxidized, 674 kcal of heat energy are released. Organisms always respire, so growth can occur only if the photosynthetic energy produced during sunlight hours exceeds the energy lost by respiration during both night and day.

Equations 14-2 and 14-3 summarize in a chemical format the gross reactions that occur during photosynthesis and respiration. This energy-capturing process is quite complex, however, and involves many steps not described by the equations. Photosynthesis takes place within the chloroplast, a subcellular element of eukaryotic plant cells. Chloroplasts contain photosynthetic pigments (e.g., chlorophyll) and enzymes. Within the chloroplast two classes of chemical reactions are observed. One class requires light energy and the other does not; thus they are called light and dark reactions. The light reactions occur on the outer membranes of the chloroplast and the dark reactions occur between inner membranes. Together, these reactions are defined as photosynthesis.

A schematic diagram of some major steps in light and dark reactions is shown in Fig. 14-6. The important aspects of the photochemical reaction include two photosynthetic pigment systems (I and II), each using different wavelengths of radiant energy and energy from the chemical breakdown of

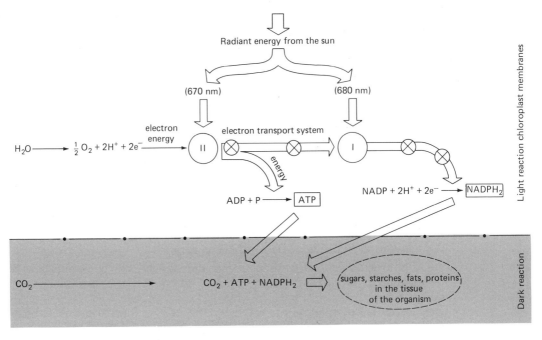

Figure 14-6 Schematic illustration of the photosynthetic process. The symbol $\otimes$ refers to other organic compounds involved in electron transfer. Broad arrows show the path of energy from the sun to the tissue of the plant.

water molecules. The System II photochemical reaction includes the splitting of water which liberates oxygen, hydrogen ions, and electrons. The electrons are transferred through a series of organic compounds which have an affinity for the electron energy. One of the byproducts of this electron transport process is the combination of the low-energy substance adenosine diphosphate (ADP) and inorganic phosphate (P) to form the high-energy substance adenosine triphosphate (ATP) as shown in Eq. 14-4.

$$ADP + P \rightarrow ATP \qquad\qquad [14\text{-}4]$$

Photosynthetic pigment System I combines energy from the electron transport process, longer wavelength radiation (680 nm), hydrogen ions, electrons, and the substance NADP (nicetinamide adenine dinucleotide phosphate) to produce a substance abbreviated as $NADPH_2$ as shown in Eq. 14-5.

$$2H^+ + NADP + 2\,e^- \rightarrow NADPH_2 \qquad\qquad [14\text{-}5]$$

Thus, the light reaction uses two wavelengths of radiant energy and water to produce two energy-rich compounds, ATP and $NADPH_2$.

The dark reaction uses ATP, $NADPH_2$, and CO_2 to synthesize a variety of organic compounds necessary for the life of the cell. The energy for this reaction is obtained from the chemical breakdown of ATP and $NADPH_2$; sunlight is not needed. This reaction is summarized in Eq. 14-6.

$$CO_2 + ATP + NADPH_2 \rightarrow \text{sugars, starches, lipids, and amino acids} \qquad [14\text{-}6]$$

In summary, the photosynthetic products that are not consumed in respiration are:

1. Converted into other forms of carbohydrate, such as glucose or cellulose for cell walls or starch for reserve food
2. Converted to lipids or fatty substances, or
3. Combined with inorganic nitrogen and phosphorus compounds to form protein.

These organic compounds are used by the cell to form the live substance, *protoplasm.* The entire process is diagrammed in Fig. 14-7.

The chemical analysis of dried phytoplankton indicates that it has the following components: carbon, 45 to 55 percent by weight; nitrogen, 4.5 to 9 percent; phosphorus, 0.6 to 3.3 percent; varying amounts of silicon (up to 25

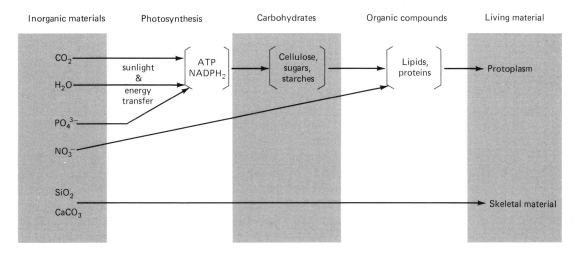

Figure 14-7 Various steps in the production of living material.

percent) or calcium carbonate (up to 25 percent), depending on the organism; and various minor elements (potassium, sodium, magnesium, calcium, and sulfur). Although these percentages vary considerably according to the organism and the state of nutrition, they do indicate the importance of the nutrient elements to the basic productivity in the sea.

In conclusion, three important deductions can be made:

1. Plants must remain in the sunlit regions of the ocean waters (i.e., the surface region) a significant portion of the time if they are to flourish.
2. During the growing season, a decrease in the nutrient concentration in stratified surface water should accompany an increase in plant growth.
3. The oxygen concentration in the surface water should increase with increased productivity if other factors remain approximately constant.

Decomposition of Organic Matter

The decomposition of waste and dead organic matter is a necessary process in the sea. It is carried out by bacteria, which convert organic compounds formed at all trophic levels into inorganic nutrients that replenish those consumed by plants at the first trophic level.

Bacteria are microscopic, one-celled organisms that are found throughout the ocean. They are usually attached to the surfaces of organic debris or to other organisms, or they may live on the sea floor. Freely suspended bacteria can be found in seawater; however, their concentration is small (on the order of 10 per cu cm).

In the presence of dissolved oxygen, bacterial remineralization proceeds as described by Eqs. 14-7 and 14-8.

$$CH_2O + O_2 \longrightarrow CO_2 + H_2O \qquad [14\text{-}7]$$

$$NH_3 + 2O_2 \longrightarrow H^+ + NO_3^- + H_2O \qquad [14\text{-}8]$$

Equation 14-7 represents the breakdown of carbohydrate by aerobic bacterial metabolism. Ammonia, NH_3, is formed by the bacterial breakdown of organic nitrogen compounds; it is also present in the excretions of zooplankton. Equation 14-8, describes the oxidation of ammonia to an inorganic nitrate nutrient. Notice that remineralization of organic matter consumes oxygen.

Remineralization completes the basic food cycle, which is shown in Fig. 14-8. In the photic zone, plants convert nutrients to organic matter. This material either sinks or is eaten by animals and carried below the photic zone. In the aphotic zone, bacteria eventually convert it back to nutrients. Nutrients are returned to the photic zone by the physical processes of diffusion and turbulent mixing. Where this process is intensified by upwelling, as along the west coast of the United States and the coast of Peru, biological production reaches some of the highest levels in the world ocean.

In basins where vertical circulation is poor, the decomposition of organic debris slowly removes oxygen from the bottom water until the processes described by Eqs. 14-7 and 14-8 can no longer occur, and *anaerobic* decomposition begins. This kind of decomposition involves the processes of *denitrification* and *sulfate reduction* (see Chap. 4). Equations for denitrification are:

$$5CH_2O + 4H^+ + 4NO_3^- \longrightarrow 2N_2 + 5CO_2 + 7H_2O \qquad [14\text{-}9]$$

$$5NH_3 + 3H^+ + 3NO_3^- \longrightarrow 4N_2 + 9H_2O \qquad [14\text{-}10]$$

and for sulfate reduction:

$$2CH_2O + 2H^+ + SO_4^{2-} \longrightarrow H_2S + 2CO_2 + 2H_2O \qquad [14\text{-}11]$$

$$NH_3 + 2H^+ + SO_4^{2-} \longrightarrow H^+ + NO_3^- + H_2S + H_2O \qquad [14\text{-}12]$$

Note that the results of these reactions are the inorganic compounds CO_2, H_2O, H_2S, and free nitrogen (N_2). Hydrogen sulfide (H_2S), produced by sulfate reduction, is toxic to most organisms. It accounts for the bad odor and lack of life in the deep portions of such stagnant basins as the Black Sea and many fiords.

The remineralization reactions complete the cycle of the generation and consumption of inorganic nutrients in the sea. Here we have considered only the first trophic level. To appreciate the cycle, we must see how other trophic levels are involved.

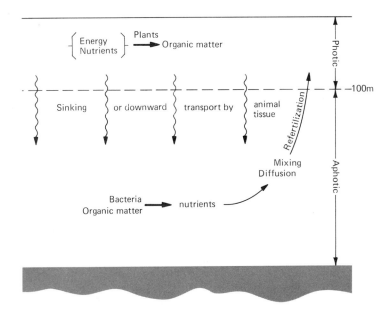

Figure 14-8 The first cycle in the food web.

Higher Levels in the Food Web

Animals cannot synthesize organic matter from inorganic substances to any appreciable extent. They must, therefore, rely on plants and other animals for their food. The primary grazers of marine plants are the zooplankton. The copepods are the largest single group of grazers. Their abundance and distribution are determined by the abundance and distribution of phytoplankton. The food relationships of other marine organisms are much more complicated. The relationships involving the herring, for example, are illustrated in Fig. 14-9, which is called a food web. This diagram shows the complex feeding relationships involved with the growth of an adult herring. Because of the varied diet of the adult herring, a number of particular food chains are intertwined into the total food web. Several food chains extracted from Fig. 14-9 are the following:

Phytoplankton—zooplankton—adult herring

Euphausid—adult herring

Phytoplankton—zooplankton—juvenile herring—adult herring

Figure 14-9 shows how animals from several trophic levels graze on phytoplankton and shows that an animal can occupy several trophic levels during its development. The figure also shows that food chains are of various lengths.

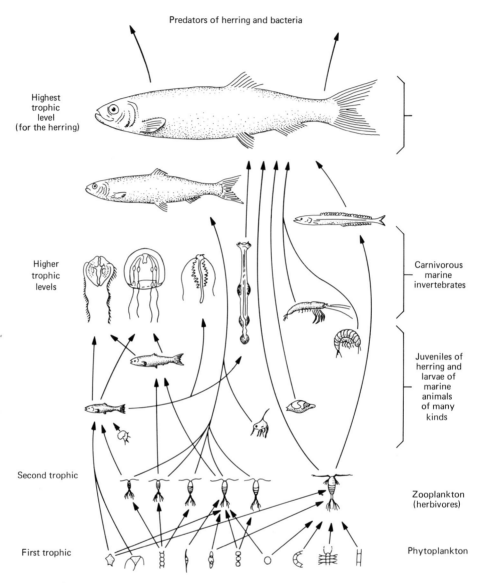

Figure 14-9 Food web of the herring at various periods of life. Organisms are not to scale. (After J.W. Hedgpeth, *Concepts of Marine Ecology;* Geological Society of American Memoir 67, 1957)

Some are short and involve only one or two transfers of food from phytoplankton to bacteria; others, as those containing the herring, involve several transfers.

Some other typical examples of food chains associated with three different oceanic communities are given in Table 14-1. The examples in Table 14-1 illustrate food transfers to higher trophic levels. This process can also be

Table 14–1   Examples of Food Chains for Three Oceanic Fisheries

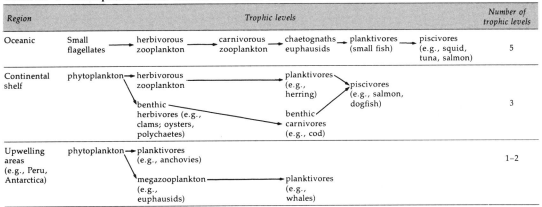

Region	Trophic levels	Number of trophic levels
Oceanic	Small flagellates → herbivorous zooplankton → carnivorous zooplankton → chaetognaths euphausids → planktivores (small fish) → piscivores (e.g., squid, tuna, salmon)	5
Continental shelf	phytoplankton → herbivorous zooplankton / benthic herbivores (e.g., clams; oysters, polychaetes); planktivores (e.g., herring), benthic carnivores (e.g., cod) → piscivores (e.g., salmon, dogfish)	3
Upwelling areas (e.g., Peru, Antarctica)	phytoplankton → planktivores (e.g., anchovies) / megazooplankton (e.g., euphausids) → planktivores (e.g., whales)	1–2

illustrated by considering the flow of energy through the ecosystem. Energy is fixed by the photosynthetic processes (at the lowest trophic level) and supplies all higher trophic levels. At any trophic level the food energy consumed is used for growth, reproduction, maintenance of life (respiration), or is excreted. Energy stored as animal or plant tissue is available to the next trophic level for its metabolic processes; however, only a small part of the total energy consumed by an organism is used in the production of tissue. The *ecological efficiency* of a food chain is defined as:

$$E = \frac{\text{Energy actually used to form tissues at a trophic level}}{\text{Total energy transferred to the trophic level from a lower trophic level}}$$

which is a ratio of the energy transferred upward to a trophic level to the total energy supplied. Estimates of a number of food chains show that the ecological efficiency varies from about 5 percent for mammals to 20 percent for zooplankton and may reach 30 to 45 percent for some stages of copepod growth. An ecological efficiency of 10 to 20 percent appears to be an average value. This means that 10 to 20 percent of the total food energy supplied to a given trophic level is used in the production of tissue and may become food for a higher level.

An organism, such as the herring, is dependent upon a huge number of phytoplankton for its growth. If this food chain has four steps and we assume a 10 percent ecological efficiency, a metric ton of herring would consume 1,000 metric tons of phytoplankton, as illustrated by the following diagram:

$$1{,}000{,}000 \text{ kg} \rightarrow 100{,}000 \text{ kg} \rightarrow 10{,}000 \text{ kg} \rightarrow 1{,}000 \text{ kg (1 metric ton)}$$
phytoplankton   zooplankton   juvenile herring   herring

Table 14–2   Estimated Fish Production for the Oceanic Communities Given in Table 14–1

Community	Oceanic	Continental shelf	Upwelling area
Estimated primary productivity g C/m²/yr	50	100	300
Percent ocean area (total area 362 × 10¹²km²)	90	9.9	0.1
Total plant production 10¹²kg C/yr	16.3	3.6	0.1
Number trophic levels (Table 14–1)	5	3	1.5
Ecological efficiency (%)	10	15	20
Estimated fish production 10⁹ kg/yr	0.2	12	12

(Adapted from J. H. Ryther, "Photosynthesis and Fish Production in the Sea," *Science* 166 (1969), 72–76)

A comparison of the productivity of the three oceanic communities given in Table 14-1 is presented in Table 14-2. This estimate uses average primary productivity values and assumes a 20 percent ecological efficiency for the shorter food chain (zooplankton-dominated) and a 10 percent efficiency for the longer food chain (dominated by fish). This simplified calculation illustrates the variations in fish production that might occur in oceanic communities depending on total area, primary productivity, ecological efficiency, and the food chain relationships. Note that over 90 percent of the fish production occurs within less than 10 percent of the ocean area; this illustrates the importance of primary productivity to the world's fisheries.

The total primary production of phytoplankton in the world ocean is estimated to be 135×10^{12} kg per year. This figure is close to the annual production of plants on land. The annual harvest of fish is 50×10^9 kg, although the potential yield could reach 180×10^9 kg, based on an overall average of a three-step food chain.

Only a small portion of the net production of the sea—that is, the fish—is readily available to humans. Fishes, however, are in the higher trophic levels. Compared to the plankton at the lower levels, fishes have small populations and slow reproductive rates. They are captured for human consumption because they yield the most food for the least expenditure of energy. An improved efficiency in obtaining food from the sea is possible if fisheries with a shorter food chain are developed. For every trophic level eliminated, seven to ten times more protein is available from the plant material formed at the first trophic level. Thus, it is much more efficient to develop and maintain the sardine, anchovy, and mackerel fisheries than to rely on tuna or cod to feed the world. The Peru anchovy fish industry, the largest catch of an individual species in the world, is a good example of a short food chain with high productivity (Table 14-2). It would be still better to use zooplankton for our basic source of protein, such as the immense euphausid stocks in Antarctica. Euphausids represent a very short food chain and high ecological efficiency.

14.3 *The Annual Cycle of Phytoplankton*

At the first two trophic levels, there is a tendency for supply and demand in the food chain to reach a balance that maintains fairly constant amounts of phytoplankton and zooplankton at any part of the ocean. The balance is easily upset, however, because of changes caused by other environmental factors. The most significant changes occur seasonally, resulting in cyclic abundance of phytoplankton. The environmental factors causing this annual cycle are: (1) the amount of incident sunlight, (2) the concentration and supply of nutrients in the surface water, (3) the thickness of the layer of surface water mixed by the wind, and (4) the abundance of zooplankton that graze upon phytoplankton.

General Environmental Factors

Sunlight. The amount of solar radiation striking the sea surface depends upon the season and upon geographic latitude. The extent of seasonal variations in irradiation also depends upon the latitude. In the ocean at high latitude, seasonal variation in sunlight is extreme, and so phytoplankton are able to grow for only a short period. In the tropics, there is always ample sunlight for phytoplankton growth because seasonal changes in solar radiation are minimal.

Nutrients. These substances are consumed from seawater in the photic zone as phytoplankton growth proceeds. If nutrients are not replenished from below the pycnocline, where most of the bacterial remineralization takes place, the nutrients become depleted, and phytoplankton growth is limited. Replenishment occurs by molecular diffusion from below and, most importantly, by turbulent mixing.

Mixed layer. During storms, wind-generated waves and surface wind stress produce turbulence in surface water. The thickness of the layer of turbulent mixing depends upon the frequency and intensity of storms and the degree of stability of the water column. Both storms and differences in density stratification occur seasonally, so the thickness of the mixed layer also varies seasonally. Phytoplankton are kept in suspension by the turbulence in the mixed layer. If the turbulence is so intense that mixing extends below the photic zone, phytoplankton will be swept down to a region of insufficient sunlight for a period long enough to kill them. On the other hand, such intense mixing will bring remineralized nutrients from below into the photic zone.

Grazing by zooplankton.   A seasonal increase in the abundance of phytoplankton increases the food supply for grazers, in turn leading to seasonal increases in the zooplankton population. As grazing increases, the population of phytoplankton is reduced and less food is available to the zooplankton.

The seasonal variations of the environment produce a corresponding imbalance between phytoplankton and grazing zooplankton. The shifts in the equilibrium of the plankton community are represented by the yearly cycle of diatoms shown in Fig. 14-9. However, the pattern of phytoplankton growth is not uniform over the entire ocean because the environmental factors and the way they are disrupted vary with location.

Environmental Factors in the Open Ocean (Oceanic Environment)

Tropical regions.   Low-latitude portions of the world ocean (between 30° north and 30° south latitude) are characterized by high incident solar radiation and a strong, permanent pycnocline. There is adequate sunlight throughout the year, but strong vertical mixing does not occur, and so the mixed layer cannot be refertilized. As a result, plant production in this region remains at a low level throughout the year.

The only variation in this pattern is at the equatorial divergence (see Chap. 8) where nutrient-rich subsurface water wells up into the sunlight (Fig. 8-12). This water supports ten times the plant production of the adjacent tropical water.

Temperate regions.   Between 30° and 55° latitude, the productivity may vary as shown in Fig. 14-10. The phytoplankton population is smallest in the winter, because the light is insufficient and the mixed layer is deep. In high latitudes, the seasonal pycnocline is destroyed as temperatures decrease and winter storms drive vertical circulation deep into the water column. The surface water becomes fertilized by mixing with the nutrient-rich water below.

In the spring, several important changes occur. Illumination increases, winter storms subside, and the weather becomes warmer. With the advent of a stratified water column, more sunlight, and more abundant nutrients, phytoplankton proliferate in a spring bloom.

During the summer season, the marine plant population decreases again. Nutrient-depleted surface water cannot be refertilized, because the highly stratified water cannot be mixed. Grazing reduces the population. Even though sunlight is at a maximum, the population cannot regenerate itself because of the deficiency of nutrients.

In the autumn, stability decreases as the surface water cools. If an isolated

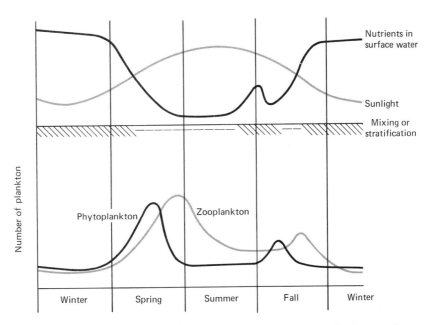

Figure 14-10 A schematic diagram of yearly phytoplankton and zooplankton production occurring in temperate latitudes. Yearly changes in nutrient concentration and sunlight are also included.

autumn storm stirs the surface but does not completely destroy the seasonal pycnocline, the surface water can be refertilized. Daily illumination, although decreasing, is still sufficient to promote an autumn bloom. If autumn storms continue and are strong, mixing extends below the photic zone and the bloom is deterred. The occurrence and magnitude of autumn blooms vary from year to year, depending on the weather.

Polar regions. The growth pattern at high latitudes is similar to that in temperate regions, but is more variable. The growing season is shorter, and storms are more frequent and more intense. A spring bloom occurs after the ice pack melts. Often there is no fall bloom because of adverse climatic conditions.

Under the permanent ice pack, there is but one bloom per year. During July and August, the snow cover disappears, and sufficient sunlight penetrates the ice to allow plant growth.

Environmental Factors
on the Continental Margins
(Neritic Environment)

The annual pattern of productivity on the continental shelf is unique. Nearly all of the water column is penetrated by sunlight, and nutrients remineralized by bacteria on the seabed are accessible when mixing occurs. As a result, nutrient depletion is not nearly as critical as in the open ocean, and productivity is considerably higher.

In tropical regions, productivity is high throughout the year. In temperate regions, the spring bloom is produced by increased sunlight and accumulation of winter nutrients. A significant summer bloom occurs when bacterial regeneration increases. In addition, coastal upwelling, caused by favorable winds (Chap. 8) produces extremely large productivity peaks. The daily productivity in some coastal upwelling areas is 100 times that in the tropical regions of the open ocean.

14.4 *Some Theoretical Aspects of Food-Chain Relationships*

Biological oceanographers are interested in knowing precisely how the variables associated with biological productivity in the sea interact. The size of a population and environmental factors can be related within a theoretical framework to predict the phytoplankton population at any given time. Several extremely simplified theoretical models have been proposed; even the simpler models depict rather well the changes observed in phytoplankton population during the seasons.

One example of a simple model is given in Eq. 14-13:

$$\text{Rate of change of population size} = (P_h - R - G)P \qquad [14\text{-}13]$$

This equation states that the rate of change in the total phytoplankton population at any instant is proportional to the size of the phytoplankton population (P) at that instant. The factor of proportionality is the coefficient of photosynthesis (P_h) minus a coefficient of respiration (R) minus a coefficient of grazing (G). $P_h - R$ is a measure of the net biological growth of the population and is related to the incident radiation, transparency of the water, nutrient supply, depth of the mixed layer, and the water temperature. The grazing coefficient (G) is related to the size and nature of the herbivore population. Phytoplankton population monitored on a seasonal basis in several areas has been compared with the theoretical predictions, and the results are surprisingly good (Fig. 14-11).

Another model, analogous to Eq. 14-13 but applicable to herbivore populations, is given in Eq. 14-14.

$$\text{Rate of change of population size} = (A - R - C - D)\,H \qquad [14\text{-}14]$$

This equation states that the rate of change of herbivore population size is proportional to the size of the herbivore population (H). The factor of propor-

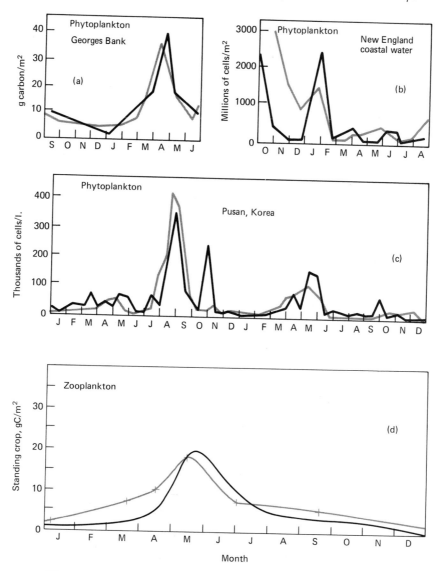

Figure 14-11 Comparison of observed seasonal cycles of phytoplankton (a,b,c) and zooplankton (d) (solid lines) with theoretical cycles (shaded lines). (a,b,c courtesy *Journal of Marine Research*; d, after Riley, 1947)

tionality includes the rate of assimilation of food (*A*) minus the rate of herbivore respiration (*R*) minus the predation rate by carnivores (*C*) minus the death rate from other causes (*D*). The coefficients in the above equation are shown as simple letters, but mathematical relationships have been developed to simulate each of the above processes. A comparison of the model prediction with measurements made over an annual period is shown in Fig. 14-11.

Indeed, with successful theoretical models, we can extend our understanding of ecological relations beyond the facts obtained by observation alone. Models of a more complex nature are being investigated by oceanographers, and they represent an important part of the study of marine ecology. One technique of ecosystem modeling is presented here to illustrate the point. The modeling technique is applied in three steps:

1. *Formulation of the model:* This step serves to define the system and provides a means of understanding the array of components recognized in the system.
2. *Mathematical description of the system:* This step provides a formal relationship of all the recognized parts of the system. It provides a means of identifying which parts of the systems are most important and which can be neglected for the sake of simplicity. It also suggests how sensitive the system response is to changes within the system.
3. *Solution of the mathematic model:* This step allows us to test desired environmental changes by introducing them into the equations that describe the model. The results represent predicted changes in the system.

As useful as it often is, environmental modeling does not always produce complete mathematical results. In some cases the system boundaries cannot be defined adequately; in other cases, the mathematical model is so complex that the describing equations cannot be solved. Nevertheless, much insight can be gained by performing the first step alone; often, valid qualitative predictions can be obtained that are quite useful in environmental planning and management. The remainder of this chapter will demonstrate how the first step is performed.

The procedure in formulating a conceptual ecological model is illustrated by means of the grossly simplified ecosystem shown in Fig. 14-12. The system consists of the upper layers of the open ocean where phytoplankton photosynthesize, consuming CO_2 and nutrients. Zooplankton graze on the phytoplankton, and bacteria convert dead organic matter into dissolved nutrient ions. Phosphate is the system aspect being modeled.

1. First we decide what particular aspects of the system are to be studied, observed, or predicted. The fewer chosen, the better. For example, it might be easier to keep track of or predict changes in dissolved oxygen than it would be to consider several species of algae that produce the oxygen.
2. Next, the system of interest is designated by a boundary chosen to include only those factors thought to be important to the aspect being studied. In the example in Fig. 14-12, the atmosphere is excluded because it is not involved in the marine phosphate cycle. The sea floor is not

A conceptual model of phosphate in the sea

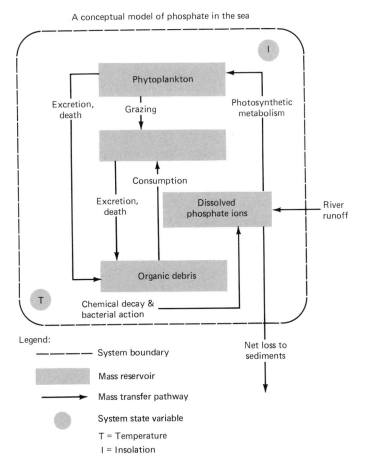

Legend:

— — — — System boundary

Mass reservoir

⟶ Mass transfer pathway

System state variable

T = Temperature

I = Insolation

Figure 14-12 Diagrammatic representation of a simplified marine ecosystem. Phosphate is the aspect being modeled.

included because we are not interested in processes affecting phosphate in marine sediments; we can sufficiently account for marine sediment phosphate lost from the system by a transfer of mass across the system boundary. The symbol for the system boundary is shown as a heavy dashed line.

3. We then place within the system boundary symbols that describe the distribution of mass (or energy) within the system. The distribution is shown by identifying the series of reservoirs where mass tends to accumulate. We use a separate reservoir for each form of mass recognized. The symbol for a reservoir is a rectangle in Fig. 14-12. The form of mass being stored in the reservoir is noted within the rectangle. All other mass that is required in the system (for example, O_2 or CO_2) is considered to

exist in infinite reservoirs. The validity of the model relies upon the validity of assumptions regarding infinite reservoirs. In actuality, no reser.·oir is truly infinite.

4. Mass is transferred across system boundaries and between reservoirs. Transfer pathways are depicted by arrows labeled with the name of the appropriate transfer process. Pathways must be chosen to account for all major mass transfer within-the system and major transfer across system boundaries. Choices are made by answering the following questions:

   a. Is there a pathway between any one reservoir and all other reservoirs in the system? We eliminate only those known to be impossible.

   b. Is mass being added to the system? There may be more than one pathway for adding mass.

   c. Is mass being removed or lost from the system? Likewise, there might be more than one pathway involved.

   d. Are the remaining pathways significant? Some pathways exist but are of little consequence in the system. Zooplankton surely ingest dissolved nutrients, but this is hardly a major pathway so it is not included in Fig. 14-12.

   e. Are there opposing pathways between any pair of reservoirs or across the system boundaries? If so, it is advantageous to combine them into a single, net-effect pathway. Phosphate exchanges between seawater and marine sediments, but the pathway is shown in Fig. 14-12 as a net loss. On the other hand, pathways that provide opposing transfer of mass by distinctly different means are not combined. Zooplankton eat organic debris and also form organic debris; hence, two opposing pathways are included in Fig. 14-12. Note that both death and excretion are combined in a single pathway in this figure. This is done to simplify the diagram.

5. Lastly, the environmental variables that describe the state of the system must be specified. State variables, as we call them, are those properties that control the *rates* at which mass transfers along the various pathways through the system. State variables are depicted by appropriate uppercase letters placed in circles drawn within the system. Temperature, insolation (amount of incident radiant energy), salinity, pressure, and flow are commonly used state variables; only temperature and insolation are important in the model in Fig. 14-12.

The most powerful physical relationship that can be applied in interpreting a conceptual model is the law of conservation. This law states that the mass transferred *into* a system must equal that transferred *out* or else there is a change (an accumulation or a net withdrawal) in the amount of mass within the system. An equivalent law applies if energy is being modeled.

If it is possible to specify the system such that it is closed (no mass is transferred across the system boundaries at all)* or such that there can be no *net* transfer across the boundaries, then the law of conservation can be applied to the reservoirs within the system. This means that an increase in mass in one reservoir *must* be balanced by a decrease in one or more of the other reservoirs in the system.

Another powerful relationship that aids the interpretation of a conceptual model is *dynamic equilibrium*. It is assumed that the conceptual model as diagrammed represents the system in a state of dynamic equilibrium. This means that the rates of transfer of mass along all pathways in the system are in balance, and no mass will accumulate in certain reservoirs and be depleted in others as long as the system is left as is. The dynamic equilibrium in the system is strongly dependent upon the system state variables because these control the transfer rates.

If the rate of transfer of mass along a pathway is altered, either by a change in a state variable or by disruption of the pathway, the trend of the adjustments that occur in the system can be predicted. For example, a decrease in insolation in the system shown in Fig. 14-12 will have the following effects:

1. Plant photosynthetic activity will decrease, so phytoplankton will reduce their rate of consumption of dissolved phosphate. This will cause the mass in the "dissolved phosphate ions" reservoir to increase because the only other pathway that removes phosphate loss to sediments is not sensitive to insolation and continues at the same rate.
2. Zooplankton activity will remain unchanged, so the transfer of phosphate along the "grazing" pathway will continue. Also, transfers along the "consumption" pathway and along the "excretion, death" pathways will remain the same. This means that phosphate will be transferred to the "organic debris" reservoir. Chemical decay and bacterial action will convert the debris into dissolved phosphate. The net effect is an increase of mass in the "dissolved phosphate ions" reservoir.

If the "photosynthesis" pathway is removed altogether, the changes described above would continue until the "phytoplankton" reservoir is empty. The "zooplankton" reservoir would become virtually empty because of starvation of grazers and because organic debris, although recycled by zooplankton, would eventually be converted to dissolved phosphate ions. Most of the phosphate would tend to accumulate in the "dissolved ion" reservoir; also the net loss of phosphate to the sediments could be expected to increase. The model described on the preceding pages is rather simplistic. It is possible to combine several system aspects on a single diagram. This has been done in

---

*Actually, the only truly closed system is the universe, as far as we know. Nevertheless, we use the principle of a closed system where exchanges across the system boundaries are small enough to be neglected.

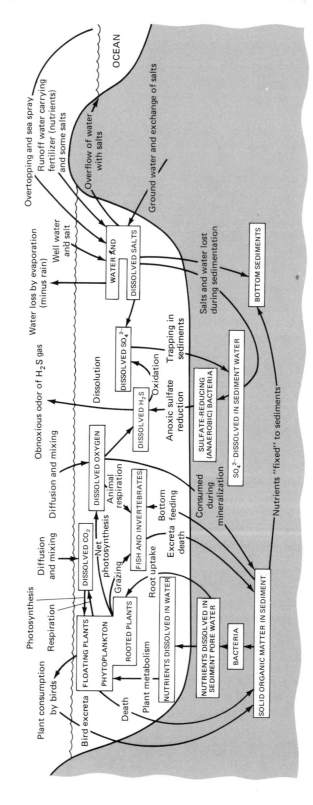

Figure 14-13 System model of a coastal pond. (After Oceanographic Services, Inc.)

Fig. 14-13, a model of several aspects of a coastal pond. The result is somewhat more realistic but considerably more complex. Writing and solving the mathematical equations that define the formal relationships between reservoir size and transfer rates is extremely difficult in such a case. Nonetheless, the model is useful in understanding how such a pond can be managed. For example, means of controlling the obnoxious odor of H_2S at the pond can be deduced by considering the reservoirs and pathways leading to the dissolved SO_4^{2-} reservoir.

reading list

DOWDESWELL, W. H., *Animal Ecology* (2nd ed.). New York: Harper & Row, Pub., 1961. 209p.

HEDGPETH, J. W., AND H. S. LADD, *Treatise on Marine Ecology and Paleoecology,* Vols. I: *Ecology*, Geological Society of America Memoir No. 67. New York, 1957. 1296p.

JORGENSEN, C. B., *Biology of Suspension Feeding*. Elmsford, N.Y.: Pergamon Press, 1966. 357p.

MOORE, H. B., *Marine Ecology*. New York: John Wiley, 1958. 493p.

PARSONS, T., AND M. TAKAHASHI, *Biological Oceanographic Processes*. Oxford: Pergamon Press, 1973. 186p.

RILEY, G. A., "A Theoretical Analysis of the Zooplankton Population of Georges Bank," *Journal of Marine Research* 6 (1947), 104–113.

STEEL, J. H., *The Structure of Marine Ecosystems*. London: Harvard University Press, 1974. 128p.

SUMICH, J. L., *Biology of Marine Life*. Dubuque, Iowa: Wm. C. Brown, 1976. 348p.

WILSON, D. P., *Life of the Shore and Shallow Sea*. London: Ivor Nicholson & Watson, Ltd., 1935. 150p.

marine sediments
15

Layers of sediments at the bottom of the sea reflect physical, chemical, geological, and biological processes in the world ocean. Geographic factors are also evident in the diversity of sediments that exists on the bottom, but this remarkable diversity usually goes unnoticed because it is hidden beneath the water. Other evidence of diversity exists, however. Everyone knows that beaches are rocky or sandy and that tidal flats are usually a sticky mud. A careful observer may also notice that the sand on the wet portion of some broad beaches is quite firm and can easily support an automobile (Fig. 15–1). Yet under the water, especially in the surf, the same sand is quite loose and yields under the weight of a person. Children are quick to notice this fact and make a sport of twisting their feet to bury them in the sand.

In addition, the coarseness and color of sand are frequently different on adjacent beaches in the same area. There are, of course, differences in sands on the various coasts of the world ocean. Variations in the grain size and color of the sediments also occur offshore. The sediments in the ocean depths are claylike and very sticky at the sea floor itself, but somewhat firmer in layers below.

The most obvious features of marine sediments are their bulk properties. Besides color and texture, the degree of *compaction* is significant. Sands are either loose-packed or close-packed, depending upon whether they are stirred by turbulence in the surf or moved to and fro by waves washing on the beach. Claylike sediments become more compact as they are buried and as *interstitial* water is expelled by the weight of overlying particles. If we study only the

Figure 15-1 Photo of cars on the beach at Daytona, Florida. (From Daytona Chamber of Commerce)

bulk properties of marine sediments, however, we usually do not find an explanation for the diversity of marine sediments. Consequently, it is necessary to analyze (i.e., separate into component parts) the sediments of the ocean bottom. Once this procedure is accomplished, each component can be examined to discover what a marine sediment is, why it appears as it does, and why it occurs where it is found.

15.1 *The Components of Marine Sediments and Their Distribution*

Examination of the sediments on the ocean bottom reveals that they are composed of a variety of solid materials that can be grouped into five categories on the basis of their sources. These categories, or components, are *terrigenous, biological, extraterrestrial (cosmic),* submarine *volcanic,* and *chemical.* The number and kinds of components represented in a particular sediment depend upon the location of that sediment in the world ocean, so they are indicative of the origin of the sediment. Terrigenous and biological components are by far the most abundant in marine sediment. However, the other sediment-producing components are important locally.

Terrigenous Components

Terrigenous components are produced by the weathering and erosion of rocks.* These rock remanents are transported to the ocean by rivers, wind, and ice. Most of this material is derived ultimately from continental masses by the processes of chemical and physical weathering. During weathering, each of the rock-forming minerals behaves somewhat differently. Calcite dissolves almost totally. Ferromagnesian minerals decompose and yield dissolved silica, clays, and other dissolved materials. Mica and feldspar behave similarly, except that mica reacts a bit more slowly, and feldspar more slowly still. Quartz is unaffected except for slight solution. Most accessory minerals are practically unaffected. When weathering has been virtually completed, the rock is reduced to (1) quartz particles in sizes from 1 mm to 0.05 mm in diameter, (2) *clay* particles (aluminosilicates) that are 0.002 mm or less in diameter, (3) accessory minerals in sizes similar to quartz, and (4) aqueous solution.

The solid products of weathering are smashed and ground into finer sizes as they are transported by rivers. In addition, winds may blow the finer materials directly into the ocean. At high latitudes, soil and rock fragments may freeze in the glaciers, which then move this material to the ocean. The combined destruction and removal of the original rock is termed *erosion*. In some cases, however, there may be no weathering and erosion at all. For example, volcanoes that erupt on land discharge rock dust (called ash) that is borne by the wind to the ocean.

The products of all these processes form the terrestrial components of marine sediments. They either make their way to the ocean bottom as a shower of discrete particles, or are transported by waves and currents, or are part of a *turbidity flow*, which is a submarine "river" of sedimentary materials flowing from the site of a submarine slide or some other event (for example, flooded rivers).

During their transportation in streams, rivers, and in the ocean, terrestrial components tend to be graded according to size and density. The sizes of sedimentary materials are classified as in Table 15–1. Because large particles are more difficult to pick up and transport than fine particles, large particles settle out of a water column sooner. Table 15–2 shows the effect of size on the settling rate. Similarly, dense mineral grains settle sooner than less dense grains, such as quartz. The concept of grading is a fundamental one in marine

---

*Definitions and descriptions of important rocks and minerals are given in the Appendix.

Table 15–1   Size Classification of Sedimentary Materials*

Name	Grade limits (diameter in mm)
Boulder	>256
Cobble	256–64
Pebble	64–4
Granule	4–2
Very coarse sand	2–1
Coarse sand	1–1/2
Medium sand	1/2–1/4
Fine sand	1/4–1/8
Very fine sand	1/8–1/16
Silt	1/16–1/256
Clay	<1/256

Mud—a term used for a mixture of silt and clay-sized particles with varying amounts of sand and organic debris

*From W. C. Krumbein and F. J. Pettijohn, *Manual of Sedimentary Petrography*. New York: Appleton-Century-Crofts, 1938, p. 80.

Table 15–2   Settling of Sedimentary Materials*

Diameter	Rate of settling in sea water ($S = 34‰$, $T = 10°$ C)	Distance traveled in sinking 1,000 m through a current of 1 cm/sec
Very fine sand (0.1 mm)	1472 cm/hr	2.4 km
Silt (0.05 mm)	31	116
Clay (0.001 mm)	0.147	24,500

After J. Gilluly, A. C. Waters, and A. O. Woodford, *Principles of Geology*. San Francisco: W. H. Freeman and Co., 1957. 631p.

geology because it relates the distribution of grain size, density, and composition of terrigenous components to the processes of transportation and sedimentation that have influenced the formation of a sediment deposit.

The principle of density grading applies to wind-carried terrigenous components. The wind is less effective than water as a carrying agent, so only the finest materials (silt and clay-sized materials) can be carried for an appreciable distance. The net effect is that considerable amounts of small materials are carried quite far by high-altitude winds. Windborne quartz fragments that occur in deep-ocean sediments are concentrated at 30° north latitude. This zone contains most of the world's deserts, areas where wind erosion and wind transport are quite pronounced. It is significant that the amount of quartz in

Figure 15-2A The LeCone glacier in Alaska transports large amounts of rock debris to the sea.

Figure 15-2B Some rocks on the sea floor are distributed in a central cluster of large rocks surrounded by smaller ones. The pattern is probably the final disposition of a load of glacial debris dumped by a mass of ice. (Photograph courtesy U.S. Naval Research Laboratory)

sediments decreases below the upper layers. We can thus conclude that deserts were not as widespread in the past as they are today and that climate in the Tertiary period was more humid than at present.

Glaciers dump undifferentiated material of all sizes, from clay to boulders, into the sea along a glaciated coast (Fig. 15–2A). These terrigenous components are found in patches close to the points where the glaciers enter the ocean. Icebergs, however, can cause *rafting* of all sizes of material, because they break off glaciers and can drift a long way. By this means, *erratic* glacial material can be part of the terrestrial component of marine sediment that is formed at a considerable distance from a continent (Fig. 15–2B).

Biologic Components

The other major sediment-forming component is of biological or organic origin. Some plants and animals living in the surface waters of the ocean have skeletons that sink to the bottom when the organisms die or reproduce. These skeletons become part of the marine sediment. The most important organisms of the sort are (1) globigerinids, microscopic animals having a shell or *test* of calcium carbonate; (2) diatoms, plants having skeletons or *frustules* of silica; (3) radiolarians, animals having a test of silica; (4) pteropods, animals having a calcareous shell; (5) coccolithophores, algae that secrete a skeleton made of tiny plates of calcium carbonate; and (6) the extinct *Discoasters*. Examples of these organisms are illustrated in Plates II and III in Chap. 12.

Other organisms contribute only very small quantities to the biological component of marine sediment. Protoplasm from marine organisms sometimes contributes 1 to 2 percent of the material in marine sediment. In areas where the supply of organic tissue is large and where decomposition on the bottom is not complete (e.g., in an anoxic environment), organic debris is abundant and the sediment that forms is called a *sapropel*. Marine algae, such as *Porolithon* and *Halimeda* (Fig. 15–3), secrete skeletal structures of calcium carbonate, and they contribute considerable amounts of biological material in certain shallow tropical regions of the world ocean. On a local basis, shell material from pelecypods and gastropods is an important biologic component (Fig. 11–15A).

Biological components of marine sediments are introduced into the ocean wherever sediment-producing organisms live. The distribution of these sediments depends upon (1) the life requirements of these organisms, (2) the chemistry of their skeletons, and (3) the depth of the water into which the remains settle.

The life requirements of an organism include, among other things, the chemical and physical properties of seawater. Because these properties are not distributed uniformly in the world ocean, particular organisms flourish in certain areas and are scarce in others.

In a similar way, water depth and body chemistry affect distribution of

Figure 15-3 The calcareous segments of the alga *Corallina*. Each plate is approximately 2 mm long. (Photograph courtesy Kent Cambridge Scientific)

biological components. Generally, sediments containing calcareous material are not found below a depth of about 4,800 m. Siliceous material disappears at a slightly greater depth. The low temperature, high pressure, and high CO_2 content (produced by the decomposition of protoplasm) of bottom water, and the activity of bottom-dwelling organsims lead to the dissolution of these materials. It is also generally observed that individual marine sediment samples rarely are rich in both siliceous and calcareous biologic components. In most cases, the reason is the geographical restriction of siliceous organisms.

Extraterrestrial Components

It is estimated that each day many tons of meteorites and cosmic dust fall on the surface of the earth. The cosmic material that falls into the ocean is often identifiable as magnetic spherules. Figure 15–4 shows a photomicrograph of such spherules. In addition, the nickel content of some sediments suggests

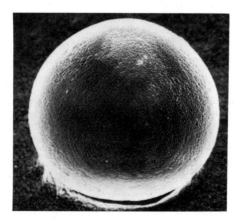

Figure 15-4 Photomicrograph of a magnetic cosmic spherule found in sediments of the equatorial Atlantic Ocean. The spherule is 280 μ in diameter and is estimated to be 900,000 years old. (Photograph courtesy Dr. B. P. Glass)

that they contain appreciable amounts of cosmic dust. In some regions, extraterrestrial materials form an important component of marine sediments. Nevertheless, this does not indicate that meteorites or cosmic dust necessarily fall more often into these regions. Because of the way in which extraterrestrial components are introduced into the ocean, they are not restricted to any particular regions; they can occur on any part of the ocean bottom.

Submarine Volcanic Components

Volcanoes have been observed erupting from the sea floor off Japan, off the western coast of Europe, off the Pacific coast of Mexico, and off the coast of Iceland (Fig. 15–5). Near volcanic islands, volcanic rock debris that ranges from ash to boulders of considerable size are added to marine sediment layers. The ash is often grayish white to tan and is usually glassy when fresh. Larger rock fragments are usually dark gray to black (basaltic) and lack a vitreous or glassy appearance.

Since volcanic components enter the world ocean after local eruptions, these

Figure 15-5 A submarine volcanic eruption forms a new island called Surtsey near Iceland. (Photograph courtesy Icelandic Airlines)

components are found in abundance only in submarine volcanic provinces (Fig. 2–16). In the South China Sea, ash from the 1883 explosion of Krakatoa is recognized even today. Ash from the 1912 Katmai eruption is used to correlate marine sediment strata in the Gulf of Alaska. Two eruptions of the Santorini volcano north of Crete in the Aegean Sea can be traced in sediments of the eastern part of the Mediterranean Sea. The upper ash layer in this area resulted from an eruption less than 5,000 years ago (possibly the origin of the Atlantis legend). The lower ash layer occurred 25,000 years ago and has a wider distribution eastward toward Sicily. Often ash deposits become altered by submarine weathering so that volcanic components are recognized by the presence of an assemblage of clay minerals (montmorillonite), phillipsite, and palagonite, a yellowish brown to deep brown material consisting of a mixture of fresh and altered basaltic glass (Fig. 15–6).

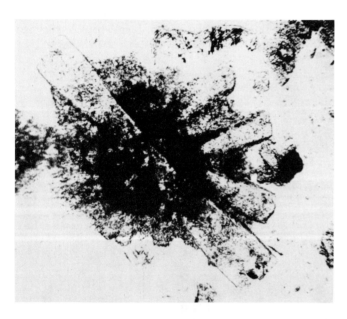

Figure 15-6 Basaltic glass with needles of zeolite and phillipsite radiating from it. It is believed phillipsite and montmorillonite are formed by the devitrification of hydrated basaltic glass. Magnification × 190. (Courtesy E. Bonatti, University of Miami)

Chemical Components

Under some circumstances, dissolved rock material brought into the sea will not remain dissolved. Eventually, it precipitates as a solid and forms a chemical component of marine sediment. The metal-rich manganese nodules (shown in Fig. 15–7A) and the minerals dolomite and aragonite are examples. The mineral phillipsite, previously mentioned as a chemical product of volcanic glass, is also included in this category. If minerals are formed chemically in the places where they are found, the process is called mineral *authigenesis* and the

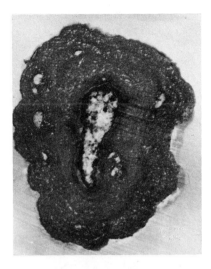

Figure 15-7A A section through a manganese nodule dredged from the Pacific Ocean floor showing a core or nucleus of volcanic rock. Other materials may act as nuclei of manganese nodules including shark teeth and ear bones of whales. Scale equals 1 cm.

Figure 15-7B Large, spherical, closely packed nodules covering the sea floor southeast of New Zealand. These nodules are 8 to 10 cm in diameter. (Photograph courtesy Lamont–Doherty Geological Observatory, Columbia University)

components are *authigenic*. *Allogenic* components are formed elsewhere and transported to the site where they are deposited. Some minerals occur in marine sediments in both authigenic and allogenic forms. Rivers introduce the clay mineral montmorillonite in suspension, but much of the south-central Pacific sediments are montmorillonite, formed authigentically from volcanic basalts. Another process called *diagenesis* occurs when certain substances in the sediment react chemically and are transformed after they become buried beneath later deposits of sediment. In almost every sense, these *diagenetic* components are metamorphosed—as are metamorphic rocks. Some clay minerals, for instance, undergo diagenetic changes in form and composition in the ocean. Calcium carbonate that has originated in organic life changes its crystal form in response to changes in the temperature and pressure in sediments on the ocean floor. Siliceous remains of marine organisms alter to form *chert,* a dense amorphous variety of silica. Volcanic debris becomes palagonite, phillipsite, and clay minerals. Animal and plant organisms are also responsible directly or indirectly for producing such diagenetic components as pyrite, glauconite (a greenish micalike mineral), barite (barium sulfate), and phosphorite (calcium phosphate). Phosphorite deposits occur frequently in areas of high biological productivity associated with upwelling. Apparently, large amounts of decaying protoplasm on the sea floor favor the formation of this mineral. The processes causing diagenesis in marine sediments are subtle and complex; consequently, they are imperfectly known. It is possible that, through further study of diagenetic effects, scientists will expand the list of diagenetic components to include material now thought to be exclusively allogenic.

Because they are mixed by ocean currents and turbulence, dissolved solids are distributed uniformly in the world ocean. Theoretically, chemical components could occur on any part of the ocean bottom. However, a low rate of deposition of the other components seems to be a prerequisite for an abundance of chemical components.

In particular areas, the bottom may be covered with a single chemical component. Manganese dioxide, for example, forms nodules, grains, slabs, coatings, and impregnations on many areas of the ocean floor. Manganese (Mn) nodules are found most frequently at the sediment–water interface, although some do exist at depth in marine sediments. This chemical component is the fourth most abundant material in marine sediments (the first three are alumino-silicate or clay minerals, calcium carbonate, and opaline silica).

Photographs of the sea floor (Fig. 15–7B) show that manganese nodules as large as 25 cm in diameter litter the ocean bottom in some areas. These accumulations can be valuable economically because they contain appreciable quantities of copper, cobalt, nickel, and traces of lead, zinc, and molybdenum. The nodules represent enormous tonnages of potential low-grade ore that await only the development of suitable marine mining technology for recovery.

Age dating of Mn nodules using Th-230, Pa-231, U-234, potassium-argon, and Be-10 techniques has established that nodules grow only 3 or 4 mm per million years. The red clay sediment upon which they rest accumulates at a rate of about 3 m per million years. The sizes of nodules recovered from the ocean floor indicate that over 5 million years' worth of Mn accumulation has managed to evade burial by the 15 m of red clay that has accumulated in the same time interval. An equal amount of nodules are found buried in the first 4 m of sediment below the sediment–water interface, suggesting that burial eventually overcomes some of the nodules.

Scientists have developed three hypotheses to explain the formation and distribution of Mn nodules. All may be valid to varying degrees. The first hypothesis holds that Mn, Fe, Ni, Co, and Cu separate from continental rocks during weathering and are removed from seawater by adsorption on particulate matter, or are incorporated in biological tissue that quickly removes these metals to the sea floor. This hypothesis gains strength from the observation that seawater is relatively impoverished in these metal ions, whereas deep-sea marine sediments are enriched in these metals relative to the parent continental rocks.

The second hypothesis maintains that the enrichment of Mn, Fe, and other metal ions is caused because the metals in and on the sediment particles are mobilized in the reducing zones in the sediments that exist below the level where the decomposition of organic matter renders the *interstitial* water anoxic. The reduced forms of the metals are quite soluble in contrast to the relatively insoluble nature of their oxidized forms. Diffusive transport moves the reduced ions upward to the sediment–water interface where they are oxidized and precipitate on nodule surfaces.

The third hypothesis explains the source of metal ions as being submarine volcanism at spreading centers at mid-ocean ridges. The ions are discharged into seawater where they oxidize and precipitate. The metal oxides in large particles settle rapidly and form a basal layer of metal-rich sediments on the flanks of the ridge. Fewer particles of oxide are distributed widely by bottom currents and eventually settle to form a chemical component of deep-sea sediments. As sea-floor spreading proceeds, the basal layer of metal-rich sediments becomes buried by carbonate-rich sediments as shown in Fig. 15–8. Lower on the flanks of the mid-ocean ridge at the carbonate compensation depth, settling carbonate debris dissolve upon reaching the sea floor, and only red clay is deposited. Cores obtained by drilling holes in a line between the mid-ocean ridge and the center of the adjacent abyssal plain reveal a sequence of sediment described above (shown in Fig. 15–8).

Calculations show that Mn accumulates in sediments almost twice as fast as in nodules. The striking aspect of manganese nodules is not that they accumulate metal ions readily (sediments have much more adsorptive surface per unit volume) but that, growing so slowly, they are not buried. Some scientists suggest that the nodules are rolled about on the sea floor by occasional strong currents, earthquakes, biological activity, or other phenomena. Others believe that they maintain their position by dissolving in the anoxic sediments below them and reprecipitating the reduced metal ions as oxides on their upper surfaces. Again, both of these effects may be occurring; the matter is not yet resolved.

Other Chemical Components

Another mineral, pyrite, is found precipitated in sediments that exist in a reducing environment, such as in restricted basins or in sediments rich in decaying protoplasm. Pyrite has been found deposited within the tests of

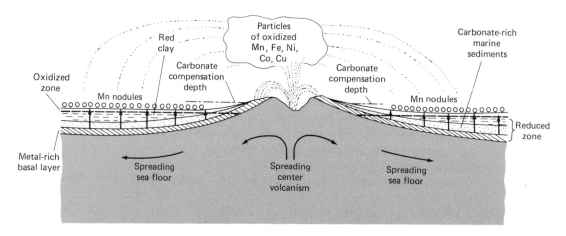

Figure 15-8 Schematic representation of the mechanism of Mn nodule formation in the ocean. Vertical·arrows represent diffusive transport of reduced metal ions dissolved in interstitial water. Sea-floor spreading leads to the formation of the sequence of sediments: basal metal-rich volcanic debris, carbonate-rich sediment, and uppermost red clay strata.

globigerinids in sediments that have contact with oxygenated seawater. This curious occurrence demonstrates that chemical reactions in the ocean probably involve elaborate biochemical and geochemical processes. For example, warm brines deep in the Red Sea contain more metal than does most seawater. When we understand the fate of these dissolved metals as the brines mix with cooler water, we will learn much about the chemistry of manganese and other trace metals in seawater.

15.2   *Classification of Marine Sediments*

The proportions of the various sediment-producing components vary from place to place in the ocean. For classification, sediment is named according to that component which is most abundant in the sediment. Common sediment types observed on the bottom of the ocean are listed in Table 15–3.

Sediments are grouped broadly into *neritic* or *pelagic* types according to whether they form by falling from the water on the continental terrace (neritic) or from the water of the open ocean (pelagic). The relationship between this system of classification and the breakdown on the basis of components is shown in Fig. 15–9.

Table 15–3   Marine Sediment Types

Component	Material	Minimum amount required (by weight)	Sediment type	
Terrigenous	clay	70%	brown clay	
	sand	70%–80%	terrigenous sands	
	silt and clay mixture, some sand	70%–80%	terrigenous muds	
Biological	globigerinids	30%*	globigerina ooze	Calcareous oozes
	pteropods	30%*	pteropod ooze	
	coccoliths	30%*	coccolith ooze	
	diatoms	30%*	diatom ooze	Siliceous oozes
	radiolarians	30%*	radiolarian ooze	
Chemical	authigenic minerals and compounds		authigenic sediments	(e.g., manganese nodules)

*Required amounts of carbonate or silicate, derived mainly from remnants of marine organisms, the dominant form determining the name.

15.3   *The Distribution of Marine Sediments*

The distribution of each sediment type is not a haphazard one; there are reasons why the sediments are found where they are. We can deduce much about the nature of marine sediments if we consider how all the components of a particular sediment type enter the ocean and how they are transported until they finally form part of a marine sediment.

Most of the components are deposited close to where they are introduced into the ocean. Sand is deposited quite close to shore, on beaches, and possibly at the continental margins. Finer material, such as silt and clay, is swept seaward, although silt is deposited closer to shore than clay. The finest clays are able to travel long distances in the ocean if they are in low concentration. Clay, therefore, is found in all parts of the world ocean. In summary, the amounts of terrigenous components decrease seaward away from the continental margins where the bulk of such materials are introduced into the ocean. Larger and heavier particles are concentrated in a band around the continents; finer sediment particles are spread over the entire ocean bottom.

Ocean currents are important in distributing fine terrestrial materials and planktonic, sediment-forming organisms. Throughout the world ocean, turbidity flows apparently cause mixing of several components or reworking of

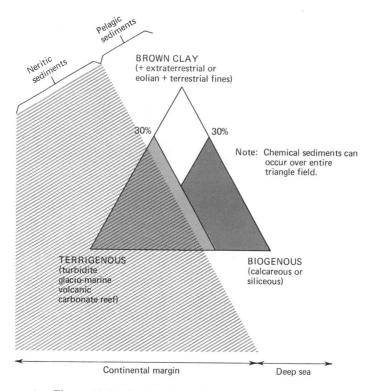

Figure 15-9 Classification of marine sediments on a component end-member basis.

sediments formerly deposited by quiet settling through the overlying water. Sediments formed this way, called *turbidites,* are distributed in a way that is predictable despite the fact that the usual distribution patterns of the components in a turbidite are often severely disrupted.

The distribution of sediment types at the bottom of the world ocean is shown in Fig. 15–10. The principles governing this distribution are demonstrated in an ocean basin like the Pacific. An east–west profile across the basin shows sediment types distributed symmetrically as in Fig. 15–11A. At the water's edge, beach sands prevail. Farther offshore, terrigenous sands and muds are the dominant sediment type. Coarse terrigenous sediments are deposited close to the continents and delineate the continental terrace fairly well. The continental rise is characterized by turbidite deposits; beyond the continental margins, biologic sediment types prevail to a depth of about 4.8 km. Brown clay is the dominant sediment type in depths exceeding 4.8 km—that is, in the deepest part of the ocean. Brown clay is composed of the finest water-borne terrigenous material and the finest airborne dust. Unusual sedi-

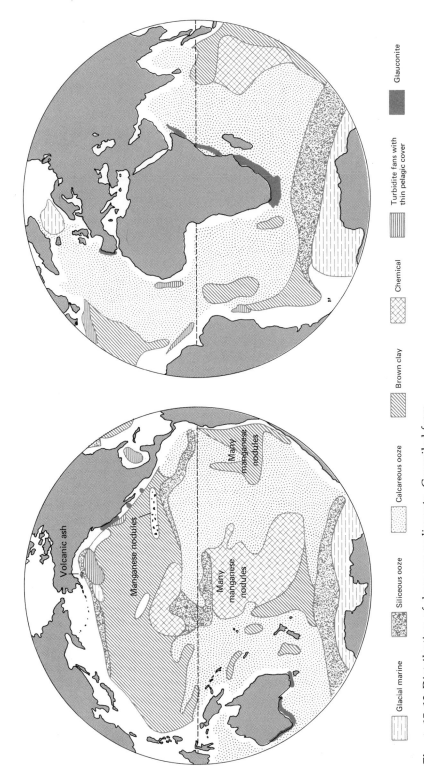

Figure 15-10 Distribution of deep-sea sediments. Compiled from information by Arrhenius (1961) and Nayudu (1959) and from suggestions by D. B. Ericson, H. W. Menard, and W. R. Riedel. It is quite likely that the areas with abundant manganese nodules cover more territory than shown and that there are many more areas where turbidite layers are interbedded with normal pelagic deposits. All boundaries should be considered as subject to extensive changes as information becomes more abundant. (By permission of F. P. Shepard)

411

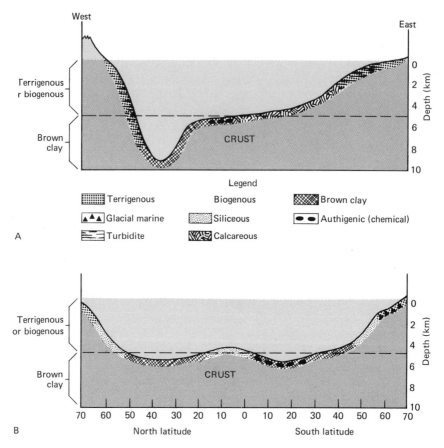

Figure 15-11 Distribution of sediment types in a hypothetical ocean basin. (A) Profile oriented east-west; (B) Profile oriented north-south. Note the importance of depth, latitude, and proximity to shore on the distribution of sediment types.

ment components, such as extraterrestrial cosmic dust, earbones from whales, teeth of sharks, and clinkers from steamships, are most noticeable in brown clay. Because their rate of deposition is rapid relative to the rate of deposition of brown clay, there is little dilution of exotic sedimentary materials.

The north–south profile in Fig. 15–11B differs from the east–west profile only in the zones occupied by biologic sediment types. Diatomaceous ooze is found in high latitudes because of the life requirements of diatoms. Likewise, radiolarian ooze is largely confined to equatorial regions, because radiolaria abound in warm, low-salinity water. The species of *Globigerina* are found in all latitudes, but individual species have limited geographic distribution. Apparently, the life requirements of individual species are stringent.

The sediment pattern presented in Fig. 15–11 usually prevails throughout the basins of the world ocean. In some places, however, pronounced discrepancies are found; rock outcrops occur at the shelf break; mud flats are found in the intertidal zone; sediment types on the continental shelf have an irregular distribution; and the fine clays in the deep-ocean basins often contain layers of silt and sand carried there by turbidity flows.

Unusual sediments are found in places in the world ocean near sources of special sedimentary materials or where there are sedimentary processes that alter the basic pattern of sediment distribution. Carbonate reefs, for instance, are surrounded by calcareous sediments consisting almost entirely of pulverized remains of reef organisms. Glacial marine sediments are found in high latitudes and at the Arctic and Antarctic margins (Fig. 15–10). These sediments are characteristically rich in silt and clay-sized crushed rocks produced by glacial action upon continental rock masses. Icebergs frequently carry coarse material of pebble size and even larger to the site of deposition (Fig. 15–2).

Volcanic sediments are found immediately adjacent to areas of volcanic activity, such as the western part of the Atlantic Ocean, Indonesia, the Gulf of Alaska, the seamount province off the Pacific northwest coast of the United States, and water adjacent to equatorial America. These sediments are rich in ash and shards of volcanic glass that have erupted from volcanoes on land and under water. Off the west coast of Central America, there are slabs of material, consisting in part of volcanic glass and phillipsite and coated with manganese oxide. These slabs are thought to represent an ancient volcanic ash layer that has undergone considerable chemical alteration.

Beaches surrounding the world ocean show the greatest variation in unusual sediments. Most of the sand on a beach is brought to the ocean by rivers that usually flow over tremendously varied terrain. Consequently, adjacent rivers along a coast discharge characteristically different assortments of minerals in their sand-sized suspended loads. Furthermore, the rocks from which beach sand is derived may be quite different from the rocks along the coast. The beach sediments mirror this difference.

Sediments in estuaries and tidal flats are abnormally fine grained, although they are in a coastal location. Tidal flats exist where currents or wave actions are too weak to cause scouring and removal of fine sediments introduced by rivers. The fine sediments are trapped there, because they are *flocculated* and form aggregates where freshwater of the river mixes with saline ocean water. The *flocs* settle more rapidly than the individual particles of which they are comprised. Their accumulation forms a hump of sediment on the bottom of the estuary. In addition, a wedge of saline water moves upstream along the bottom in response to tides and the hydraulic forces associated with river flow (see Chap. 11). The upstream motion of the salt wedge inhibits the seaward transport of flocs so that the estuarine bottom sediment remains as a more or less permanent feature.

Conditions offshore can also cause local variations in beach sediments. An example is the calcite sand of Daytona Beach, Florida. The source of this material is thought to be chemical precipitation of calcium carbonate just off the coast.

Sediment Color

The color of marine sediments varies considerably with location, and more specifically with the sedimentary environment. Those beach sands at Daytona, Florida, are almost white. Elsewhere, in the tropics and subtropics, carbonate-reef sands have a cream to tan color. The colors reflect differences in form and genesis of the carbonate materials. At Daytona, carbonate is precipitated chemically, whereas tropical carbonate-reef sands are comminuted fragments of reef algae and other organisms and therefore contain considerable organic impurities. Terrigenous sediments are usually light olive green to gray green or gray blue. The colors are caused by organic matter and reduced iron compounds. The decomposition of organic compounds consumes oxygen in the sediment and keeps iron in the ferrous (reduced) state. Ocassionally, organic matter decomposes completely and imparts a black color to the enclosing sediments. The black color is usually lost when the sediment is exposed to air.

Deep-ocean sediments from the sediment surface to a few tens of centimeters below usually have different colors than the sediments beneath them. Contact with oxygen in the overlying seawater keeps iron in the ferric (oxidized) state, so colors tend toward yellowish tan or red brown tints. Where organic matter is scarce, the oxidized zone may entend for tens of meters below the sea floor.

Sediments from anoxic basins are dark greenish gray or black. These colors are produced by sulfides or sulfur compounds precipitated in the sediments and sometimes by large quantities of organic matter. Sufficiently pure ash layers are cream to buff. Beach sands are often strikingly colored. On the island of Hawaii, there are green sands made of olivine crystals weathered from lava and black sands made of black lava fragments. Red sands rich in the mineral garnet occur on New England coasts, and brown sands rich in the mineral monazite are mined for rare earth elements in Southeast Asia. Sands composed of heavy accessory minerals are often concentrated by wave action and occur as dark streaks on lighter-colored beaches (Fig. 11–15B).

Effects of Transport in Turbidity Flows

Turbidites are formed when the processes of erosion, transportation, and deposition take place under particular conditions of geography and ocean bottom configuration. Submarine slides, for instance, occur in areas where sediments accumulate: at the heads of submarine canyons, on the continental slope, on the slopes of seamounts and ridges, and on the walls of trenches. These slides dislodge masses of more or less compact sediments and throw them into suspension, forming a turbidity flow. The seaward extent of a turbidity flow is often determined by bathymetric features. Where submarine trenches or seamount chains occur near the sediment source, they act as barriers to the flow, and so the seaward extent of the resulting turbidite deposit is limited. On the other hand, ocean basins frequented by turbidity currents can contain turbidite deposits thousands of kilometers from land.

The irregular distribution of a turbidite sedimentary sequence is demonstrated by differences in the degree of smoothness of the ocean floor. If a basin floor has no turbidites, it usually has quite rough regions of abyssal hills; areas with turbidites have smoother bathymetry (i.e., abyssal plains). The rock surface underlying abyssal plains is probably rough but is buried under the thick turbidite sedimentary sequence.

Layering in Marine Sediments

Many of the sediments of the world ocean lie in layers of different compositions. Samples of brown clay that are several meters thick often show a uniform composition except near the sediment-water interface. However, samples obtained by drilling through the entire sediment sequence reveal that uniformity is not the rule. Instead, there seems to be an alternation of abyssal clays, carbonate oozes, chert (amorphous silicon dioxide), and turbidites.

Turbidites occur in distinct layers of graded terrestrial mud (or reworked sediments) that alternate with layers of pelagic sediments. The sedimentary characteristics of turbidite layers derive largely from their manner of transport and sedimentation. Turbidites originating from nearshore areas carry into deeper water sedimentary materials having shallow-water, terrestrial characteristics. In the turbidity flow, all sizes of sedimentary materials are transported. When suspended materials settle at the site of deposition, they are graded vertically in the order of size and density. The coarse, heavy particles settle first; the fine, light particles, last. Between flows, the pelagic interbeds deposit materials in the same scheme of formation and distribution that governs their occurrence elsewhere in the world ocean. The resulting bottom deposit exhibits an alternation in size, color, mineralogical, and biological composition.

Unlayered sediments form where a population of bottom-dwelling organisms rework the sediment by scavenging for food or by digging burrows into the bottom. Layering cannot occur even if a considerable variety of sedimentary materials is deposited. Consequently, a homogeneous unlayered bottom sediment is formed. Often, however, the uppermost layer of these sediments contains evidence of the activity of these organisms. There may be distinct burrows or chaotic mottling of colors of the sediment. These effects extend downward as much as $1/3$ m from the water-sediment interface.

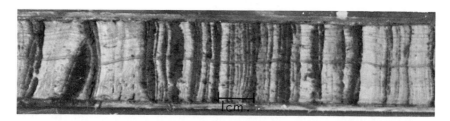

Figure 15-12 A cross section of a submarine core showing varves or layers that reflect seasonal difference in deposition in the area. The thickness of the dark layers varies from 1 to 10 mm. (Photograph courtesy Joe S. Creager)

If there are no bottom-dwelling organisms, sediments will form layers wherever there are changes in the sedimentation conditions. Certain estuaries, marginal seas, and lakes contain *varved*, or thinly laminated, sediments. These sediments lie in thin layers (a few millimeters thick) that are alternately light and dark, reflecting an alternating or cyclic change in sediments reaching the bottom. The most striking laminae are produced by diatoms having periodic blooms (Fig. 15–12). Light layers rich in diatom tests alternate with darker layers containing fewer diatoms. In such sediments, each light-dark pair of layers usually represents a single cycle of diatom growth. In areas where the cycle is annual, each pair—or varve—represents a single year of deposition. If the cyclic sedimentation has continued to the present day, the sediments are dated easily. By dating the sediments and interpreting the oceanic conditions prevailing at the time of the deposition of each sediment layer, scientists learn about the history of the ocean and the earth.

The arrangement of strata, or *stratigraphy*, is studied by examining the layers of ocean sediments; the younger layers, of course, overlie the older ones. The sediment is collected by core samplers that are driven vertically into the bottom (described in Chap. 16). Samples obtained in this fashion usually do not exceed a few meters in length. Much longer cores have been obtained by the deep-sea drilling ship *Glomar Challenger* (see Fig. 16–10). These core samples permit direct observation of the layers of ocean-bottom sediments. In this way, the ocean's history from the Jurassic (160 million years ago) to the present can be studied in detail.

Drill cores from the North Pacific Ocean show that basement rocks (*lithified* sediments or volcanic rocks) are youngest at the west coast of North America where Miocene basalts are found. The basement becomes progressively older toward the west. Jurassic (or older) rocks are found just seaward of the Mariana Trench. The sediments lying on the basement are carbonate (coccolith) oozes. Above these are brown clays. Layers of chert are found at the contact of these two sediment layers and in the carbonate ooze. Clay minerals and zeolites, both from partially altered volcanic ash, are found in layers within the brown clay layer. The ages of the lowermost sediments parallel those of the basement.

Mid-Cretaceous sediments are found in the western North Pacific; Oligocene sediments, in the central North Pacific.

There is little doubt that these sediment samples establish that sea-floor spreading in the North Pacific Ocean has proceeded westward from the East Pacific Rise since at least Jurassic time. Equally dramatic evidence of the sea-floor spreading is found in drill cores obtained in the South Atlantic Ocean. The basement and initial sediments become older farther away from the Mid-Atlantic Ridge. The ages of these materials indicate a rate of sea-floor spreading nearly identical to that determined by a study of magnetic anomalies in the South Atlantic.

The lithologies of the samples from the South Atlantic are similar to those in the North Pacific; that is, an initial carbonate ooze is overlain first by brown clay and then by carbonate sediments. Chert layers are absent in the South Atlantic, but in the North Atlantic and Caribbean they are present just as in the North Pacific.

In general, the evidence from shorter sediment cores indicates a wider zone of tropical climate during the Teritiary, alternating cold glacial and warmer interglacial stages during the Pleistocene, and a warm condition in the Recent (Holocene) epoch that is not as extensive as in the Tertiary.

This climatic sequence is inferred from differences in the relative concentrations of calcium carbonate in deep-sea cores that were collected from the equatorial Pacific. The deposition of calcium carbonate in the deep sea is a function of both supply by biological productivity near the sea surface and removal by dissolution of the calcium carbonate detritus as it settles to the sea floor. Figure 15–13 shows how the concentration of calcium carbonate in the sediment column is related to relative depth below the sediment-water interface and the latitude. The compensation line refers to the latitude at which dissolution of carbonate detritus just equals its supply.

The sequence of layers exhibiting high (60 percent) and moderate (1 to 60 percent) carbonate concentrations are thought to reflect the differences in surface productivity during the Pleistocene epoch. Carbonate-rich layers are related to glacial stages when trade winds were more intense; hence, equatorial upwelling and associated biological productivity were greater. During the interglacial periods, the trade winds died down, upwelling decreased, and biological productivity slowed. During the Tertiary, the compensation line migrated from 15° north to 7° north latitude. Evidence indicates that this change may reflect a warming trend in the bottom waters (thus decreasing the rate of dissolution) rather than an increase in surface productivity. In the early Tertiary, the compensation line may have extended to 45° latitude. However, the warming trend subsequently decreased, and the compensation line reached its present location by the late Miocene epoch.

There are other indications of climatic control on the nature of pelagic sediments: (1) coiling directions of certain forms of planktonic globigerinids, (2) isotope ratios of oxygen O–16/O–18, (3) changes in mineralogy and

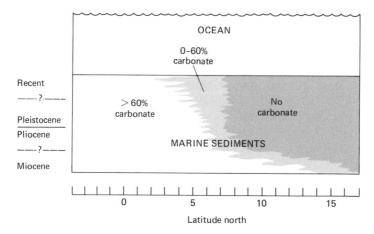

Figure 15-13 The east equatorial Pacific Ocean is a site of high biological productivity because of upwelling produced by trade winds. During glacial times the earth's climatic zones were "compressed," resulting in more intense winds—especially the trade winds. This led to greater upwelling, hence, greater productivity and more calcium carbonate deposition on the ocean floor. High calcium carbonate concentrations are thus correlated with glacial times in sediments from the east equatorial Pacific. (Modified after Arrhenius, 1963, in *The Sea*, ed. by Hill, by permission of John Wiley & Sons, Inc.)

deposition rates of pelagic clays, (4) the distribution of ice-rafted sediments, and (5) the relative abundance of cold-water and warm-water species of planktonic foraminifera, coccoliths, diatoms, radiolarians, or pteropods. All of these are important indicators of past climates and must be considered in reconstructing the paleoclimates of the earth.

Dating Marine Sediments

The interpretation of marine sediments depends critically upon the scientists' ability to ascertain the age of each of the strata. If there were no method of dating earth materials, scientists could not understand the history of the ocean. Fortunately, a system of earth chronology has been developed by dating geological materials. Several techniques are used; each serves to complement the others. The dating techniques most important in oceanography are radionuclide geochronology, paleontological chronology (using fossil remains of plants and animals), magnetic reversal chronology, and chronology of the climatic reversals of the Pleistocene and Recent (Holocene) epochs.

Radionuclide dating is practically the only system that yields age in years, or absolute time. It is based on the phenomenon of radioactive decay, in which a parent radioactive atom emits electromagnetic energy spontaneously and becomes a more stable daughter atom. The rate of decay of parent atoms to daughter atoms at any moment is proportional to the number of parent atoms present at that moment. The proportionality factor is called the *decay rate constant*. This factor is different for each kind of parent atom (or radioactive element), and it determines how long a given amount of radioactive material will last after it begins to decay.

Dating is possible only if the radionuclide is segregated from its daughter atoms at the time of the formation of the material being dated. Once the material has formed, there cannot be migration in or out of it or else erroneous dates are inferred.

Three kinds of radionuclides have been used for dating marine sediments: *primary, secondary,* and *induced.* Primary radionuclides decay so slowly that measurable amounts of these materials remain 5 billion years after they formed within our solar system. The daughter products of some primary radionuclides are also radioactive. These secondary radionuclides decay at intermediate rates; that is, measurable amounts remain after hundreds of thousands of years of decay. Induced radionuclides are formed by the bombardment of the earth's atmosphere by cosmic rays. These materials decay rather rapdily but are useful for dating relatively young materials and for tracing ocean currents.

The radionuclides most frequently used to date marine sediments are thorium-230 (Th-230), which is also called ionium (Io), protactinium-231 (Pa-231), and carbon-14 (C-14). Potassium-40 (K-40) is also used. The span of geologic ages that can be measured with each radionuclide is shown in Table 15–4.

Carbon-14 is useful for geologically young materials (formed since the middle of the last glaciation of the Pleistocene). Additional range into the Pleistocene is obtained with Pa-231, Th-230, and U-234, but the major part of geologic time is measured with the K-40 radionuclide. The K-40 technique is applied to igneous rock dating, because the gaseous daughter product argon-40 (Ar-40) is driven from molten rock but begins to accumulate in crystal lattices when the rock solidifies and cools below 300°C. The K-40 technique is not suitable for dating marine sediments, but fortunately it is useful for dating the continental lava flows that reveal the succession of reversals of the earth's magnetic polarity throughout much of geologic time (see Fig. 3–2B).Magnetic reversals are measured in marine sediments and basement lava flows in the world ocean, so a marine sediment that dates back to the mid-Pleistocene or earlier can be assigned an age expressed in years.

Before the advent of magnetic reversal dating, only *relative* geological ages could be assigned to any (except the youngest) marine sediment. This type of dating was based upon (1) paleontology or climatic changes that were reflected by changes in the relative abundance of clay minerals in sediments, (2) the sequence of seawater temperature reversals indicated by oxygen isotope measurements, or (3) coiling direction of certain foraminifera.

Table 15–4   Useful Ranges of Radionuclides in Dating

C-14	0 to 40,000 years
Pa-231	0 to 150,000 years
Th-230	0 to 300,000 years
K-40	700,000 to 4.5 billion years

Marine sediments contain small quantities of magnetite that orient to the prevailing magnetic field as they settle through the water to the sea floor. Consequently, marine sediments contain a record of the variation in the earth's magnetic field. This fact permits magnetic reversal dating to assign *absolute* ages to marine strata and the oceanographic events they represent. As a result, scientists can understand the history of sedimentation of the ocean and particularly the ages of several important dating horizons used to describe events in the history of the world ocean. Magnetic reversal dating permits the correlation of these horizons in marine sediments from different parts of the earth.

15.5   *The Thickness of Marine Sediments and Sedimentation Rates*

The determination of the age of sediment layers by the various dating procedures can also help us to calculate the rates of accumulation of marine sediments. On the average, sediment layers have a thickness of about 1 km, although they vary from place to place at the bottom of the world ocean. Sediments are about 3 km thick in the Argentine basin and about 50 m thick on the Mid-Atlantic Ridge. The thickest sediments occur at the continental margin and on the continental terrace. Both the total thickness and sedimentation rates vary according to sediment composition. Brown clay accumulates at considerably less than 1 cm per 1,000 years; globigerina ooze, at about 1 cm per 1,000 years; and terrigenous mud, at about 6 cm per 1,000 years. At the highest sedimentation rate, the 3 km of sediments in the Argentine basin would accumulate in 50 million years. This is only 1 percent of geologic time. It is not likely that the sedimentation rate prior to the Pleistocene was far slower than it is today. Apparently, therefore, sediment is being removed. Presumably it is being swept under the continents during sea-floor spreading. If the rate of sea-floor spreading is 5 cm per year (actually quite rapid), then it would take 50 million years for a piece of the floor to travel from its point of origin at the Mid-Atlantic Ridge to the Argentine basin, which is 2,500 km away. In other words, at no time during the history of the South Atlantic Ocean could there be more than a 50 million years' accumulation of sediments on the ocean floor. Indeed, a decade of deep-sea drilling through the sediments of all the basins of the world ocean has failed to reveal sediments older than Jurassic (137 million years before present) age.

Nondeposition

The bottom of the ocean is almost totally covered with layers of more or less fine sediment. Exceptions do occur where strong currents tend to sweep sediments away, such as at the break between the continental shelf and slope. In these cases, rocks are exposed. In other cases, conditions are such that sediments no longer accumulate, so the floor of the ocean is an ancient (or *relict*) deposit formed thousands of years ago.

Continental shelves are outstanding examples of such nondeposition. Sediments in these regions are not graded according to distance from land. Instead, the shelves are covered with patches of coarse terrigenous materials that show evidence of shallow-water or even subaerial and fluvial sedimentary processes. Dating, as well as physical evidence, indicate that these sediments were formed by deposition or even by weathering when the sea level was much lower during Pleistocene glaciation.

Under the normal condition of a relatively wide shelf and moderate influx of sediment from land, insufficient time has elapsed for a recent sedimentary veneer to bury the existing Pleistocene deposits. Hence, many of the sediments of the continental shelf represent a disequilibrium between existing oceanic conditions and the sediment texture. These relict sediments are occasionally redistributed by large storms passing over the continental shelf. Generally, however, their existence is associated with the environmental conditions prevailing during a previous epoch in geological time.

Suspended Particulate Material in the Ocean

Most of the materials in marine sediments arrived at the sea floor as particulate material originally in suspension in seawater. Studies of the *suspensoids,* or suspended particulate phase, in the ocean have revealed that these particles play important roles in regulating the chemistry and biology of the ocean as well as determining the nature of marine sediments.

The ocean contains an average of 1 to 2 g of suspended solids per 100 T of seawater. Organic matter in sizes from 1 μm to 1 mm comprise 30 to 70 percent of the particles in the upper 100 m of the ocean; 25 to 50 percent of the particulate matter is skeletal $CaCO_3$ and SiO_2. The concentration of particles larger than 10 μm is small; most of the particles are sized between 1 and 10 μm. Concentrations are greatest at high latitudes, and a pronounced minimum concentration exists in tropical latitudes. Coarse (> 5 μm) particulates introduced to the ocean by rivers and the wind seldom travel beyond the continental shelf, but biological fecal pellets occur everywhere in the ocean and appear to be an important transport pathway for introducing Ca, Si, and C to the water of the deep ocean.

The distribution of sizes of siliceous and calcareous particles suspended in the ocean does not appear to change with depth for particles between 1 and 10 μm, the size range of the most abundant particles. The skeletons of planktonic organisms are considerably larger than the particles, so we must conclude that the skeletons become comminuted by fragmentation and dissolution.

Biogenic particle sizes appear to follow a *power law* distribution described by the expression:

$$\frac{\text{Number of particles in a small interval of sizes}}{\text{size of interval}} = Ar^{-b}$$

where r is the average size of particles in the interval of sizes and A and b are constants. The constant A represents the number of particles in a small interval of sizes about a value of $r = 1$ μm and is an index of the concentration of particles in a given volume of seawater. The constant b is related to processes comminution, particle settling, and possibly water motion and usually has a value between 4 and 5. A typical particle size distribution is shown in Fig. 15–14.

Particles settle through water according to *Stokes' law* which is formulated as solid particle settling velocity, $V_s = Br^2$. B is a constant that accounts for particle shape, the effect of gravity is g, the effect of water viscosity is η (itself influenced strongly by water temperature), the difference between the density of the particle is ρ_b, and the density of water is ρ_w. The formula expressing B is

$$B = \frac{2g}{9} \frac{(\rho_b - \rho_w)}{\eta}$$

Particles smaller than 0.5 μm are suspended by molecular collisions so they do not settle according to Stokes' law and can be considered to behave as if they were dissolved. The flux of particles settling through the ocean is the number of particles times the velocity of particles settling. Hence for a particle of size r the flux is

$$Ar^{-b}Br^2 \qquad \text{or} \qquad ABr^{(2-b)}$$

This is the theoretical form of the distribution of sizes that reach the bottom and form marine sediments (Fig. 15–14). However, the distribution of particle sizes in marine sediments suggests that the appropriate Stokes' law expression describes the settling of hollow spheres, not solid particles, and the flux is $ABr^{(c-b)}$ where $c = 1$. Further, clays tend to cluster together, or *flocculate* in seawater, so they settle as particles larger than their individual sizes would indicate.

As particles settle through the ocean, their sizes, r, change because they

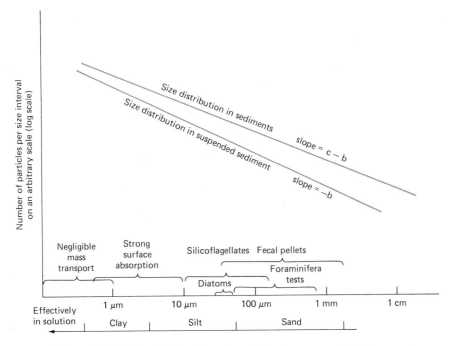

Figure 15-14 The distribution of particle sizes suspended in seawater and accumulated in marine sediments.

fragment, dissolve, or grow by accretion. Small particles tend to adsorb molecules from seawater and their effective settling sizes may change as a result of the modification of the sheath of hydration around the particle. Where upwelling occurs, a dissolving particle may reach a size such that its settling velocity is just balanced by its velocity of advection upward. In such circumstances particles of a certain size would become concentrated in distinct horizontal zones a few meters thick. This is one of the mechanisms postulated for the formation of *nepheloid layers* observed in the ocean. Other mechanisms that have been suggested include resuspension of bottom sediments, accumulation of particles at sharp pycnoclines, and concentration of sinking phytoplankton at the base of the euphotic zone.

Particles in sizes between 1 and 10 μm are capable of adsorbing ions from seawater. The residence time of Th, Pu, Fe, Pb, and Cu in the ocean appears to be controlled by this mechanism.

Fecal pellets are formed by zooplankton that feed upon smaller plankton and suspended debris in the surface layer of the ocean. The pellets provide food for benthic organisms because they settle to the sea floor relatively rapidly and without being reduced in size by dissolution as are small particles. The rate of size reduction of dissolving particles is proportional to $1/r^3$ where r is the diameter of the particle. We see that small particles become smaller at higher rates than the rates for larger particles. The mass flux of fecal pellets is quite large because they settle rapidly, are relatively large, and are produced in large numbers by biological metabolism; they represent a substantial pathway for the transport of organic matter from the surface of the ocean to bottom water and marine sediments.

Metal Deposits in Marine Sediments and Oceanic Crust

Marine sediments act as the host for minerals formed by chemical precipitation at the sea floor. Several of these minerals are of great economic importance. The concepts of plate tectonics and the chemistry of seawater provide a basis for understanding how certain metal-bearing minerals form, distribute, and ultimately become concentrated into the ore deposits mined today. Figure 15–15 illustrates present concepts of the relation between marine processes and ore mineral emplacement. Evidence gathered from recent observations of marine sediment on the sea floor at tectonically active areas and the studies of economic ore deposits indicate that many ore minerals are forming today as they have throughout the geologic history of the ocean. The metallic elements in the ore minerals originate in the earth's mantle and crust where they are dispersed in rather small concentrations. Melting of the mantle and crust at spreading centers (constructive margins of oceanic plates) mobilizes the metallic minerals. Some segregate in the molten material and form primary deposits (Ni and Pt sulfides and chromium oxide). The rest of the metals are brought upward toward the sea floor in effusive volcanic rocks. Reaction of hot molten basalt with cold seawater fractures the rock and permits the seawater to circulate deep (several kilometers) into the crust. The downward circulation of cold bottom water on the flanks of a spreading center is thought to cause the *geothermal anomaly* observed at mid-ocean ridges and rises (see Fig. 3–8). The descending seawater is heated to a few hundred degrees and it leaches silica, calcium, iron, manganese, copper, nickel, cobalt, lead, zinc, tin, tungsten, and other metals into solution. The chloride ion in seawater facilitates the leaching. In the process, seawater becomes acidic and reducing. Magnesium and water are extracted from the seawater to form new minerals as basalt is altered. As the resulting solution ascends, it cools and forms a *hydrothermal* deposit of metal (mainly iron and copper) sulfides. The sulfur is derrived from sulfate ions initially present in the original seawater as well as from sulfur species in the crustal rocks. The sulfides and quartz precipitate in open fractures within the altered basalt. Sulfides continue to precipitate when the solution reaches the sea floor if the bottom water is anoxic as in the Red Sea. Otherwise, the solution reacts with the cold, oxygenated bottom water and precipitates *hydrogenous* iron and manganese oxides which become incorporated in bottom sediments near the spreading center. Manganese does not form sulfides as readily as iron, so fractionation occurs and the sediments are

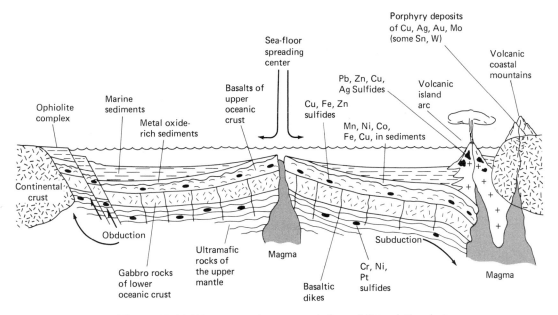

Figure 15-15 Diagrammatic representation of the relation between processes of marine sedimentation, sea-floor spreading, and the emplacement of economic mineral deposits.

enriched in manganese relative to iron. Trace metals in the solution become adsorbed on the metal oxide particles and are carried to the bottom sediment also. As the oceanic crust moves away from the spreading center the metal-rich layer is buried by sediments. Hydrogenous deposition continues but is somewhat masked by detrital or biogenic material. Where the detritus contains enough organic carbon, the interstitial water becomes reducing by consuming its dissolved oxygen. Manganese and iron become mobilized because the reduced forms of these metals are much more soluble than the oxidized forms. The mobilized metals in the interstitial solution diffuse upward and also are advected as compaction expels interstitial water upward. Ultimately the reduced metal ions reach the zone of oxygenated water at the sediment-water interface where they become oxidized and precipitate to form ferromanganese nodules and crusts containing appreciable quantities of iron, nickel, cobalt, copper, zinc, and barium. Manganese is fractionated from iron even more in this *diagenetic* process owing to its higher solubility in the reduced state and to the tendency of iron to combine with sulfur to form relatively insoluble sulfides.

Sea-floor spreading carries the sediments and their hydrogenous deposits to destructive continental margins where oceanic crust is subducted under the continental plates or obducted onto the surface of the continental rocks.

Melting and volcanism occur here and the hydrogenous deposits in the sediments and hydrothermal deposits in the oceanic crustal rocks become mobilized once more. Where obduction occurs, a suite of rocks called an *ophiolite* complex is brought to the surface of the continent. The ophiolite complex represents a fragment of oceanic crust and its covering of sediments and it contains metal deposits formed hydrothermally, hydrogenously, and diagenetically during the history of the oceanic plate. An ophiolite, as typified by exposures in the Appennine Mountains of northern Italy, Cyprus, Newfoundland, and Luzon, consists of an ultramafic (rich in Fe and Mg) layer of igneous rocks from the oceanic upper mantle, overlain by a zone of gabbro (lower oceanic crust), and then a layer of basalt (upper oceanic crust) that often displays a pillow structure evidencing its sudden cooling upon eruption into seawater. Vertical dikes of basaltic rocks extend downward from the basalt layer. These represent the conduits through which molten material from the upper mantle and lower oceanic crust passed to the ocean floor to form the upper oceanic crust. A layer of sedimentary rocks rests on top of the crustal series of igneous materials. Manganese oxide deposits are found at the base of the sedimentary layer and massive deposits of copper sulfide containing iron sulfide and sometimes zinc sulfide, all of hydrothermal origin, occur in the basalt. These mineral deposits are often altered to a rock called greenstone, so named because of its color.

Small amounts of chromite and asbestos are found in the ultramafic layer which is often altered to a rock called serpentinite. In some places (e.g., Zambales Mountains, Luzon) the ultramafic rock is thought to have contained substantial quantities of nickel sulfide, because of the nickel-rich deposits in laterites that formed when the rock weathers.

Subduction at the destructive margin of an oceanic plate results in volcanism that forms island arcs or coastal mountain ranges. Melted oceanic crust may undergo magmatic differentiation such that the volcanic rocks that are extruded at the edge of the continental plate are andesitic, that is, richer in silica and alumina than was the original oceanic crust. Metals mobilized in the magma form large disseminated deposits of copper sulfides called *porphyry* deposits which have lesser quantities of gold, silver, and molybdenum. These large, low-grade deposits are found along the western margins of the North American and South American continents and are important sources of these metals.

Where volcanism forms island arcs, massive sulfides of lead, zinc, copper, and silver form high-grade deposits in basaltic rocks (e.g., the Kuroko sulfides in Northeast Japan) or in andesitic rocks (e.g., the Besshi sulfides of Shikoku Island, Japan). These deposits are thought to form during submarine volcanic activity in shallow, nearshore areas.

Economic mineral deposits in the interiors of continents bear convincing evidence of having been involved in marine processes similar to those described earlier. Ample reason exists for believing that such processes have been taking place during much of geologic history. The metal deposits associated with greenstone belts in the shield areas of Canada, Australia, and South Africa seem to be examples of pre-Cambrian island arc deposits.

reading list

Bonatti, E., "The Origin of Metal Deposits in the Oceanic Lithosphere," *Scientific American*, CCXXXVIII, No. 2 (February 1978), 54–61.

Broecker, W. S., *Chemical Oceanography*. New York: Harcourt Brace Jovanovich, Inc., 1974. 214p.

Hill, M. N., ed., "The Sea, Ideas and Observations," in *The Earth Beneath the Sea*, Vol. III. New York: Interscience Publishers, 1963. 963p.

Komar, P. D., *Beach Processes and Sedimentation*. Englewood Cliffs, N.J.: Prentice-Hall, Inc., 1976. 429p.

Lal, D., "The Oceanic Microcosm of Particles," *Science*, CIXVIII, No. 4321 (December 9, 1977), 997–1009.

Shepard, F. P., *Submarine Geology* (2nd ed.). New York: Harper & Row, Pub., 1963. 557p.

Trask, P. D., *Recent Marine Sediments* (Rev. ed.). Tulsa: Society of Economic Paleontologists and Mineralogists, Special Publication No. 4, 1955. 736p.

oceanographic instruments

16

The oceanographer uses a wide variety of instruments that either obtain a sample of seawater or tell something about the oceanic environment—for example, the water depth, or its temperature, or the thickness of the sediment. Many such electronic and mechanical instruments are now being used routinely on oceanographic ships. These instruments can collect and record vast amounts of data that are then analyzed by high-speed computers. Oceanographic data that are collected by scientists throughout the United States are sorted and stored in national collection centers like the U.S. National Oceanographic Data Center in Washington, D.C. This agency serves as a clearinghouse and makes the data available to all scientists.

16.1 Positioning

Observations, measurements, or samples taken at sea have little value unless their location is known. Several instruments for locating a point on the ocean are used in oceanography. Although they are not strictly oceanographic instruments, they are as indispensable as any used in the marine sciences and should be mentioned here.

Navigation by dead reckoning was probably the earliest form of positioning used at sea. By this method, the speed and direction of a ship's travel is determined by compass and speed log (a device for measuring the distance the ship travels in a measured interval of time). The duration of travel on a known

428

course is used to plot the ship's position on a navigational chart. This technique is still used today, even though sophisticated navigational equipment has been developed. *Celestial navigation* (also an ancient technique) is based upon an angular measurement between the horizon and celestial objects (the sun and stars) to determine latitude. Longitude is determined by measuring the local time of the sun's zenith with a chronometer set to indicate the time at the Greenwich (0°) Meridian. Navigation satellites of known orbit are now used to determine a ship's position at sea. Knowledge of the satellite's position at any moment during its passage overhead is used to calculate the position of a ship relative to the satellite and then relative to the earth. *Satellite navigation* is quite precise: A ship can be located within 1 m of any point on the globe using this technique.

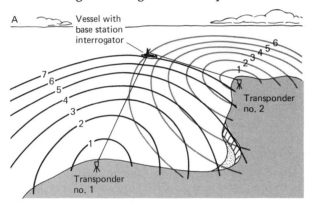

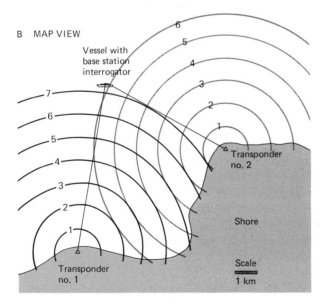

Figure 16-1 The range-range electronic navigation system showing the geometry of positioning (A) and a map view (B) of the range arcs from each transponder. The vessel is located as being 7.32 km from transponder 1 and 5.96 km from transponder 2.

Navigation by radio frequency ranging is a standard technique for finding a ship's position. Transmitters on land broadcast signals which are intercepted by a receiver aboard ship. Signals from two transmitters are compared to determine the distance from the ship to each transmitter. The *Loran* system of radio navigation is in widespread use in the world ocean; the U.S. Coast Guard maintains Loran transmitters on the shores and islands of every ocean basin. A smaller, portable version of radio ranging and positioning is used in nearshore oceanography. Transponders (combined receivers and transmitters) are placed temporarily at appropriate locations (stations) on shore. Operating within 30 miles of the shore stations, a ship carries an interrogator and timer that sends an interrogation signal to each shore station. Upon receiving the interrogation, the shore transponders immediately broadcast a signal back to the ship. The elapsed time from interrogation to receipt of each signal is converted to ranges between the ship and each shore station. The ranges are plotted on a navigational chart bearing the location of the shore stations to fix the ship's position (Fig. 16-1).

In oceanographic operations close to shore, *radar* navigation is often used. It is based upon the imaging of reflected high frequency signals transmitted from the ship in a swept beam (much like a searchlight). The configuration of coastlines and harbors and nearby ships or other obstructions are displayed on a circular screen from which range and bearings can be obtained.

Acoustic beacons placed in the water at locations surrounding a point of interest serve as an accurate positioning system. This technique is used in deep-sea drilling where it is necessary to keep a drill ship over the drill site for an extended interval of time. A hydrophone (marine microphone) system detects the sonic pulses emitted by each acoustic beacon, and a shipboard computer converts this information to a navigational fix and creates a set of instructions for maneuvering the ship to hold it over the drill site (see Fig. 16-12B).

16.2 *Geological Measurements*

Topographical Measurements

As early as 1504, depth measurements appeared on maps. Possibly the first deep-sea sounding was made by Magellan in the Pacific Ocean in 1521. The technique used then, and until the end of the 1800's, was to lower a rope and lead weight to the sea bed and measure the length of rope paid out. In the 1870's piano wire was used, because it had several advantages over rope: smaller volume, lighter weight, and less drag in the water. Nevertheless, the process of making a deep-sea sounding was difficult and time consuming.

In the 1920's, an electronic sounding device, called an *echo sounder* or sonic depth finder, was developed. This device measures the time for a sound pulse

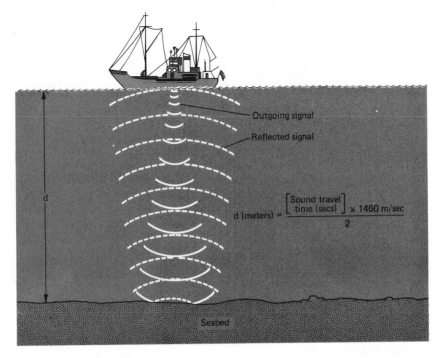

$$d \text{ (meters)} = \frac{\left[\begin{array}{c} \text{Sound travel} \\ \text{time (secs)} \end{array}\right] \times 1460 \text{ m/sec}}{2}$$

Figure 16-2 An echo sounder determines the depth by measuring the time interval required for a sonic pulse to travel from the ship to the sea floor and back.

transmitted from a vessel to travel to the sea bed and return to a listening device. The speed of sound in seawater is known; it is approximately 1,460 m per sec. Thus the travel time can be converted to a distance indicating the water depth (Fig. 16-2).

The echo sounder was first used as an oceanographic tool by the German research vessel *Meteor* on an expedition from 1927 to 1929. It was better than previous sounding methods, because soundings could be made while the vessel was underway. Hence, a continuous bottom profile (shown in Fig. 16-3) could be obtained. Before this development, there were only several thousand deep-sea soundings. After development of the echo sounder, millions of soundings became available. In fact, it has become standard practice for vessels to make continuous soundings as they sail throughout the world ocean. The compilation of these data has provided the geological oceanographer with an invaluable picture of the surface of the sea floor.

The side-scanning *sonar* (Sound Navigation and Ranging) apparatus is a refinement of the echo sounder. It sweeps the sea floor beneath and to the sides of the observation vessel with a beam of sound pulses and constructs a photolike image of the bottom from the echoes.

Figure 16-3 Two oceanographers study an echogram on board ship. (Photograph courtesy Sarah Barnes)

Observation of the Sea Floor

Geological oceanographers studying processes of sedimentation in the deep sea routinely use underwater cameras to obtain pictures of the sea floor. Equipment of this sort is also used by biological oceanographers to study marine life. The oceanographer's camera can be lowered to any depth and is prepared to take up to 500 photographs either automatically or upon command (Fig. 16-4A). Cameras are used singly or in pairs that provide stereoscopic viewing of the bottom (Fig. 16-4B).

Closed-circuit television has also been adapted for oceanographic use (Fig. 16-5). A television camera is often used either to monitor the operation of other equipment or to observe phenomena in the marine environment.

Direct observation and sampling by persons equipped with scuba gear (self-contained underwater breathing apparatus) is feasible in water no deeper than 45 m (Fig. 16-6). At depths of several kilometers, persons in deep-diving submarines are capable of routine observations. The bathyscaphe *Trieste* took scientists 11 km down into the Mariana Trench.

Sediment Samplers

Several types of sediment samplers are available to the geological oceanographer. *Dredges, grab samplers,* or *coring tubes* can be used, depending upon the nature of the bottom in the area of investigation and the degree of sophistication of the sampling program.

432

Figure 16-4A An underwater camera and deep-sea housing. (Photograph courtesy Hydro Products)

Figure 16-4B A lowering frame mounted with stereo cameras ready to lower to the sea floor. (Photograph courtesy the Office of Information Services, University of Washington)

Figure 16-5 Underwater television camera and light, monitor, and video tape recorder. (Photograph courtesy Hydro Products)

Figure 16-6 A scuba diver exploring the pinnacle of Cobb Seamount 450 km off the Washington coast. (Photograph courtesy Walter Sands)

Figure 16-7 A biologist's dredge ready to be lowered over the side. (Photograph courtesy Joe S. Creager)

A dredge is a strong boxlike apparatus that is dragged along the bottom of the sea. It can operate at any depth. A wire mesh or cloth mesh lining is placed inside the dredge to keep sedimentary material from being lost. The size of the mesh determines the size of material retained in the dredge (Fig. 16-7). Dredges are also designed to chip rock fragments from submarine rock outcrops.

Grab samplers obtain a relatively unoriented and somewhat disturbed volume of sediment from the layer at the sea floor. Grab samplers operate at any depth, but they are usually specialized in order to sample a particular sediment type. The Shipek sampler (Fig. 16-8) is used if coarse or hard-packed

Figure 16-8 A Shipek grab sampler. (Photograph courtesy Hydro Products)

435

Figure 16-9 Large clam shell type grab sampler.

materials form the bottom. Other types of samplers are used for sampling sand or finer materials (Fig. 16-9). The box sampler (Fig. 16-10) collects large-volume, mildly disturbed samples from the sediment–water interface.

Marine sediment samples for stratigraphic study must be obtained from successive layers extending as deep as practical. These samples must also represent the order of deposition on the bottom. A gravity corer is the simplest instrument that can penetrate marine muds and obtain samples of this kind. It consists of a hollow tube, weighted on top, that is driven into the bottom by the force of gravity (Fig. 16-11A). As it penetrates the bottom, the tube fills with sediments that remain inside as a core when the tube is brought back to the vessel. Core samples operate poorly in sandy sediments but in silt and clay-sized material, cores as long as 1 m can be obtained regularly.

The piston corer is a more complicated and effective type of coring mechanism. It consists of a coring barrel, weighted on top, with a tightly fitting piston inside. The piston is adjusted on the lowering cable in such a way that, when the barrel reaches the sediment interface, the barrel slides over the piston into the mud (Fig. 16-11B). The piston corer fills with mud more easily than the gravity corer, because a decreased pressure is produced within the barrel of the piston corer. Cores ranging from 25 to 30 m in length are obtained with this device.

Drills, such as percussion drills and various rotary drills, have obtained

Figure 16-10 A box sampler for collecting undisturbed samples of the sea floor. (Photograph courtesy G.M. Mfg. and Instrument Corp.)

sediment cores considerably longer than those obtained with gravity or piston corers. The drill ship *Glomar Challenger* has taken core samples as long as 1,000 m from the floor of the open ocean where the water depth exceeds 5 km (Fig. 16-12). This vessel combines a drill similar to a full-scale oil drill with acoustical position-sensing and automatic dynamic-positioning gear. Much of the sedimentary evidence supporting the sea-floor spreading hypothesis has been obtained by the *Glomar Challenger* during its participation in the Deep-Sea Drilling Project, which was begun in 1969 and is sponsored by the National Science Foundation.

Figure 16-11 A gravity corer (A) and piston corer (B) ready to be lowered to the sea floor. (Photographs courtesy Joe S. Creager and Dean A. McManus)

Figure 16-12A Deep-sea drilling ship *Glomar Challenger*. (Photograph courtesy Scripps Institution of Oceanography, University of California at San Diego)

16.3   *Geophysical Measurements*

Because geophysical measurements have been made on a worldwide basis, we can study the structures of the ocean basins and their relationships to the continental masses. In addition, by using these measurements we can make a model that accounts for the structure and mechanisms of the crust of the earth.

A number of different instruments are needed for these measurements. The earth's magnetic field, measured throughout the world ocean by ships carrying magnetometers has provided a visualization of the remanent magnetization of the sea floor that gives strong support to the sea-floor spreading hypotheses. To measure the thermal gradients in the sediments, sensitive thermal sensors are mounted on sediment core barrels and thrust into the sea floor. The gradients are interpreted to obtain the magnitude of heat flow through the sea floor. These data provide information on tectonic processes at work in the world ocean today. Gravity measurements are made at sea using a pendulum device corrected for the ship's accelerations. Data on the variation of the magnitude of gravity in the world ocean reveals how rocks of different density are distributed beneath the sea floor.

Seismic techniques are also used for measurement. For example, the elastic properties of the earth are measured through the propagation of seismic waves

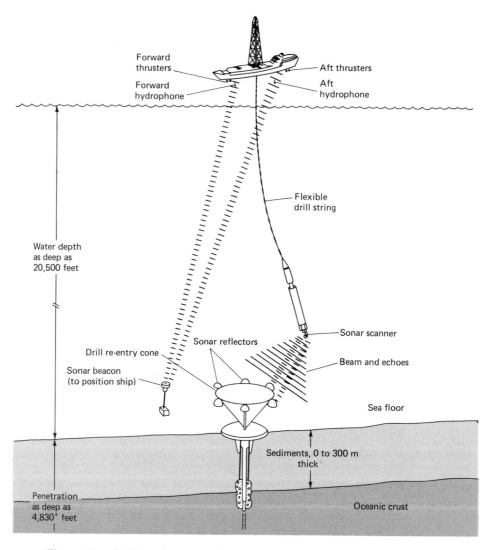

Forward thrusters

Aft thrusters

Forward hydrophone

Aft hydrophone

Flexible drill string

Water depth as deep as 20,500 feet

Sonar scanner

Sonar reflectors

Beam and echoes

Drill re-entry cone

Sonar beacon (to position ship)

Sea floor

Sediments, 0 to 300 m thick

Penetration as deep as 4,830⁺ feet

Oceanic crust

Figure 16-12B Dynamic positioning and re-entry technique for deep-sea drilling. (Photograph courtesy Scripps Institution of Oceanography)

that occur naturally as earthquakes or that are produced artificially by high-energy sound. The seismic reflection profiling technique uses sound energy to determine the structure beneath the sea floor. This technique is similar to echo sounding except that high-energy sound pulses are transmitted. These pulses not only reflect from the sea floor but also penetrate the bottom. Energy is reflected at discontinuities in the layers of bottom sediments. The result is a profile of all reflecting layers within the range of penetration (Fig. 16-13). Several types of energy sources are used to generate the penetrating signal.

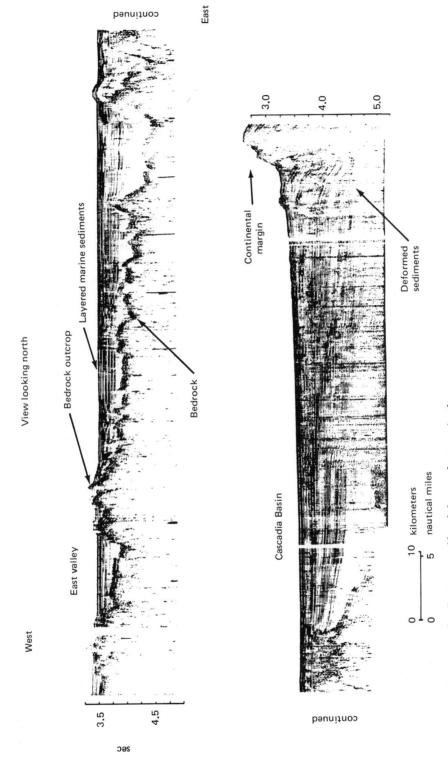

Figure 16-13 A typical reflection profile of the sea bottom in the Northeast Pacific Ocean Basin. One second of sound penetration represents approximately 750 m. (Photograph courtesy Dean A. McManus)

441

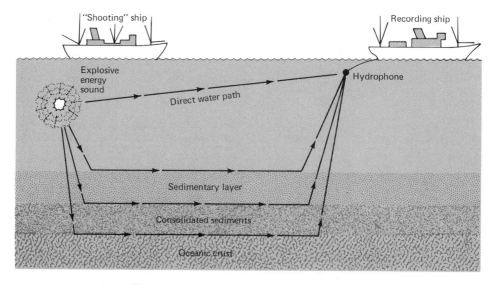

Figure 16-14 Seismic refraction technique.

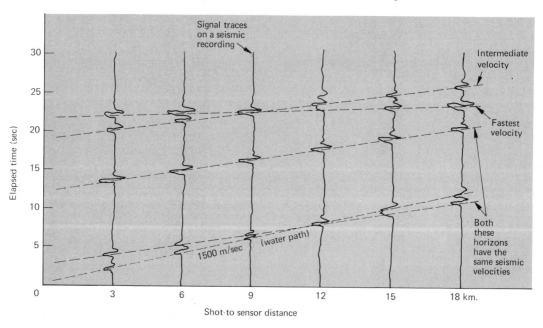

Figure 16-15 An example of a seismic refraction record.

Low-frequency sound is not absorbed by rock as extensively as are the higher frequencies, but it affords less resolution of small features at the bottom. The sound signal is produced in the water by an electrical discharge, sudden release of compressed air, an explosion, or any device that converts electrical energy into sonic energy. Each energy source produces a signal of unique acoustical quality, so that its use is limited to particular applications.

442

Refraction profiling uses the principle that energy impinging upon a sediment layer will refract depending upon the angle of incidence of the energy and its propagation velocity. In a series of strata of different compositions, energy propagates rapidly along paths in certain layers and slowly along the others (Fig. 16-14). A single pulse of energy refracted by sediment strata becomes separated into a series of pulses that represent the various propagation paths through each layer. In practice, one ship produces a seismic pulse and another ship or sensor buoy detects the refracted energy from some distance away. Energy traveling horizontally through the water arrives at the receiving sensor first, provided it is close to the seismic source. Energy that penetrates deeply into the bottom may arrive at a sensor deployed several kilometers from the source sooner than the direct signal that passed horizontally through the water. Analyzing the times of arrival of energy at sensors deployed at several distances permits interpreting the geologic structure beneath the sea floor (Fig. 16-15). A refraction profile is constructed by making a series of refraction measurements along a cruise track.

16.4   *Chemical Measurements*

Routine measurements of the properties of seawater include temperature, oxygen, salinity, and nutrients (phosphate, nitrate, and silicate ions). Techniques for measuring these properties are either semiautomatic or fully automatic; in many cases, the analytical data is reduced by a digital computer for storage, collation, and interpretation.

An instrument of great help to chemical and physical oceanographers is the STD (salinity, temperature, and depth) probe, shown in Fig. 16-16. This device consists of a sensing unit, which is lowered through the water column, and a data-receiving unit on shipboard. The sensing unit, containing an electronic thermometer, a pressure transducer, and an induction salinometer, transmits continuous electronic signals through a cable connecting it with the ship. As the sensors are lowered through the water column, the receiving unit plots the signals on graph paper. Thus, the oceanographer obtains an immediate graph of temperature, salinity, and depth while on station. Often, this information is fed directly into a shipboard computer for additional computations and display.

Collection of Seawater Samples

For most chemical determinations, it is necessary to retrieve a sample of seawater from several predetermined depths. A common sampling device is a Nansen bottle (Fig. 16-17), which is a metal tube (lined with a chemically inert plastic) having valves at both ends. The bottle, with the valves open, is lowered on a wire to the desired depth. Then a messenger (a metallic weight)

A

B

Figure 16-16 An S.T.D. sensing head ready to be lowered through the water column (A), while a shipboard computer plots vertical profiles of temperature and salinity (B).

is slid down the wire to hit the bottle, causing it to reverse *in situ* and close its valves, enclosing water. In practice, several bottles (up to twelve) are mounted at standard intervals on the hydrographic wire. When tripped by a messenger, each bottle drops another messenger to the bottle below, thus closing all bottles on the wire in succession. On board the exploration vessel, seawater samples are transferred to smaller sample bottles and subjected to a variety of chemical analyses.

Temperature Measurements

The reversing thermometer is the device used frequently to measure the temperature of seawater. It is a mercury-in-glass thermometer that is lowered

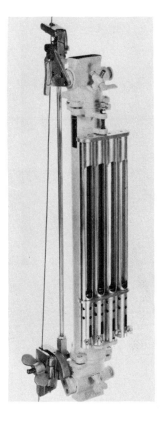

Figure 16-17 Nansen bottle mounted on a wire. The thermometer rack is designed to hold four thermometers. (Photograph courtesy G.M. Mfg. and Instrument Corp.)

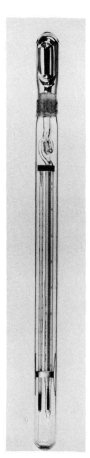

Figure 16-18 Reversing thermometer in the reversed position. (Photograph courtesy G.M. Mfg. and Instrument Corp.)

to the desired depth and inverted (Fig. 16-18). This reversal causes the mercury column to break in such a way that a quantity of mercury representing the *in situ* temperature is isolated from the mercury reservoir. In practice, the thermometers are mounted on the outside of a Nansen bottle so that the reversing process that closes the valves of the bottle also causes the *in situ* temperature to be recorded.

Reversing thermometers are manufactured either to respond to or to ignore pressure. When one of each type of thermometer is mounted on a Nansen bottle, the difference in the temperature readings indicates the pressure affecting the unprotected thermometer. This pressure is used to calculate the actual depth where the Nansen bottle was reversed. Reversing thermometers are considered reliable only to the nearest 0.02°C.

Today, extremely precise electronic temperature-measuring devices are used routinely. For example, the crystal thermometer uses the vibrational frequency of a quartz crystal to indicate temperature. This thermometer can resolve temperature changes as slight as 0.0001°C and has been used to measure the small temperature fluctuations that occur at the deep-sea floor.

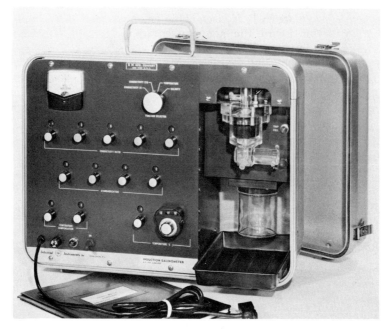

Figure 16-19 Portable salinometer. (Photograph courtesy G.M. Mfg. and Instrument Corp.)

Salinity Measurements

Seawater conducts an electrical current according to the temperature, salinity (ion content), and pressure. Therefore, if the temperature and pressure are known, the conductivity of seawater can be used to determine its salinity. Many oceanographic vessels have a salinity bridge aboard as standard equipment. This device compares the conductivity of a seawater sample to that of a known, standard sample (Fig. 16-19). If the temperature is controlled carefully, the salinity of the sample is easily determined. The salinity bridge, as other salinometers, must be calibrated with seawater of known salinity. The titration described in Chap. 4 still serves as the fundamental method for determining calibration salinities.

Measurement of Nutrients

Biological consumption of nutrients continues in a water sample after it has been collected, so it is necessary either to analyze nutrient ions in a water sample immediately or to arrest changes in nutrient ion concentrations during storage. Nutrient ion determinations chosen for use aboard a ship are simple and can be performed quickly, so that chemists can analyze samples as fast as they are collected.

Recorders for:

Nitrate Silicate   Phosphate ammonium

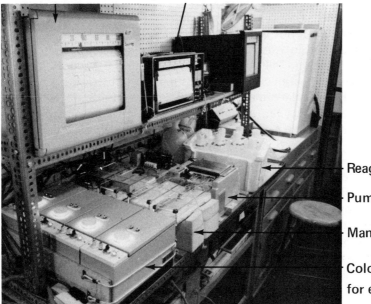

Reagents

Pump

Manifolds

Colorimeters
for each nutrient

Figure 16-20 This automatic analyzer can continuously analyze seawater samples for nitrate, phosphate, silicate, and ammonium concentrations. (Photograph courtesy the Bureau of Commercial Fisheries)

Colorimetry is the usual technique used to measure the concentration of nutrient ions in seawater. The seawater sample is treated chemically in such a way that a color is produced having an intensity depending on the concentration of the nutrient ion. The solution is transferred to a special glass cell and placed in a *spectrophotometer*. In this device, a beam of light passes through the flask, and the relative absorption is measured. Calibration curves are used to convert relative absorption values to nutrient ion concentration. Colorimetric techniques that take approximately 20 min have been developed for determining phosphate, nitrate, and silicate ions in seawater.

Instruments are now available that make nutrient determinations virtually automatic. The autoanalyzer, shown in Fig. 16-20, samples the seawater collection bottles in sequence, mixes reagents, and measures relative light absorption. This instrument can perform as many as 60 samples and analyses per hour. The measured concentrations of each sample are plotted on a graphic recorder, or the results can be fed directly into a computer.

Measurement of Dissolved Gases

The concentration of a gas dissolved in seawater can be measured by chemical analysis or by chemical instruments depending upon the chemical nature of the gas. Dissolved oxygen formerly was measured chemically by its ability to react with chemical reagents. An analytical procedure, called the Winkler method, precipitates an oxidized compound of manganese using oxygen dissolved in a seawater sample. The manganese compound then causes an iodate compound to liberate an amount of iodine proportional to the oxygen dissolved in the sample. The iodine is measured by titrating with a thiosulfate solution. The Winkler method is still used to calibrate instruments for the measurement of oxygen dissolved in seawater. Such instruments include a dissolved *oxygen electrode*, or probe, the *polarograph*, and the *gas chromatograph*. The oxygen probe involves the measurement of an electrochemical effect produced when dissolved oxygen diffuses across a membrane fixed at the end of a cell containing a solution whose *redox* state is sensitive to oxygen. The polarograph induces an electrical potential in seawater and causes oxygen to convert from a dissolved molecule (O_2) to a pair of separate oxygen atoms. The electrical current passing through the system is proportional to the concentration of dissolved oxygen in the seawater. The technique of gas chromatography involves passing a stream of gases extracted from a seawater sample through both a molecular sieve and a column packed with a material that retards the passage of gases selectively by adsorption. The molecular sieve is a porous material so fine that molecules larger than a particular size cannot pass through it. The gases swept through the adsorption column become fractionated and emerge into a gas detector in sequence. The time of arrival or removal by the molecular sieve determines the chemical identity of the gas. The amount of each type of gas in the stream is measured by the detector at the end of the absorption column. The gas chromatograph is used to measure oxygen, carbon dioxide, nitrogen, and other atmospheric and organic gases in trace quantities dissolved in seawater.

Trace Element Measurement

Trace elements, as the term suggests, are present in seawater in extremely small concentrations (a few ppm to a few ppb) that cannot be measured by ordinary chemical analysis. Instruments that sense minute concentrations of trace elements are used; these employ atomic properties of the elements for detection. The *atomic absorption spectrometer* is used widely for trace element analysis. A seawater sample is aspirated into a flame through which is passed a beam of light composed of radiation excited from the elements sought. As the trace elements are made alternately more and then less energetic by the heat energy of the flame, they absorb radiant energy from the light beam in proportion to their concentrations. In some cases a seawater sample must be concentrated to assure that a sufficient amount of the trace element is introduced into the flame of this instrument.

Activation analysis is useful in trace element measurement because the particles emitted during the radioactive decay of elements irradiated (activated) by neutron (or other particles) bombardment of the sample are easily detected and measured instrumentally. In an analagous fashion, the fluorescence induced in a trace element upon bombardment by X rays is a quantitative measure of trace element concentration obtained with an *X-ray fluorescence spectrometer.*

Trace elements as well as more abundant elements in solid phases from the ocean can be measured by the *electron microprobe.* This device scans an extremely small area of a solid sample with a beam of electrons in a manner similar to that in a cathode ray tube (or ordinary television screen). The nature of the secondary radiation induced by the electron beam is monitored to provide a map of the distributions and concentrations of specific elements in this sample. In the *scanning electron microscope,* secondary electron emission is detected and supplied to a television circuit, providing a visual display of the configuration of the surface of the sample. Examples of scanning electron microscope photos appear on Plates II and III in Chap. 12.

16.5 *Physical Measurements*

Measurement of Ocean Currents

Oceanographers use a variety of methods for measuring ocean currents. Some current-measuring techniques are simple, but detailed measurements of currents in the open ocean are difficult to make. For example, let us assume that we want to obtain a 1-month record of the South Equatorial Current in the middle of the Pacific Ocean. First, we must have devices that will operate and record continuously for that period. The parts of the meters must be corrosion-resistant, strong, and reliable. Second, we must anchor the meters, so they remain fixed with respect to the sea floor and orient themselves properly with respect to the current flow, despite severe attack by storm waves. Furthermore, the instruments must be retrievable. We will have to identify the instruments by a radio beacon or flashing light and then collect all equipment. Even this simplified list of considerations indicates that direct current measurements anywhere in the world ocean require considerable effort, an advanced marine technology, and sophisticated equipment.

Early indications of the speeds and directions of ocean currents were obtained by devices cast adrift at sea. A square rig sail weighted at its clews (lower corners) was used to test currents in 1576. This design is used today (but now is called a window shade drogue) with hardly any change other than materials. The drogue area must be at least 100 times the cross-sectional area of the float, flag, or spar that protrudes above the sea surface in order to minimize the effect of the wind upon the drogue's motion. Drogues with a cruciform, cylindrical, spherical, or parachute shape have been employed at one time or another since 1850. Fig. 16-21 illustrates some of the many designs.

In the early 1900's, scientists used drift bottles, which were small bottles

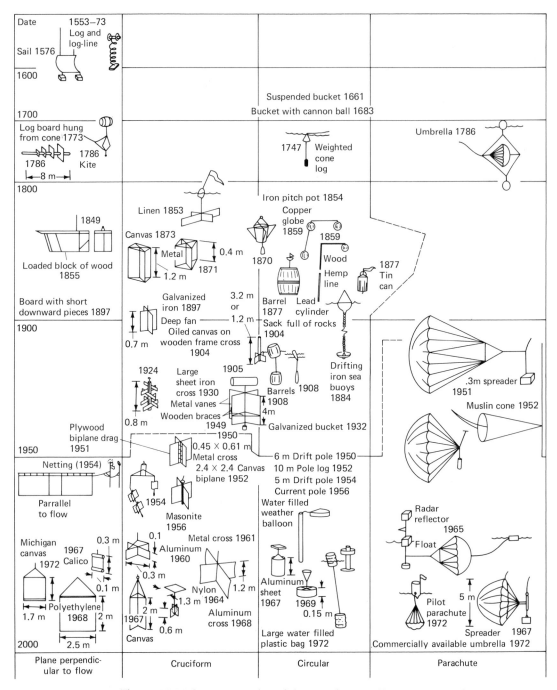

Figure 16-21 Some examples of drogue designs. Dates given indicate the approximate time of the first use of the design. (Courtesy Michigan Sea Grant Program)

that contained an identification card giving the time and place of release and the bottle number. The card requested that the finder fill in the time and place at which the bottle was found and return it to the oceanographic laboratory. A variety of other drifting devices, ships, plastic cards, drift poles, and even inflated plastic mattresses have been used to observe currents. Drifting objects have been used for measuring deep currents also. The Swallow float, for instance, is a device that can be weighted to sink to a predetermined depth when thrown overboard. It then emits sonic signals that allow it to be traced by a vessel as it moves with the deep currents (Fig. 16-22). Bottom currents are detected by drifters designed to be bounced and dragged along the bottom by currents at the sea floor.

The current measuring devices described so far all move with the water and must be tracked by ship, radio beacon, or some other position-locating system. The movement of the drogues traces the *trajectory* of a parcel of water in the vicinity of the drogue; the trajectory represents the sum effect of all kinds of forces inducing motion in the water.

Another class of current-measuring device includes *current meters* that are fixed in space with respect to the sea floor. Current meters moored by buoys or anchors, hung from anchored ships, or attached to fixed structures measure the water motion at a point in the ocean at a particular moment. If a continuous display or recorder is connected to the meter, the motion of seawater from moment to moment can be studied.

An example of such a current meter is the classic Ekman meter. This device contains a vane that orients the instrument to the flow of the current and a propeller that rotates as a function of current speed (Fig. 16-23). A simple and ingenious mechanism records the rotation rate of the propeller and the current direction. A circular container that is free to turn 360° about a vertical axis is located beneath the instrument. This container is a magnetic compass and is partitioned in 10-degree compartments. Above the propeller is a reservoir of small metal balls. The meter is lowered to some depth and is activated by a messenger. The mechanism is so designed that, for each 100 turns of the propeller, a ball is dropped from the reservoir into the magnetically oriented compartments. After a given time, another messenger deactivates the propeller, and the instrument is then returned to the ship. The number of balls that dropped during the measurement time indicates the average speed at that depth. The particular compartments into which the balls fell indicate the direction of the flow relative to magnetic north.

Fixed current meters measure the sum effect of all water motions that occur at a point. These include steady flow associated with hemispheric oceanic gyres, inertial flow, tidal currents, boundary flow at the sea surface, bottom, and coasts, wave motion, and random motion associated with turbulence of all scales down to the lower limit of the current sensor. Different meter designs measure the components of water motion to different degrees, so a meter must be selected to provide the measurements sought.

Figure 16-22 Swallow float which can be set to be neutrally buoyant at a predetermined depth and tracked by an acoustic beacon.

The Savonius Rotor current meter measures the rotation rate of an impeller, which has a shape completely different from a propeller. These meters are omnidirectional and hence do not have to be oriented to the current flow. Because they are sensitive at low speeds (approximately 1 cm per sec), they are used for deep-sea current measurements. To measure flow direction, a separate vane must be placed in the vicinity of the rotor. In Fig. 16-24, the rotor and direction vane are coupled to a shipboard unit that gives a continual visual display of the speed and direction of the current. This complete unit is light enough to lower by hand from a small boat. The deck unit can be coupled directly to a recording device if desired.

A Savonius Rotor meter is not particularly effective for detecting steady flow near the ocean surface because oscillatory wave motion is rectified by the omnidirectional rotor and is added to steady flow as a large component of motion. A better device is the *electromagnetic current* meter (Fig. 16-25). This device senses the vector of motion as seawater moves through the electromag-

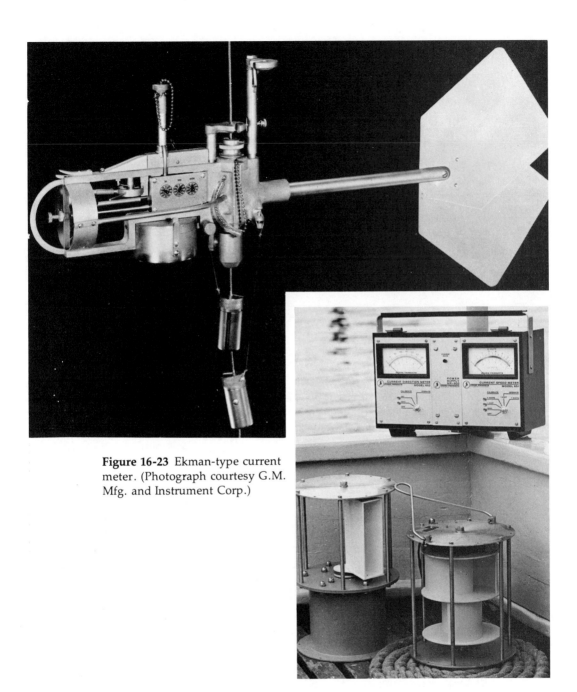

Figure 16-23 Ekman-type current meter. (Photograph courtesy G.M. Mfg. and Instrument Corp.)

Figure 16-24 Savonius rotor-type current meter. (Photograph courtesy Hydro Products)

Figure 16-25 An electromagnetic current meter ready to be lowered over the side. (Photograph courtesy Environmental Devices Corp.)

netic field induced by a magnet in the sensor. The vector is derived from electrical potentials that are measured on an array of electrodes that protrude from the meter's sensor. The instantaneous water current vectors are averaged over a prescribed sampling interval and the result is displayed or recorded. By choosing the sampling interval properly, the oscillatory motion of waves is removed from the current automatically.

Another approach is the tethered, neutrally buoyant, *ducted impeller meter* (Fig. 16-26). The impeller responds only to the steady water motion; current speed is measured in terms of the rate of impeller rotation. The direction of alignment is sensed by a compass contained within the meter housing.

Measurement of Waves and Tides

When a wave passes through shallow water, it is associated with a fluctuation of hydrostatic pressure at the bottom. The pressure increases under the wave crest and decreases under the trough. The magnitude of the pressure change is a function of the wave characteristics and the depth of water. This effect makes it possible to use a pressure-measuring device as a wave gauge. Pressure

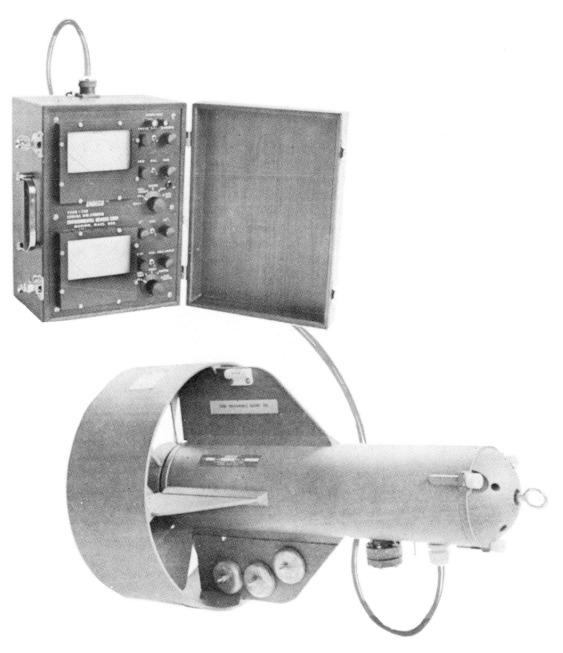

Figure 16-26 A ducted impeller-type current meter with a deck read-out unit. (Photograph courtesy of Environmental Devices Corp.)

transducers often consist of specially packaged strain gauges or potentiometers in which the pressure exerted on a metal diaphragm causes a change in a calibrated electronic signal. Another type of transducer uses a quartz crystal that is made to vibrate at its resonant frequency. As the surrounding pressure varies, the vibrational frequency of the crystal changes. Thus, changes in

Figure 16-27 In situ wave and tide recorder. (Photograph courtesy Hydro Products)

signal strength or frequency can be recorded as pressure fluctuations. One such device is shown in Fig. 16-27.

Waves at sea are measured and recorded by a *wave rider buoy* (Fig. 16-28). The buoy measures the vertical accelerations induced as it follows the motion of the sea surface. The accelerations are converted to wave height values recorded within the buoy or are transmitted to a shore- or ship-based receiver where the time history'of waves is displayed and recorded. Waves as high as 20 m can be measured. The period of the waves can range from 2 sec to 15 sec and can be recorded faithfully. Waves of longer period (to 28 sec) are recorded with less precision.

At the coast, waves and tides are measured by a wave staff bearing a pair of bare wires. The seawater immersing the wires provides a conducting path for an electrical current at that level. Thus, the total current path of the staff becomes shortened as the water level rises. Tides are measured at the coast by recording the position of a float in a stilling well, or of a pipe set to extend

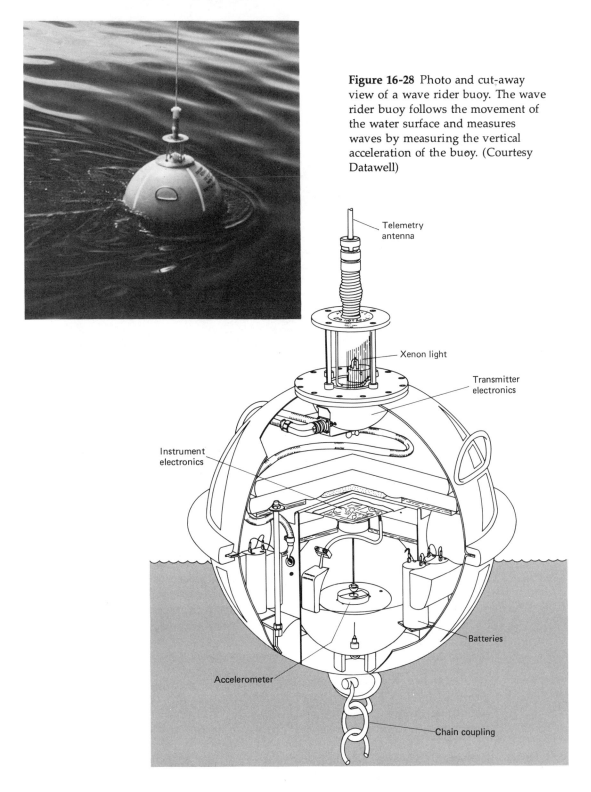

Figure 16-28 Photo and cut-away view of a wave rider buoy. The wave rider buoy follows the movement of the water surface and measures waves by measuring the vertical acceleration of the buoy. (Courtesy Datawell)

Telemetry antenna

Xenon light

Transmitter electronics

Instrument electronics

Batteries

Accelerometer

Chain coupling

Figure 16-29 An oceanographer deploying a secchi disk. This 30 cm white disk is lowered into the water until it disappears. The depth of disappearance, called the secchi depth, is a measure of the clarity of the water and of the thickness of the euphotic zone at the site.

through the sea surface. Bubbler tide gauges release a small bubble of inert gas at a point below the sea surface. The pressure on the bubble at its moment of release is converted to tidal height in the tidal recorder connected to the device.

Measurement of Light in the Ocean

Perhaps the most simple oceanographic instrument in use is the *secchi disk*, a thin white disk about 30 cm in diameter (Fig. 16-29). It is weighted to orient horizontally and is lowered on a rope into the sea. The depth at which it disappears, termed the secchi depth, is a measure of the transparency of the surface water of the ocean. The secchi depth is related to the extinction coefficient, a parameter that is a measure of the optical clarity of the water. The clarity of the water, or specifically the ability of the water to absorb light, is measured deeper in the ocean by a *transmissometer*. This device contains a calibrated light source separated a fixed distance from a light detector. The attenuation of the light over the fixed path is measured and expressed as an absorption coefficient.

The scattering of light by particles in seawater is measured by a *nephelometer*. This instrument is similar to the transmissometer except that the detector is situated at an angle to the light path where it senses light scattered from the direction of light propagation. The intensity of the scattered light is a measure of the concentration of scatterers (small suspensoids and molecules) in the seawater.

16.6 *Biological Measurements*

Biological oceanographers have developed a variety of mechanisms to obtain specimens from all parts of the water column and the sea floor. Representative devices are discussed here according to the mode of life of the organisms sampled.

Collection of the Benthos

The benthos is sampled with dredges (Fig. 16-7), which are dragged along the bottom and indiscriminately collect material in their paths. Samples of the benthos are also made with grab samplers (Fig. 16-8) that obtain those organisms living wherever the sampler happens to fall. The ocean bottom and the benthic organisms living there can be observed by underwater cameras (Fig. 16-4) and by underwater television devices (Fig. 16-5). These devices are similar to those used by geological oceanographers for sampling and observing bottom sediments and rocks.

Collection of the Plankton

The sampling of plankton is done by some form of filtration. A variety of fine-mesh nets, such as the half-meter net (Fig. 16-30) and the Clarke-Bumpus sampler (Fig. 16-31), are lowered to the ocean and dragged behind a moving ship. The plankton pump is another variation. A hose that can be lowered to any desired depth is attached to a pump that draws water from depth and discharges it into a barrel containing a graduated series of nets. With this instrument, the distribution of plankton at depth and with time can be sampled. The continuous plankton sampler (Fig. 16-32) is a filtering mechanism that is dragged at a predetermined depth behind a moving ship. It filters a sample of water on a continuously moving roll of netting. This apparatus provides a lateral profile of plankton distribution in surface water along a known path of travel over the world ocean. Nannoplankton are too small to be effectively filtered through a net. These organisms are collected in water

Figure 16-30 A ½-m plankton net being cleaned in preparation for a tow.

samples and either centrifuged or pumped through a special filtering apparatus that filters out organisms as small as 0.5 μm.

Collection of the Nekton

The Nekton are gathered with various trawls or coarse nets. The nets are drawn through the water at high velocity to trap organisms that could otherwise evade capture. In the trawls, there are arrangements of doors or rigid bars to hold the mouth of the trawl open, and depressors to prevent the net from inadvertently rising to the surface (Fig. 16-33). Traps (Fig. 16-34) are used in certain cases where organisms can be lured into the apparatus and thereby sampled.

Productivity Measurements

In practice, primary productivity is measured by observing the change in any of the substances involved in photosynthesis. In the oxygen method, a water sample containing phytoplankton is obtained and split into two bottles:

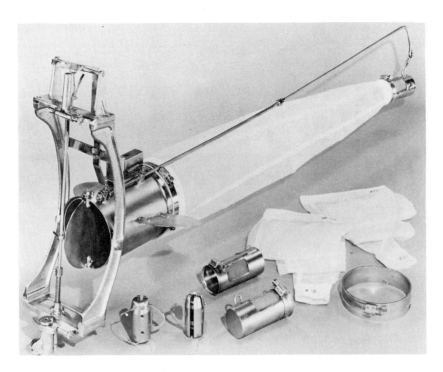

Figure 16-31 A Clarke-Bumpus automatic plankton sampler that can be opened and closed at depth by the use of wire messengers. (Photograph courtesy G.M. Mfg. and Instrument Corp.)

the water in one is illuminated, and the water in the other is kept dark. The dissolved oxygen in both bottles is measured to verify that both subsamples have the same initial oxygen concentrations. Both bottles are returned to the ocean for a period of time. The oxygen in both bottles is then remeasured. In the light bottle, photosynthesis and respiration show a net productivity, whereas the dark bottle shows the effects of respiration only. The concentration of dissolved oxygen in the water in the light bottle minus that in the dark bottle equals the gross photosynthetic production.

Productivity is measured instrumentally by inoculating the light and dark bottles with radioactive sodium carbonate initially and counting the C-14 radiation emitted by each after incubation in the ocean. The gross productivity is related to the counts of beta radiation per unit time detected by a gas-flow, beta-particle counter.

16.7 Data Recording and Processing

Oceanographic instruments, by making use of an advanced technology, are capable of gathering data in large quantities and at fast rates. The storing and rapid processing of masses of data have become a necessary and specialized aspect of oceanography.

461

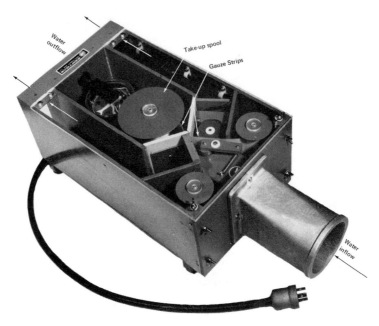

Figure 16-32 The Cod-end of the Longhurst-Hardy plankton sampler. (Photograph courtesy Benthos Company)

Figure 16-33 Oceanographic vessel preparing to lower a beam trawl. (Photograph courtesy T. S. English)

Figure 16-34 Spring-loaded plankton trap. (Photograph courtesy G.M. Mfg. and Instrument Corp.)

Analog recording of data in chart form continues to be a useful way to display data for verification of sensor performance and for visual analysis. Digital recording and processing is advantageous for handling large quantities of data rapidly. Digital circuitry in the form of analog–to–digital voltage or frequency converters, amplifiers, and other signal conditioning devices, and digital processers are available as inexpensive, compact components that allow complex storage, analysis, and manipulation of data with deceptively small devices. In many cases such a device can be placed within the instrument housing where it programs the sampling cycle (duration and interval), digitizes the sensor signal, performs averaging, spectral analysis, or other statistical processing, and stores the reduced data on magnetic tape according to a prescribed format. Using such equipment, months of observational data can be stored on ordinary data cassettes (Fig. 16-35).

Digitally recorded data can be processed by high-speed digital computers

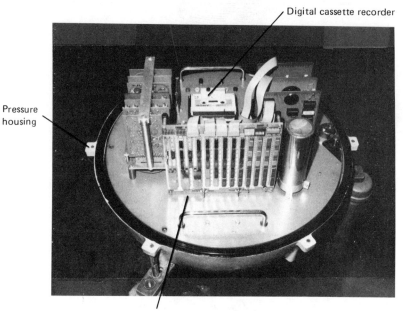

Figure 16-35 Data acquisition system mounted within a sphere for remote recording of sensors on the sea floor.

capable of performing millions of computations per second. Peripheral equipment, such as printers, graphic plotters, and cathode ray tube displays, provides the means for presenting the analysis of oceanographic data in a variety of ways. The processing units of such computers called micro-processors are often used to control complex data sampling and manipulation functions within the oceanographic instrument or on board ship. These processors are capable of controlling an unlimited number of sensors, clocked functions, telemetry, communications, and displays.

reading list

BARNES, H., *Oceanography and Marine Biology, A Book of Techniques.* New York: The Macmillan Company, 1959. 218p.

Instruction Manual for Oceanographic Observations (3rd ed.), U.S. Naval Oceanographic Office Publication 607. Washington, D.C.: U.S. Government Printing Office, 1968. 180p.

ISSACS, J. D., AND C. O. ISELIN, *Symposium on Oceanographic Instrumentation,* National Academy of Sciences—National Research Council Publication 309. Washington, D.C., 1952. 233p.

appendix:
physical and chemical concepts

The reader with no background in the physical sciences, particularly chemistry and physics, may find some parts of the text difficult to understand because of a language barrier. Therefore, we present here explanations of some of the terms and elementary concepts used in several chapters. The Appendix is not intended, however, to be a comprehensive treatment, as found in introductory textbooks on physics or chemistry.

A.1 Some Initial Considerations

The Metric System

Most scientists use one of the various metric systems of measurement. Generally, oceanographers use the *centimeter–gram–second*, or cgs, system for measuring length, mass, and time. This system should become familiar to nonscientists because of its consistency in nomenclature (denoting powers of 10) and because of certain other advantages over the so-called English or U.S. system of measurements.

In the metric system, both the magnitude of any physical property (mass, volume, length, and so on) and the fundamental measure of the property are named. The root of the name defines the property (length, time, mass, and so on); the prefix denotes the order of magnitude (Table A–1).

Length. The fundamental metric unit of length is the *meter*, defined as

Table A-1   Common Prefixes Used in Metric Systems

kilo = 1,000 units
deci = 1/10 part of a unit
centi = 1/100 part of a unit
milli = 1/1,000 part of a unit
micro = 1/1,000,000 part of a unit
nano = 1/1,000,000,000 part of a unit
pico = 1/1,000,000,000,000 part of a unit

1,650,763.73 wavelengths of Kr-86 orange red radiation. The length of the meter is very close to 1/40,000,000 the circumference of the earth. Table A–2 gives the most important metric units of length and some approximate equivalents.

Two units, the *fathom* and the *nautical mile*, persist in oceanography; they are holdovers from early maritime usage. The fathom is equal to 6 ft. The nautical mile is equal to 1,852 m, approximately 1 minute of arc on any great circle route on the earth's surface. These units are still found on most nautical charts printed by the U.S. Coast Survey.

Table A-2   Some Common Metric Length Units and Their U.S. Equivalents

kilometer = 1,000 meters = 3,281 feet = 0.62 statute miles
    = 0.54 nautical miles
meter = 100 centimeters = 3.28 feet = 39.4 inches
centimeter = 10 millimeters = 0.39 inches = 0.00328 feet
millimeter = 1,000 microns = 0.039 inches

Mass.   Mass is most simply defined as a quantity of matter. In the cgs system, the primary quantity is the *gram*, which is equivalent to the mass of 1 cu cm of pure water at 4°C. Other common units based on the gram are the kilogram and milligram (see Table A–1).

Time.   The fundamental unit of the time, the *second*, is approximately equal to 1/86,400 part of a mean solar day. The other subdivisions of time in the metric system are the same as in the U.S. system. In a geologic sense, time is reckoned in units of thousands, millions, and billions of years. For convenience, geologic time is divided into named intervals, which are shown in Table A–3.

Forms of Energy

Physical properties are best understood if they are related to some underlying scheme. The concept of energy is taken as the basic concept in this text, because, by relating physical phenomena this way, we can demonstrate how

Table A-3 Geologic Time*

Era	Period	Epoch	Stages	Began years ago	Dominant life and important events
Cenozoic	Quaternary	Recent (Holocene)		11,000	man
		Pleistocene	Wisconsin	0.2 million	glacial
			Sangamonian	0.4 "	interglacial
			Illinoisian	0.6 "	glacial
			Yarmouthian	0.9 "	interglacial
			Kansan	1.4 "	glacial
			Aftonian	1.7 "	interglacial
			Nebraskan	3.0 "	glacial
	Tertiary	Pliocene		6 million	
		Miocene		22 "	
		Oligocene		37 "	mammals
		Eocene		54 "	
		Paleocene		62 "	
Mesozoic	Cretaceous			130 million	
	Jurassic			180 "	reptiles
	Triassic			230 "	
Paleozoic	Permian			280 million	
	Pennsylvanian			325 "	amphibians
	Mississippian			340 "	trees
	Devonian			400 "	grasses
	Silurian			450 "	fish
	Ordovician			500 "	
	Cambrian			580 "	invertebrates
Precambrian				1.8 billion	development of oxygen in atmosphere; appearance of eucaryotic cells
				2+ billion	life originated as a procaryote cell
				3+ billion	formation of ocean
				4+ billion	oldest rocks
				5+ billion	origin of earth and solar system
				12 billion	origin of the universe according to the present rate of expansion

*A person not familiar with the geologic time scale would realize that 5 billion years is a long time but would have no understanding of what that age represents relative to other important occurrences throughout geologic time. Therefore, this table is presented to familiarize the reader with the scope of geologic time and with some important occurrences within this time span.

all physical processes on the earth are ultimately dependent upon the sun.

It seems that the best way to describe energy succinctly is to say that everything in the universe seems to consist of energy. We cannot say what energy is, however. Nevertheless, inquiries into the nature of energy have revealed some of its characteristics. One characteristic is that the manifestations of energy occur in several forms. One form is *matter.* Einstein postulated the formula, $E = mc^2$, where c equals the celerity or speed of light (approximately 300,000 km per sec), so that any quantity of matter, m, can be represented as a definite amount of energy, E. The validity of this equation was demonstrated dramatically by the explosion of the first atomic bomb in New Mexico on July 16, 1945.

Another manifestation of energy is the form of *radiant energy.* We can show that any radiation—light, for example—is equivalent to a definite quantity of energy by the equation: $E = hf$, where h is Planck's constant and f is the frequency of the radiation (i.e., a particular color of light).

Further, *magnetism* and *electricity* are electrical forms of energy. *Chemical energy* is the energy that motivates chemical reactions between chemical substances. *Thermal energy* is energy that we recognize as heat. *Mechanical energy* is energy that matter possesses by virtue of its position in the universe *(potential energy)* or its motion through space *(kinetic energy).* Waves in the ocean represent a combination of potential and kinetic energy. Sound energy is also a form of mechanical energy.

Other Characteristics of Energy

A fundamental characteristic of energy is that it is conserved; that is, energy is neither created nor destroyed. This fact is asserted as a physical law because no observations or experiments have ever disproved it.

Another characteristic of energy is that it can change from one form to another. Many examples exist. A battery contains chemical substances that convert chemical energy into electrical energy. Electrical energy can be made to operate an incandescent lamp that emits light (radiant energy) and heat (thermal energy). Imagine yourself in an automobile. If it is parked on a hill, it has potential energy with respect to the bottom of the hill. Should the brakes be released, the potential energy is converted into kinetic energy as the automobile moves down the hill. If you bring the automobile under control by applying the brakes suddenly, the skidding of the tires converts kinetic energy into thermal energy. If you were burned by touching the hot tire, an amount of thermal energy would cause a nervous impulse to be sent to the brain in the form of electrical energy. Your burned finger demonstrates that thermal energy can be converted to chemical energy in coagulating the protein in skin. Your cry of dismay represents the conversion of chemical energy obtained from your last meal into sonic energy, a form of mechanical energy.

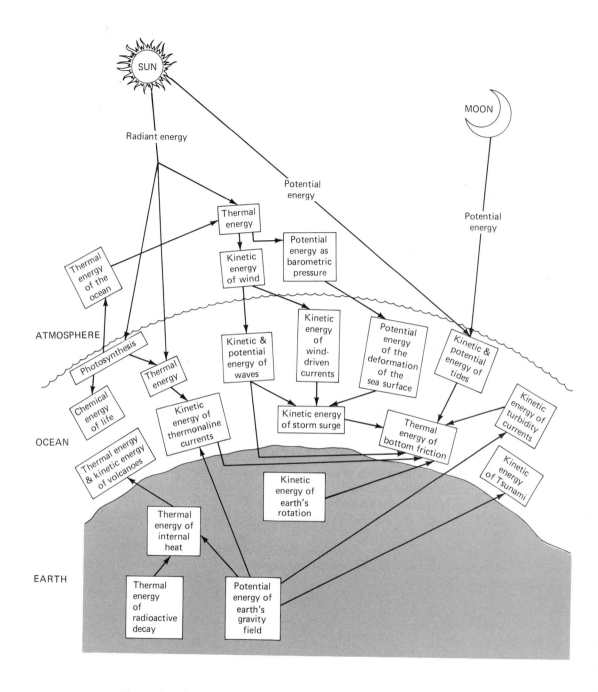

Figure A-1 Sources, transformations, and reservoirs of the earth's energy.

Last, energy can be considered to exist in discrete amounts called *quanta*. The size of the quanta is small and depends upon the form of energy considered. Note that just as matter has a particulate nature—that is, atoms are made from subatomic particles—so also does energy have a particulate nature. The sources and the transformations of energy in the ocean are demonstrated in Fig. A–1. The principal sources of the earth's energy are extraterrestrial. The sun supplies radiant energy, and potential energy is supplied by the gravitational attraction of the moon and sun. A smaller amount of energy as heat (about 0.008 percent of solar irradiation) is supplied by decay of radioactive elements within the earth, but even they had their source elsewhere in the universe.

A.2 *Properties of Energy in the Form of Matter*

Density

The quantity of matter in a body is termed its *mass,* and the amount of space that the body occupies is its *volume*. Mass is assigned the basic unit of grams; volume is assigned the basic unit of cubic centimeters. These two properties are related and can be considered simultaneously by using the term *density*. The amount of matter in a specified amount of space is the density of the matter under consideration: density (ρ) = mass/volume. The standard density is that of water at a temperature of about 4°C. This density is arbitrarily set as equal to 1 g per cu cm. The same standard defines mass. One gram of mass is the mass in 1 cu cm of water at 4°C.

The densities of different types of matter differ because their molecules have different masses and different spacings in their structures. The densities of a few substances are given in Table A–4.

Table A-4   Density of Some Common Substances

Substance	Density (g per cu cm)
Pure water at 4°C	1.00
Seawater	approx. 1.03
Gold	19.3
Air	0.0012
Rock (granite)	2.7
Steel	7.8
Mercury	13.6
Cork	0.2
Ice	0.92

It is possible to crowd more molecules into a given unit of volume; therefore, the density of a single type of matter can vary. Gases, in particular, are readily compressible.

Buoyancy

The *buoyancy* of an object is its tendency to float in a fluid. According to Archimedes' principle, a body floats if its mass is less than the mass of the water it displaces.

The volume of water displaced is the same as the volume of the immersed body. An object with a volume of 1 cu cm displaces a volume of water containing approximately 1 g of mass. The immersed object will float if its mass is less than 1 g and will sink if its mass is greater than 1 g. For example, 1 cu cm of iron contains a mass of 7.8 g. This cube of iron displaces only 1 g of water, so it will sink. One cubic centimeter of pure ice contains a mass of 0.92 g; therefore, it floats on water. These phenomena are usually described in terms of density. Bodies more dense than water will sink and bodies less dense than water will float. An object whose density is less than water is said to have *positive buoyancy,* or a tendency to rise toward the surface of the liquid. If an object is more dense than water, it has *negative buoyancy. Neutral buoyancy* occurs when the object and the water have the same density. A neutrally buoyant substance will remain where it is placed and has no tendency to rise or sink.

A. Stable   B. Unstable   C. Indifferent stability

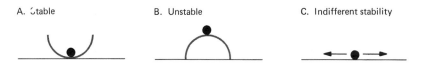

Figure A-2 Diagrammatic representation of the concept of stability.

Stability

The concepts of buoyancy and density are combined in the concept of *stability*. Stability can be stated as the tendency of a displaced body to return to its original position. The black ball in Fig. A–2A is in a stable position, because it has a tendency to return to its original position if displaced in any direction. An unstable configuration is illustrated in Fig. A–2B. Here, the ball, once displaced, has a tendency to seek a new position rather than return to its original position. Figure A–2C illustrates a configuration of indifferent stability, in which the displaced black ball has no tendency to move in any direction.

In seawater, stability is related to density and therefore to buoyancy. In this case, the black ball in Fig. A–2 is analogous to a small parcel or volume of

472

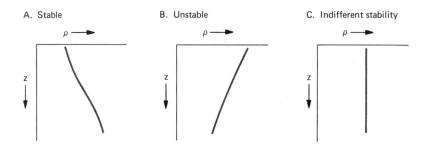

Figure A-3 The concept of stability as applied to a water column.

$Z = depth$

$P = density$

seawater, and the bowl or plane is analogous to the surrounding water. Figure A–3A represents a stable configuration, because at every level, water of low density is floating in water of greater density. If a parcel of water is displaced downward, there is a tendency for it to rise to the level of its own density—that is, to return to its original position. An unstable configuration is illustrated by Fig. A–3B. Here, water of greater density is floating over less dense water, and there is a tendency for the surface water to sink spontaneously through the low-density water. Likewise, the low-density water tends to rise through the water of higher density. A uniform density profile (Fig. A–3C) is one of indifferent stability. In this situation, a displaced parcel of water has no tendency to return to its original position or to seek a new position.

Mechanical Energy and Force

Mechanical energy is measured by the work that a body produces. Work is done when matter is moved; the amount of work done equals the distance the body is moved times the force required to make the move. *Force* is commonly thought of as being a push or pull applied to the body. Hence, force is meaningless unless a definite quantity of matter, or mass, is also considered. To understand how force is related to mass, consider a force applied to a stationary object. Initially, the body is at rest and has a velocity equal to zero. One second after applying directed force to the body, the velocity of the body was increased to, say 10 cm per sec. In other words, its velocity has changed from 0 cm per sec to 10 cm per sec within the span of a second. This change in velocity is called *acceleration*. If the force on the body is varied, the acceleration varies directly; that is, force is proportional to acceleration for a given object. If the same force is applied to different masses, the acceleration of those masses varies inversely. Mass is proportional to the reciprocal of acceleration; or bigger objects accelerate more slowly. If we combine these observations, we obtain the relation between force, F, mass, m, and acceleration, a. This is Newton's second law, often called the equation of motion:

$$F = ma \qquad \text{[A-1]}$$

So far, we have shown that, in order to measure the amount of mechanical energy in a body, it is necessary to determine the amount of work being done. To determine work, it is necessary to know the force acting, as calculated from Eq. A-1.

The principle of gravitation states that any two objects in the universe are attracted toward each other by virtue of their masses. The force of attraction is related to the masses of the two objects and to the distance separating them. Newton observed the phenomenon and was able to write the equation:

$$F = \frac{Gmm_e}{r_e^2} \qquad \text{[A-2]}$$

where G equals the universal gravitational constant, m equals the mass of an object on earth, m_e equals the mass of the earth (a constant), and r_e equals the radius of the earth (a constant). The constants in this equation can be combined and designated by g; that is:

$$m_e G / r_e^2 = g$$

From this statement is obtained the force of the earth's gravitation upon a mass, m, on the earth's surface:

$$F_G = mg \qquad \text{[A-3]}$$

By comparing this formula with the equation of motion (Eq. A-1), we see that g is an acceleration. Consequently, it is called the acceleration of gravity (on the earth). It has a value of about 980 cm per sec per sec (it varies slightly from place to place on earth).

The principle of gravitation is used in conjunction with the fact that a spring will stretch a distance proportional to the force causing it to stretch. If an object is suspended from a spring, the force of the earth's gravity pulls the object downward. The elongation of the spring is directly proportional to the force that gravity exerts. This force is called the *weight* of the object. Weight is actually a force; that is:

$$\text{weight} = mg \qquad \text{[A-4]}$$

Because g is known on earth, it is possible to calculate the mass of the object from its weight. The unit of force is defined by saying that 1 dyne is the force required to accelerate 1 g of mass 1 cm per sec per sec. On the earth, the weight of 1 g of mass is 980 dynes.

The kinetic energy possessed by a moving body is summarized by the equation:

$$E = \frac{1}{2} mv^2 \qquad \text{[A-5]}$$

where v = the velocity of a moving object.

Dynamic Equilibrium

On the earth, gravity also accounts for the acceleration that is assigned to even a stationary object. When all forces acting on a body are in balance—that is, when the net force acting on that body is equal to zero—the body is in dynamic equilibrium. Conversely, if the forces are not balanced, its state of motion will change in such a way that dynamic equilibrium is approached. Thus, just because a body is stationary does not mean that no forces are acting on it. Indeed, all bodies on the surface of the earth are attracted to the earth by a force of gravitation; however, the force of gravitation is equally opposed by other forces, so that a net force does not exist. Because the force of gravity is acting on a body at all times, it is always possible to assign an acceleration of gravity to that body.

As another example of dynamic equilibrium consider an object sinking in water. The force of gravity acting on the object causes a definite acceleration in this case. However, as the velocity increases (as the body accelerates), the friction between the body and the water increases and presents a force opposing the sinking of the object. At a certain velocity, the acceleration by gravity just equals the deceleration by frictional drag, and the body sinks at a constant rate. The net acceleration is zero, implying that the net force acting on the body is also zero, the condition for dynamic equilibrium. It is important to realize that, in this case, the velocity of the body is not zero and that a constant, finite motion exists.

Force Diagrams

The forces acting on a body to produce either dynamic equilibrium or disequilibrium are visualized by displaying them graphically in a *force diagram*, sometimes called a *vector diagram*. In force diagrams, forces are depicted as arrows; the orientation of the arrow indicates the direction in which the force acts and the length of the arrow is drawn to be proportional to the magnitude of the force.

In Fig. A–4A, two forces, one twice as large as the other, are shown to be acting in the same direction but on separate bodies. In Fig. A–4B, two equal forces are shown acting in opposite directions on separate bodies.

Where several forces act on a single body, they can be resolved into a single net force. Figure A–4C shows two equal but opposing forces acting to produce a zero net force on a body. In Fig. A–4D, two forces (1 and 2) acting on a body are of unequal magnitude and directions. If a parallelogram (dashed line) is drawn, the resultant (or net) force can be drawn (3) as the combination of forces 1 and 2. This force system can be represented by *either* forces 1 and 2 or by 3 alone, because they are equivalent. Likewise, a simple force can be separated into various component forces. In Fig. A–4E, vector 1 has been divided into a north (3) and a west (2) component force. In this case, force 1

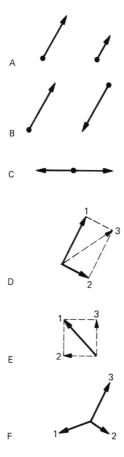

Figure A-4 Introduction of force vectors and the resolution of forces.

is equivalent to forces 2 and 3, and the physical system can be illustrated by either 1, or by 2 and 3.

Figure A–4F shows a body acted on by forces 1, 2, and 3. In this example, the net force is zero. This calculation is determined by (1) resolving any two of the three forces and (2) comparing the resultant with the third force. It makes no difference which two forces are picked initially, provided that the resultant force *replaces* the two chosen and is in turn compared to the third force. This technique is important to oceanographers as a tool for analyzing the dynamics of ocean currents. Some actual examples are given in Chap. 8.

Pressure

One common force is *pressure*. Strictly speaking, pressure is the force acting on the quantity of matter divided by the area over which that force is acting. A person whose mass is 100 kg (and therefore weighs 98 million dynes) and whose shoes have an area of 300 cm exerts a pressure on the floor of about 32,666 dynes per sq cm. A unit such as dynes per sq cm is rather unwidely; others, therefore, have been devised. The pressure of the earth's atmosphere has been calculated as approximately 1 million dynes per sq cm. It is called 1 bar by meteorologists and is equal to the pressure at the bottom of a column of mercury 76 cm high, a quantity easily measured with a mercury barometer. This pressure is approximately equal to 1 atmosphere (actually 0.987 atm).

Thermal Energy and the Structure of Matter

Amorphous—no particles visible (obsidian, glass,

In matter, the organization of atoms or molecules (henceforth called *particles*) depends upon the phase, or state, in which the matter exists. In the solid state, matter is either crystalline or amorphous. A crystalline material like salt has its particles arranged in space according to a definite geometric pattern. The particles in such a crystal are continuously vibrating. The vibration of any particle occurs around a point in space determined by the position of the particle in the crystal lattice. Amorphous materials like glass differ from crystalline materials in that the particles have no recognizable geometric arrangement. The particles do, however, have vibrational motion around some mean position in space.

In the liquid phase, the particles move farther through space in such a way that any previous position is not "remembered," and the organization of the particles in space is transitory. In addition to vibrating, these particles are free to translate and to rotate around their own axes. Furthermore, the particles are cohesive; that is, they attract and repel one another in such a manner as to maintain an average spacing between particles and a constant volume. Furthermore, the aggregate of particles in a liquid is influenced by the force of gravity, so that it tends to remain in an open container, such as a cup, and maintain a free surface.

In the gaseous state, particles vibrate and translate too, but they move so far apart that virtually no cohesive attractive forces act between them. For this reason, a gas will not remain in an open container but will tend to leave to fill a larger enclosure. For example, gas that is allowed to escape from a bottle will distribute its particles uniformly throughout the room in which the bottle is situated.

Definitions of these states of matter are merely conventional to some extent. Wax, for example, represents a gradation between a crystalline and an amorphous solid. At certain temperatures and pressures, it is impossible to distinguish between the liquid and gas phases of water. Note, however, that all phases of matter contain mechanical energy manifested as vibrational, rotational, and translational motion of particles. Potential energy is represented by the energy involved in maintaining a mean separation between the particles in matter.

Partitioning of thermal energy. When thermal energy is supplied to matter, it is stored in the body of matter in several ways. Part of the thermal energy is used in opposing the attraction of the molecules (potential energy), and part of the thermal energy increases the vibration, rotation, and translation of the molecules. The amount of energy stored in each of these ways depends upon the type of molecule in the body, the phase of the body (gas, liquid, or solid), and the amount of energy already in the body.

Temperature and heat. The amount of energy that each molecule in a body stores as motion is indicted by the temperature of that body. Heat, on the other hand, is the total amount of thermal energy in a body of matter. We cannot feel how much heat (or thermal energy) a body has any more than we can feel how much potential energy is contained in a rock located at the top of a hill. It is necessary to specify the size of a particular body, its temperature, and its heat capacity in order to state how much thermal energy it contains.

Temperature is the intensity of molecular motion and can be felt as hotness or coldness of a body. The size of a body need not be specified to state its temperature; it is necessary only to bring a thermometer into contact with the body.

Thermometers and the Measurement of Temperature

Two scales are commonly used for the measurement of temperature: Fahrenheit (F) and Celsius (C), also called centigrade. Both of these scales are based on properties of water. Two fixed points, the freezing point and the boiling point, provide a standard for comparison of temperatures. On the Fahrenheit scale, the freezing point of water is 32° and the boiling point is 212°. On the Celsius scale, the freezing point is 0° and the boiling point is 100°. It is immediately evident that the size of the Fahrenheit degree is different from that of the Celsius degree. Between the freezing point and boiling point of water, there are 180 Fahrenheit degrees and 100 Celsius degrees. They are in a ratio of 180 to 100 or 9/5. To convert from degrees Celsius to degrees Fahrenheit, multiply the temperature on the Celsius scale by 9/5 and add 32 to account for the fact that the Fahrenheit scale is already at 32° when the Celsius scale is only at 0. That is, $F = 9/5C + 32$. To convert from F degrees to C degrees, solve this equation for C: $5/9 (F - 32) = C$. This relationship is explained in Fig. A–5.

Most temperature-measuring devices are designed to respond to characteristic thermal properties of matter. A change in temperature in a liquid results in a change in the density of that liquid, because the liquid tends to occupy a different volume of space. Mercury has a characteristic, uniform thermal expansion, so it is commonly used in thermometers. Oceanographers, how-

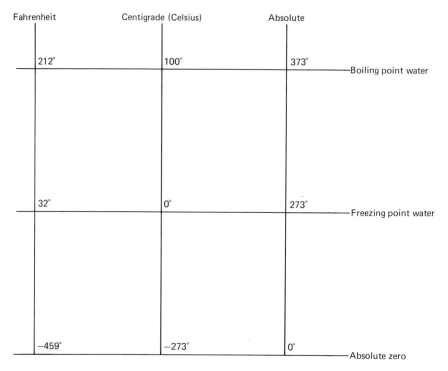

Figure A-5 Comparison of different temperature scales.

ever, measure temperature with electronic thermistors, devices in which electrical resistance is proportional to temperature.

Scientists sometimes use another scale of temperature, the absolute or Kelvin temperature scale, which is based on the energy of molecular motion. At the zero degree point of the absolute scale, matter has only slight molecular vibration and no translation or rotation. The absolute degree is of the same magnitude as the Celsius degree. The boiling point of water is at about 373° absolute, and the freezing point of water is at about 273° absolute. Absolute 0° is at −273.16°C or −469°F.

The Relationship Between Temperature and Thermal Energy

Each kind of molecule stores energy as motion in different amounts; therefore, one unit of heat energy will raise the temperature of one substance more than another. The relationship between the change in temperature and the change in the amount of thermal energy in a given mass of a substance is called its *heat capacity*. The heat capacity of water is taken as the standard and is arbitrarily assigned the value of 1°C per gram calorie. Thus, the unit of heat energy is defined as the *calorie*. Note that this calorie is not the one used in the calculation of food energy in dieting; in that case, a Calorie is equal to 1,000 calories. One calorie of heat energy is required to raise the temperature of 1 gm of water 1°C (in the vicinity of 16°C). The heat capacities of some substances are listed in Table A–5.

Although water is the standard for defining units of thermal energy, temperature, and heat capacity, it has some of the most unusual thermal properties of all the naturally occurring substances on earth.

Table A-5   Heat Capacity of Selected Substances

Substance	Amount of energy absorbed in causing a 1° change in temperature in 1 gm of substance
Ice	0.55 cal/°C
Mercury	0.03
Copper	0.093
Air	0.33
Rock	0.20

Substance	Number of degrees that temperature of 1 gm of substance can be raised by 1 cal of thermal energy
Water	1°C/cal
Ice	1.8°
Mercury	33.3°
Copper	10.8°
Air	3°
Rock	5°

Latent heat energy of fusion.   Part of applied thermal energy opposes attraction of molecules and tends to hold molecules apart. If sufficient heat energy is supplied to the molecules in a solid body, the molecules will stay far enough apart to give liquid properties to it. If still more energy is supplied, the molecules tend to stay even farther apart, and then the substance becomes a gas. The amount of thermal energy that must be supplied to 1 gm of matter to convert it completely from a solid at its melting point to a liquid at the same temperature is the latent heat energy of fusion. For water, 80 cal are required. It makes no difference which way the phase change proceeds. When water passes from the liquid to the solid phase of water, 80 cal of heat energy per gm are released rather than absorbed.

Latent heat energy of evaporation.   The amount of thermal energy that must be supplied to 1 gm of matter to convert it completely from a liquid to a gas is the latent heat energy of evaporation. Water requires 540 cal per gm at its boiling

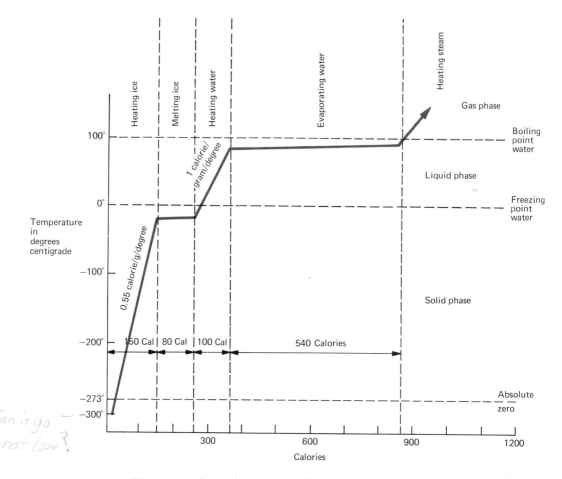

Figure A-6 Thermal properties of water. The graph shows the thermal energy (calories) required to raise the temperature of one gram of water from absolute zero to above 100°C.

point. The latent heat energy of fusion and of evaporation for mercury is 70 cal per gm. The fact that a temperature of phase change is specified does not imply that a phase change must occur at this temperature; water can pass from the liquid to gas phase at any temperature. However, the temperature at phase change determines the exact amount of the latent heat energy absorbed or released at the change of phase. For example, evaporation of water at 0°C requires 595 cal per gm. At 18°C, the phase change absorbs 585 cal per gm. The thermal properties of water are illustrated in Fig. A–6. This curve shows the changes in temperature when heat energy is supplied gradually to 1 gm of water (ice) at absolute zero.

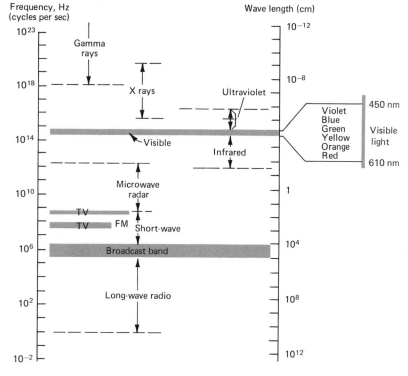

Figure A-7 The electromagnetic spectrum.

Radiant Energy

Energy in the form of electromagnetic radiation is characterized by either wave or particulate properties. Radiant energy waves can be assigned a constant speed of 300,000 m per sec, a frequency in cycles per sec, and an amplitude that is a measure of the intensity of the radiation. The same energy can be considered as particles called *photons*. Each photon contains a discrete amount of energy called a *quantum*. Experimental evidence shows that electromagnetic radiation is explained best as waves when observed in one manner and as particles when observed in a different manner. Wave properties of radiant energy are related to particulate properties by the following formula: $E = hf$, where h is 16×10^{-35} cal sec and f is the frequency of the radiation. This formula states that the amount of energy in the radiant form is proportional to the frequency of radiation. All possible frequencies of electromagnetic radiation are described in a spectrum, as shown in Fig. A–7.

Energy is emitted from matter as electromagnetic radiation because of fluctuations in the distribution of energy among the molecules. Collisions of molecules and the vibration of molecules cause these particles to have first greater, then lesser energy. Both the frequency (energy of the photon) and the intensity (number of photons leaving per sec) are governed by the amount of energy in the matter and, indirectly, by the temperature of the matter.

Matter will absorb electromagnetic radiation but only in quanta of certain size (frequency). The size of the absorbed quanta is dependent upon the molecular structure of the matter absorbing the radiation; that is, the photon must "fit" into the molecule or it is not absorbed.

A.3 *Some Basic Chemical Definitions*

Classification of Matter

Atoms are the basic particles from which all matter is made. They have different compositions, depending upon the amount of subatomic particles contained. Two types of subatomic particles, the *proton* and the *neutron*, constitute the nucleus of an atom; the third type, the *electron*, is outside the nucleus. The number of protons in the nucleus of an atom determines its chemical nature. The common form of each atom has an equal number of neutrons and protons in the nucleus. Elements can have less common forms *(isotopes)*, because the nuclei of these atoms may have more or fewer neutrons, hence a different mass, than the common isotope.

At present, 104 different kinds of atoms are known to exist. Each kind of atom is called an *element* and is generally considered to be unalterable. In truth, alteration can be accomplished by applying a tremendous amount of energy. Some atoms change by spontaneous radioactive decay; hence, their elemental properties change with time. Examples of some common elements are listed in Table A–6.

Two or more atoms of any kind in chemical combination form a *molecule*. There are essentially two types of molecules: those formed by the combination of two or more different kinds of atoms, and those formed by the combination of two or more atoms of the same element. Examples of the first type are water (H_2O), carbon dioxide (CO_2), and sucrose, a common sugar $(C_{12}H_{22}O_{11})$. Examples of the second type are oxygen (O_2), nitrogen (N_2), and hydrogen (H_2).

Matter composed of molecules of the first type is called a *compound*, implying that it is a substance with fixed composition that is separable by chemical means into two or more elements. Compounds are of two general kinds— organic and inorganic. *Organic compounds* contain carbon, and many of these can be synthesized by living organisms. They are the building blocks of living matter. Examples are sugars, fats, and proteins. *Inorganic compounds* include all other compounds.

Table A-6   Some Common Elements and Their Chemical Symbols

Aluminum	Al	Iodine	I	Potassium	K
Argon	Ar	Iron	Fe	Protactinium	Pa
Boron	B	Lead	Pb	Silicon	Si
Bromine	Br	Magnesium	Mg	Strontium	Sr
Calcium	Ca	Manganese	Mn	Sulfur	S
Carbon	C	Nitrogen	N	Thorium	Th
Chlorine	Cl	Oxygen	O	Uranium	U
Copper	Cu	Phosphorus	P	Zinc	Zn
Hydrogen	H				

A *mixture* consists of atoms and molecules that are not in chemical combination with each other and have no fixed composition. The ocean illustrates the difference between a compound and a mixture. Water is a compound. Seawater is a solution (a homogeneous mixture) consisting of solids, liquids, and gases (solutes) dissolved in water (the solvent). The relationships between these different terms are illustrated in Fig. A–8. *Colloids*, relatively large aggregates of molecules in suspension, are common in the sea; they are intermediate between a solution and a mixture.

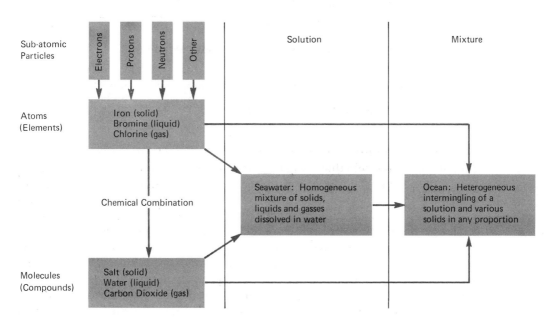

Figure A-8 Relationship between subatomic particles, atoms, molecules, solutions, and mixtures. In this scheme, water is a compound, seawater a solution, and the ocean a mixture.

A *solution* has one important property: There is a maximum quantity of solid, liquid, or gaseous material that can be dissolved in it. A solution containing a maximum quantity of solute is said to be *saturated* with that substance. The concentration of this dissolved material is called the *saturation concentration*, or *saturation solubility*.

Chemical Nomenclature

Most people, whether trained in chemistry or not, realize that chemists use symbols rather than the formal names of elements. This chemical shorthand allows a chemist to refer to any form of matter in a simple and concise manner.

The first step in understanding the language of chemistry is to know the symbol for each of the elements. Table A–6 presents the chemical symbols for those elements mentioned in this text.

Next, it is important to learn how these abbreviations for elements fit together to form the names of compounds. Since compounds represent elements in fixed chemical combinations, each different compound has a name and a specific set of symbols to represent the particular combination of elements. For example, a water molecule is composed of two atoms of hydrogen combined chemically with one atom of oxygen. The chemical symbol for water is H_2O. In many cases, the name of the compound refers to the composition, just as does its symbol. Some example are given in Table A–7.

Table A-7 Some Common Compounds and Their Chemical Symbols

Table salt	NaCl	Calcium carbonate	$CaCO_3$
Carbon dioxide	CO_2	Silicon dioxide	SiO_2
Silver chloride	AgCl	Hydrogen sulfide	H_2S

The concept of an ion is of great importance in chemical oceanography. An *ion* is an atom or molecule that, when put into solution, acquires a net positive or negative charge by gaining or losing one or more electrons. The electron carries a negative charge, so an atom or molecule that has gained one electron will have a net negative charge, and one that has lost an electron will possess a positive charge. The chemical symbol for an ion is made by placing one positive or one negative sign for each electron lost or gained above and to the right of the normal abbreviation for the compound in question. For example, the element sodium readily gives up one electron in solution and becomes the sodium ion (Na^+). Likewise, chlorine in solution gains an electron to become the chloride ion, written Cl^-. Positively-charged ions are called *cations*; negatively-charged ions are *anions*.

The ions of some metals can exist in solution in two or more states. Iron, for example, can give up two or three electrons in solution, depending upon the demand for electrons imposed by the ions of other elements in the solution. If the demand is low, iron exists in the divalent (2^+) or *reduced* state; if the solution is oxidizing (i.e., has a high electron demand), iron exists in the trivalent (3^+) or *oxidized* state. The iron ions are called *ferrous* and *ferric:* the *-ous* and *-ic* endings are used consistently to indicate the oxidation states of polyvalent ions.

Acids and *bases* are two important classes of compounds that dissociate and liberate ions in solution. The strength of an acid or base depends upon the completeness of ionization. Acids dissociate into hydrogen (H^+) ions and an anion; bases dissociate into a cation and the hydroxyl (OH^-) ion. The chemical reaction between an acid and a base (the neutralization reaction) produces water and a compound called a *salt.* Most salts ionize readily. The most common salt is sodium chloride (table salt), which ionizes completely in water. There are many such salts, both organic and inorganic. Organic salts generally do not ionize in solution as completely as do inorganic salts; indeed, some inorganic salts hardly dissolve at all. A solution containing ions is called an *electrolyte,* which refers to its ability to conduct an electrical current. When a salt dissolves in water, an equal number of positive and negative ions are produced, so that the net charge in the solution is zero. However, the dissolved substance is present as ions and not as salts, even though the term *dissolved salts* is commonly used. Salts can be removed from an ionic solution by freezing or by evaporation, because individual ions do not exist independently in the solid state.

Modes of Chemical Aggregation

Chemical substances come together in solutions, gases, solids, and liquids in several ways. In solutions, there are two general modes of aggregation. One is called a *complex,* in which each chemical substance is capable of independent existence in solution. The other mode includes such discrete chemical entities as ions and dissolved molecules. The degree of association varies in strength and includes (1) strong chemical bonding; (2) hydrogen bonding, in which pairs of oxygen molecules in water are bonded via a hydrogen atom; (3) formation of ion pairs by electrostatic attraction between the protons (positive charges) of one ion and the electrons (negative charges) of another ion; and (4) chemisorption of ions or charged (polar) aggregates on solid surfaces where there are unsatisfied charges. This last process occurs because atoms at the surface of a substance are not completely surrounded by other atoms of that substance. In the sea, for example, the unsatisfied charges on suspended sediment particles are negative, so cations are usually absorbed on these materials. The bonding is relatively weak. Thus, there can be considerable exchange of cations on these surfaces, particularly where they pass from a river to seawater.

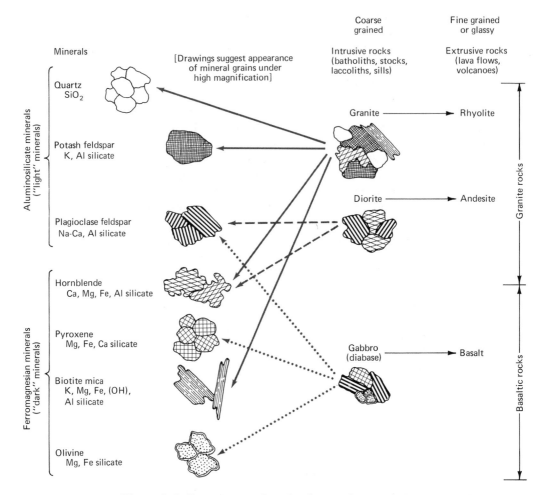

Figure A-9 Component minerals of several common igneous rocks. (Modified after Strahler, *Physical Geography*, 1960, John Wiley and Sons, New York)

Chemicals of the Earth

In nature, insoluble chemical aggregations are called *minerals*.* A mineral is a naturally occurring inorganic substance with characteristic chemical composition, internal structure, and physical properties. A *rock* is a cohesive aggregate of minerals.

The minerals commonly forming rocks are *quartz*, which is silicon dioxide

_____

*This statement is not totally accurate. Minerals formed by the evaporation of natural bodies of water (notably halite, or rock salt) are quite soluble in water.

or silica; *feldspar,* an alkali aluminum silicate; *mica,* a hydrous aluminosilicate; *ferromagnesian* minerals, dark-colored iron and magnesium silicates; and *calcite,* calcium carbonate. Minor amounts of *accessory minerals* are also present in rocks. Accessory minerals have various compositions and are relatively heavy and resistant to decomposition by weathering.

Minerals can be formed into rocks in several ways. *Igneous rocks* are mineral aggregates that have solidified upon cooling from a molten state (Fig. A–9). *Sedimentary rocks* are aggregates of individual mineral or rock particles that have been deposited together under conditions at the earth's surface and cemented. Other sedimentary rocks form from minerals precipitated chemically from seawater. *Metamorphic rocks* are mineral aggregates that result when heat, stress, and hot fluids not common at the earth's surface are applied to any preexisting rock—a condition that often occurs after burial of such rocks.

glossary

ABYSSAL—(or *abyssobenthic*). Pertaining to the great depths of the ocean, generally below 3700 meters (2000 fathoms).

ACCELERATION OF GRAVITY—The acceleration of a freely falling body due to the gravitational attraction of the earth. Its true value varies with latitude, altitude, and the nature of the underlying rocks.

ADVECTION—In oceanography, advection refers to the horizontal or vertical flow of seawater as a current.

AEROBIC—Conditions in which oxygen is present in the environment. Aerobic respiration refers to metabolic processes carried out in the presence of oxygen.

ALGAE—A thallophyte possessing chlorophyll. Algae are single-celled, colonial, or multicelled plants having no true roots, leaves, or stems.

ALKALINITY—The excess base that exists in seawater because the total charge of the major cations exceeds that of the major anions.

ALLOGENIC—The term applied to rock or sediment constituents which originated at a different place and at a previous time to the rock of which they now constitute a part.

AMPHIDROMIC POINT—A no-tide or nodal point on a chart of *cotidal lines* from which the cotidal lines radiate.

ANAEROBIC—Conditions in which oxygen is excluded from the environment. Some bacteria can, however, live in these conditions.

ANTARCTIC CONVERGENCE—(or *Antarctic Convergence line, Antarctic Convergence zone*). The Southern Hemisphere *polar convergence*. It is the best defined convergence line in the oceans, being recognized by a relatively rapid northward increase in the surface temperature. It can be traced around the world in the broad belt of open water between Antarctica to the south and Africa, Australia, and South Africa to the north.

ASTHENOSPHERE—The lower part of the mantle of the earth.

ATOLL—A ring-shaped coral reef that encloses a *lagoon* in which there is no preexisting land, and which is surrounded by the open sea. Low, sandy islands may occur on the reef.

AUTHIGENIC—Formed in the sea. Products of chemical and biochemical action in marine sediments occurring during and after deposition but before burial and consolidation.

AUTOTROPHIC NUTRITION—That process by which an organism manufactures its own food from inorganic compounds.

BALEEN—(or *whalebone*). The horny material growing down from the upper jaw of large plankton-feeding whales, which forms a strainer or filtering organ consisting of numerous plates with fringed edges.

BARRIER BEACH—(also called *offshore barrier*). A *bar* essentially parallel to the *shore,* the crest of which is above *high water.*

BARRIER REEF—A *coral reef* parallel to and separated from the coast by a *lagoon* that is too deep for coral growth.

BASALT—A basic *igneous (extrusive) rock* composed primarily of calcic plagioclase, pyroxene, and with or without olivine.

BATHYPELAGIC—A depth zone of the ocean which lies between depths of 900 and 3700 meters (500 and 2000 fathoms).

BEACH—The zone of unconsolidated material that extends landward from the *low water line* to the place where there is marked change in material or physiographic form, or to the line of permanent vegetation (usually the effective limit of storm waves).

BENIOFF ZONE—A planar zone containing the foci of shallow, intermediate, and deep earthquakes. The zone dips 30° to 60° away from spreading centers and extends 600 km deep.

BENTHIC—(also called *benthonic*). 1. That portion of the marine environment inhabited by marine organisms which live permanently in or on the bottom. 2. Pertaining to all submarine bottom terrain regardless of water depth.

BERM—The nearly horizontal portion of a *beach* or *backshore* having an abrupt fall and formed by deposition of material by wave action, that marks the limit of ordinary high tides.

BIOLOGICAL OCEANOGRAPHY—The study of the ocean's plant and animal life in relation to the marine environment, including the effects of habitat, sedimentation, physical and chemical changes in the environment, and other factors on the spatial and temporal distribution of marine organisms, as well as the action of organisms on the environment.

BIOLUMINESCENCE—The production of light by living organisms as a result of a chemical reaction either within certain cells or organs or extracellularly in some form of secretion.

BODY WAVE—A seismic, or earthquake, wave that travels through regions having uniform mechanical properties. Such waves travel through the interior of the earth and are of two major types—P-waves and S-waves.

BROWN CLAY—A brownish mud that accumulates in the deep sea and contains less than 30 percent biogenous remains.

BUFFER SOLUTION—A solution that is resistant to changes in acidity or basicity. A buffer solution contains a weak acid and its salt or a weak base and its salt.

CAPILLARY WAVE—(also called *ripple, capillary ripple*). A wave whose velocity of propagation is controlled primarily by the *surface tension* of the liquid in which the wave is travelling. Water waves of lengths less than one inch are considered to be capillary waves.

CARBON[14] METHOD—A method of radioactive dating which utilizes the ratio of radiocarbon (Carbon[14]) to Carbon[12] to determine the age of samples containing formerly living matter.

C/G/S SYSTEM—The system of physical measurements in which the fundamental units of length, mass, and time are the centimeter, gram, and second, respectively.

CHALLENGER EXPEDITION—The expedition mounted by the British in H.M.S. *Challenger,* 1873–1876, which made the first extensive oceanographic cruise.

CHART DATUM—(or *datum, tidal datum*). The permanently established surface from which soundings or tide heights are referenced (usually *low water*). The surface is called a tidal datum when referring to a certain phase of tide. In order to provide a factor of safety, some level lower than *mean sea level* is generally selected, such as *mean low water* or *mean lower low water.*

CHEMICAL OCEANOGRAPHY—The study of chemical composition of the dissolved solids and gases, material in suspension, and acidity of ocean waters and their variability both geographically and temporally in relationship to the atmosphere and the ocean bottom.

CHERT—A hard siliceous rock of organic or precipitated origin.

CHLORINITY—(symbol Cl ‰). A measure of the chloride content, by mass, of seawater (grams per kilogram of seawater, or parts per mille). Originally chlorinity was defined as the weight of chlorine in grams per kilogram of seawater after the bromides and the iodides had been replaced by chlorides. To make the definition independent of *atomic weight,* chlorinity is now defined as 0.23285233 times the weight of silver equivalent to all the halides.

CHLORINITY RATIOS—The constant ratios of major ions (also alkalinity) to the chlorinity of seawater.

CHLOROPHYLL—A group of green pigments, identified as *a, b,* and *c,* which occur chiefly in bodies called *chloroplasts* and are active in *photosynthesis.* The concentration of each of these pigments has been employed as a means of estimating the rate of photosynthesis (*primary production*).

CLAY—As a size term, refers to sediment particles ranging from 0.0039 to 0.00024 millimeter in diameter. Mineralogically, clay is a hydrous aluminum silicate material with plastic properties and a crystal structure. Common clay minerals are *kaolinite, montmorillonite,* and *illite.*

COCCOLITH—Very tiny calcareous plates, generally oval and perforated, borne on the surface of some planktonic marine algae (*coccolithophores*).

COLLOID—A particle so small (.001 to 1 micron in diameter) that it can remain in suspension indefinitely, diffract light, and be moved by molecular collisions.

COMMENSALISM—A symbiotic relationship between two species in which one species is benefitted and the other is not harmed.

CONTINENTAL RISE—A gentle slope with a generally smooth surface, rising toward the foot of the *continental slope.*

CONTINENTAL SHELF—(also called *continental platform*). A zone adjacent to a continent or around an island, and extending from the *low water line* to the depth at which there is usually a marked increase of slope to greater depth.

CONTINENTAL SLOPE—A declivity seaward from a shelf edge into greater depth.

CONVECTION—In general, mass motions within a fluid resulting in transport and mixing of the properties of that fluid. Convection, along with *conduction* and *radiation,* is a principal means of energy transfer. Distinction is made between *free convection* (or gravitational convection), motion caused only by density differences within the fluid; and *forced convection,* motion induced by mechanical forces such as deflection by a large-scale surface irregularity, turbulent flow caused by friction at the boundary of a fluid, or motion caused by any applied external force.

CONVERGENCE—Situation whereby waters of different origins come together at a point, or more commonly, along a line known as a convergence line. The recognized convergence lines in the oceans are the polar, subtropical, tropical, and equatorial convergence lines. Regions of convergence are also referred to as convergence zones.

CORAL REEF—A ridge or mass of limestone built up of detrital material deposited around a framework of the skeletal remains of *mollusks, colonial coral,* and massive *calcareous algae.*

CORE—The innermost region of the earth composed of material having the properties of a mixture of iron and nickel.

CORIOLIS FORCE—An apparent force on moving particles resulting from the earth's rotation. It causes the moving particles to be deflected to the right of motion in the Northern Hemisphere and to the left in the Southern Hemisphere; the force is proportional to the speed and latitude of the moving particle and cannot change the speed of the particle.

CRUST—The outer shell of the solid earth, the lower limit of which is taken generally to be the *Mohorovičić discontinuity.* The crust varies in thickness from approximately 5 to 7 kilometers under the ocean basins to 35 kilometers under the continents.

CURIE TEMPERATURE—The temperature below which magnetization of a body can occur.

DECLINATION—The angle that the sun, moon, planets, or stars make with the plane of the equator. The maximum declination of the sun is about 23-1/2° and of the moon is about 28-1/2°.

DEEP-WATER WAVE—(also called *short wave*). A surface wave the length of which is less than twice the depth of the water.

DENSITY—A property of a substance defined as its mass per unit volume.

DENTRIFICATION—The chemical reduction of nitrate and nitrite compounds to nitrite, ammonia, or free nitrogen. This process is commonly caused by bacteria under anoxic marine conditions.

DESICCATION—Drying up, or loss of moisture.

DETRITUS—(or *debris*). Any loose material produced directly from disintegration.

DIAGENESIS—The chemical and physical changes that sediments undergo after their deposition, compaction, cementation, recrystallization, and perhaps replacement, which result in *lithification*.

DIAPIR—A mass of plastic, mobile material (such as rock salt under extreme pressure) that pierces and deforms the overlying rocks.

DIFFUSION—The spreading or scattering of matter under the influence of a concentration gradient with movement from the stronger to the weaker solution.

DIPOLE—An object that is oppositely charged at two points. It usually refers to the charge distribution on a water molecule.

DISPERSION—Separation of waves as they propagate because long waves travel faster in deep water than do shorter waves.

DIURNAL—(*daily*). Actions that recur every 24 hours. When considering lunar tides, tides that recur once each lunar day.

DIVERGENCE—A horizontal flow of water away from a common center, often associated with upwelling.

DOLDRUMS—The equatorial trough that is characterized by the light and variable nature of the winds.

DYNE—A force which, acting on a mass of 1 gram, imparts to that mass an acceleration of 1 centimeter per second every second. The dyne is the unit of force of the *cgs system*.

EDDY MIXING—Mixing caused by the turbulence in the ocean.

EKMAN SPIRAL—A theoretical representation of the effect that a wind blowing steadily over an ocean of unlimited depth and extent and of uniform *viscosity* would cause the surface layer to drift at an angle of 45° to the right of the wind direction in the Northern Hemisphere.

ELECTRONEUTRALITY—A state in which the net electrical charge within a region is zero.

ELECTROSTRICTION—The immobilization of water molecules by the electrostatic field of an ion.

EPICENTER—A point on the surface of the earth lying directly over the *focus* of an earthquake.

EQUATIONS OF MOTION—Specifically, Newton's laws of motion which relate force, velocity, and acceleration.

EQUATORIAL TIDES—Tides that occur approximately every 2 weeks when the moon is over the equator. At these times, the moon produces minimum inequality between two successive *high waters* and two successive *low waters*.

EQUINOXES—The two points in the celestial sphere where the celestial equator intersects the ecliptic; also the times when the sun crosses the celestial equator at these points. At this time day and night are of equal duration throughout the earth.

ERRATIC—A rock fragment found out of place with regard to its place of origin. Usually indicative of transport in floating glacial ice, called *rafting*.

ESTUARY—(or *drowned river mouth, branching bay, firth*). A tidal bay formed by submergence or drowning of the lower portion of a nonglaciated river valley and containing a measurable quantity of sea salt.

EURYHALINE—Adaptable to a wide range of salinity.

EURYTHERMAL—Tolerant of a wide range of temperature.

FETCH—(also called *generating area*). An area of the sea surface over which seas are generated by a wind having a constant direction and speed.

FIORD—A narrow, deep, steep-walled *inlet* of the sea, formed either by the submergence of a mountainous coast or by entrance of the sea into a deeply excavated glacial trough after the melting of the *glacier*.

FLOCCULATE—To aggregate into lumps, as when fine or colloidal clay particles in suspension in fresh water clump together upon contact with salt water and settle out of suspension; a common depositional process in estuaries.

Focus—The point in the earth at which stress is released causing an earthquake.

Food Web—The interaction of marine organisms with regard to the production, consumption, and decomposition of food in the sea. The interrelated sequences of organisms in which each is food for a higher member of the sequence.

Fringing Reef—A *reef* attached directly to the shore of an island or continental landmass. Its outer margin is submerged and often consists of algal limestone, coral rock, and living coral.

Frustule—The siliceous shell of a *diatom*, consisting of two valves, one overlapping the other. It is the principal constituent of *diatomaceous ooze*.

Fully-developed Sea—(also called *fully-arisen sea*). The maximum height to which ocean waves can be generated by a given wind force blowing over sufficient *fetch*, regardless of *duration*, as a result of all possible wave components in the spectrum being present with their maximum amount of spectral energy.

Geodosist—A scientist specializing in the determination of the size and shape of the earth.

Geological Oceanography—The study of the floors and margins of the oceans, including description of submarine relief features, chemical and physical composition of bottom materials, interaction of sediments and rocks with air and seawater, and action of various forms of wave energy in the submarine crust of the earth.

Geophysics—The physics or nature of the earth. It deals with the composition and physical phenomena of the earth and its liquid and gaseous envelopes; it embraces the study of terrestrial magnetism, atmospheric electricity, and gravity; and it includes seismology, volcanology, oceanography, meteorology, and related sciences.

Geostrophic Current—A current defined by assuming that an exact balance exists between the horizontal pressure gradient and the *Coriolis force*.

Geothermal—Heat produced from within the solid earth. A *geothermal anomaly* is formed at mid-ocean ridges where cold bottom water is mixed with ascending geothermal water.

Glacial Ice—Ice found floating in the ocean produced by terrestrial glaciers.

Glauconite—A green mineral, closely related to the micas and essentially a hydrous potassium iron silicate. Occurs in sediments of marine origin and is produced by the alteration of various other minerals in a marine reducing or *anaerobic* environment.

Gram—A cgs unit of mass; originally defined as the mass of 1 cubic centimeter of water at 4°C; but now taken as the one-thousandth part of the standard kilogram.

Granite—A crystalline plutonic rock consisting essentially of alkali feldspar and quartz. Granitic is a textural term applied to coarse and medium-grained granular *igneous rocks*.

Grazing—The feeding of zooplanktonic organisms upon phytoplanktonic organisms. Generally in reference to the feeding of *copepods* upon *diatoms*.

Groin—A low artifical wall-like structure of durable material extending from the land to seaward for a particular purpose.

Heterotrophic Nutrition—That process by which an organism utilizes only preformed organic compounds for its nutrition.

Holoplankton—Organisms living their complete life cycle in the floating state.

Hot Spot—A place on the surface of the earth where molten rock rises persistently.

Hydration—Surrounding an ion with a sheath of water dipoles.

Hydrogenous—Formed in or by reaction with water.

Internal Wave—A wave that occurs within a fluid whose density changes with depth.

Intertidal—*see* Littoral.

Ion—An electrically charged group of atoms either negative or positive. The dissolved salts in seawater dissociate into ions.

Island Arc—A term used for a group of islands usually having a curving archlike pattern, generally convex toward the open ocean, with a deep *trench* or *trough* on the convex side and usually enclosing a deep sea *basin* on the concave side.

ISOSTASY—The balance of large portions of the earth's crust as though they were floating in a denser medium.

ISOTOPE—A species of atom that differs from its ordinary counterpart by the number of neutrons in its nucleus and hence its mass number.

KNOT—A speed unit of 1 nautical mile (6,076.12 feet) per hour. It is equivalent to a speed of 1.688 feet per second or 51.4 centimeters per second.

LITHOSPHERE—The crust, both continental and oceanic, on the upper part of the mantle of the earth.

LITTORAL—The benthic zone between high and low water marks.

LUNAR DAY—(or *tidal day*). The interval between two successive upper *transits* of the moon over a local meridian. The period of the mean lunar day, approximately 24.84 solar hours, is derived from the rotation of the earth on its axis relative to the movement of the moon about the earth.

LUNITIDAL INTERVAL—The interval between the moon's *transit* (upper or lower) over the local meridian and the following *high* or *low water*.

MAGNETIC ANOMALY—A linear zone in which the magnetism of the underlying rocks is greater or less than expected.

MAJOR CONSTITUENTS—Those chemical elements present in seawater which together make up over 99.9 percent of the known dissolved solid constituents of seawater. These include the following ions: chloride, sulfate, bicarbonate, bromide, fluoride, boric acid, sodium, magnesium, calcium, potassium, and strontium.

MANGROVE—One of several genera of tropical trees or shrubs which produce many prop roots and grow along protected low-lying coasts into shallow water.

MANTLE—1. The relatively plastic region between the *crust* and *core* of the earth. 2. In biology, the body wall of some organisms, or the soft tissue next to the shell of mollusks.

MARINE ECOLOGY—The science which embraces all aspects of the interrelations of marine organisms and their environment and the interrelations between the organisms themselves.

MEGALOPLANKTON—Plankton larger than 1 cm.

MEROPLANKTON—Chiefly the floating development stages (eggs and larvae) of the benthos and nekton.

MICRON—(abbreviated μ). A unit of length equal to one-millionth of a meter or one-thousandth of a millimeter.

MIXED TIDE—A type of tide characterized by large inequalities in heights and/or durations of successive high and/or low waters.

MIXING—A general term that refers to the stirring or homogenation of seawater. Common mixing processes include wind, waves, and convection due to density instabilities or turbulence.

MOHOROVIČIĆ DISCONTINUITY—(abbreviated Moho). The sharp discontinuity in composition between the outer layer of the earth (the *crust*) and the next inner layer (the *mantle*). This was discovered by Mohorovičić from seismograms.

MONSOON—A name for seasonal winds derived from Arabic "mausim," a season. It was first applied to the winds over the Arabian Sea which flow for 6 months from northeast and for 6 months from southwest, but it has been extended to similar winds in other parts of the world.

MUD—Pelagic or terrigenous detrital material consisting mostly of silt and clay-sized particles (less than 0.06 millimeter) but often containing varying amounts of sand and or organic materials. It is a general term applied to any sticky fine-grained sediment whose exact size classification has not been determined.

NANNOPLANKTON—(or *centrifuge plankton*). Plankton within the size range 5 to 60 microns. Includes many *dinoflagellates* and smaller *diatoms*. Individuals will pass through most nets and usually are collected by centrifuging water samples.

NEAP TIDE—(or *neaps*). Tide of decreased range which occurs about every two weeks when the moon is in quadrature.

NEKTON—Those animals of the *pelagic division* that are active swimmers, such as most of the adult squids, fishes, and marine mammals.

NEMATATH—A "thread ridge," or linear array of volcanic peaks produced by the passage of a crustal plate over a relatively stationary hot spot.

NEMATOCYSTS—The stinging mechanism of coelenterates, consisting of a chitinous sac filled with venom and pointed at one end. The pointed end can be everted by mechanical or chemical stimuli.

NEPHELOID LAYER—Layers of seawater near or at the sea floor that are characterized by a high degree of light scattering and attenuation.

NERITIC—The waters that overlie the continental shelf extending from low water level to the shelf break.

NUTRIENT—In the ocean any one of a number of inorganic or organic compounds or *ions* used primarily in the nutrition of primary producers. Nitrogen and phosphorus compounds are essential nutrients. Silicates are essential for the growth and development of *diatoms*. Vitamins such as B_{12} are essential to many *algae*.

OBDUCTION—The upthrusting of one lithospheric plate upon another during collision at a plate boundary.

OCEANIC PROVINCE—The water filling the ocean basins seaward of the 100 m isobath. Often referred to as the "open ocean."

OCEANOGRAPHY—The study of the sea, embracing and integrating all knowledge pertaining to the sea's physical boundaries, the chemistry and physics of seawater, and marine biology.

OOZE—A fine-grained pelagic sediment containing undissolved sand- or silt-sized, calcareous or siliceous skeletal remains of small marine organisms in proportion of 30 percent or more, the remainder being clay-sized material.

OPHIOLITE—A complex of rock types representing the uplifted part of a destroyed lithospheric plate.

P-WAVE—A wave that transmits energy by means of travelling compressions and rarifactions of the medium.

PARASITISM—A relationship between two species in which one lives on or in the body of its host, and obtains food from its tissues. Some authorities distinguish between a "commensal parasite," which obtains nourishment from its host without causing harm, and a "pathogenic parasite," which benefits at the expense of its host.

PELAGIC DIVISION—A primary division of the sea which includes the whole mass of water. The division is made up of the neritic province which includes that water shallower than 100 fathoms, and the oceanic province, that water deeper than 100 fathoms.

PHASE—1. A homogeneous, distinct, and physically separable part of an inhomogeneous system. 2. A particular configuration of the earth, moon, and sun in the lunar cycle. 3. The position of a wave with respect to its configuration at some designated starting time.

PHOTIC ZONE—The layer of a body of water which receives ample sunlight for the photosynthetic processes of plants. The depth of this layer varies with the water's *extinction coefficient*, the angle of incidence of the sunlight, length of day, and cloudiness; but it is usually 260 feet (80 meters) or more.

PHOTON—A quantity of electromagnetic energy whose value in *ergs* is the product of its frequency (*v*) in cycles per second and *Planck's constant (h)*. The equation is: $E = hv$.

PHOTOSYNTHESIS—The manufacture of carbohydrate food from carbon dioxide and water in the presence of *chlorophyll*, by utilizing light energy and releasing oxygen.

PHYSICAL OCEANOGRAPHY—The study of the physical aspects of the ocean, such as its density, temperature, ability to transmit light and sound, and sea ice; the movements of the sea, such as tides, currents, and waves; and the variability of these factors both geographically and temporally in relationship to the adjoining domains, namely, the atmosphere and the ocean bottom.

PHYTOPLANKTON—The plant forms of *plankton*. They are the basic synthesizers of organic matter (by *photosynthesis*) in the *pelagic division*. The most abundant of the phytoplankton are the *diatoms*.

PLANKTON—The passively drifting or weakly

swimming organisms in marine and fresh waters.

PORPHYRY DEPOSIT—A dissemination of metallic minerals in a ground mass of porphyritic (visually inhomogeneous) rock of igneous origin.

PRIMARY PRODUCTIVITY—(or *gross primary production, primary production*). The amount of organic matter synthesized by organisms from inorganic substances in unit time in a unit volume of water or in a column of water of unit area cross section and extending from the surface to the bottom.

PROGRESSIVE WAVE—A wave which is manifested by the progressive movement of the wave form.

PYCNOCLINE—The vertical gradient of *density*.

QUADRATURE—The position in the phase cycle when the two principal tide-producing bodies (moon and sun) are nearly at a right angle to the earth; the moon is then in quadrature in its first quarter or last quarter.

RADIANT ENERGY—(also called *radiation*). The energy of any type of *electromagnetic radiation*.

RADIOACTIVE DECAY—The disintegration of the nucleus of an unstable *isotope* by the spontaneous emission of charged particles and/or *photons*.

RADIONUCLIDE—An atom that undergoes radioactive decay. There are three types of radionuclides. *Primary* radionuclides are naturally radioactive. They decay to form stable atoms or *secondary*, radioactive daughter atoms. *Induced* radionuclides are formed by bombardment of atoms with energetic particles, such as cosmic rays.

REFRACTION OF WATER WAVES—The process by which the direction of a wave moving in shallow water at an angle to the contours is changed. That part of the wave advancing in shallower water moves more slowly than the part still advancing in deeper water, causing the *wave crest* to bend toward alignment with the underwater contours.

RESIDENCE TIME—The mean time that a substance remains in a reservoir within the ocean. It is the quotient of the concentration on a substance divided by its rate of addition or removal.

RESONANCE—The phenomenon of amplification of a *free wave* or oscillation by a forced wave or oscillation of exactly equal period.

RESPIRATION—An oxidation-reduction process by which chemically bound energy in food is transformed to the other kinds of energy required by living cells.

REVERSED POLARITY—A condition in which the magnetic poles of the earth are opposite to what they are today (*normal polarity*).

RING—A water circulation pattern found near major, swift currents in the ocean. The rings are nearly circular bands of swiftly flowing water several hundred kilometers in diameter.

RIP CURRENT—The return flow of water piled up on shore by incoming waves and wind; a strong narrow surface current flowing away from the shore. A rip current consists of three parts: the *feeder* current flowing parallel to the shore inside the *breakers*; the *neck*, where the feeder currents converge and flow through the breakers in a narrow band or "*rip*"; and the *head*, where the current widens and slackens outside the breaker line.

S-WAVE—A wave that transmits energy by means of a travelling shear deformation of the medium.

SALINITY—A measure of the quantity of dissolved salts in seawater. It is formally defined as the total amount of dissolved solids in seawater in parts per thousand (‰) by weight when all the carbonate has been converted to oxide, the bromide and iodide to chloride, and all organic matter is completely oxidized. These qualifications result from the chemical difficulty in drying the salts in seawater. In practice, salinity is not determined directly but is computed from *chlorinity, electrical conductivity*, refractive index, or some other property whose relationship to salinity is well established.

SAND—Loose material which consists of grains ranging between 0.0625 and 2.0000 millimeters in diameter.

SAPROPEL—A marine sediment rich in the organic debris of plants and animals.

SEA ICE—Ice formed at sea or the seashore. Includes *grease ice, slush ice,* and *pancake ice,* formed at successive stages of the freezing of seawater; *pack ice,* caused by coalesced floes; and *fast ice,* a sheet or pile of ice formed in contact with the sea bottom and shore.

SEAMOUNT—An approximately cone-shaped feature that rises at least 1000 m above the sea floor.

SEDIMENT—Particulate organic and inorganic matter which accumulates in a loose unconsolidated form. It may be chemically precipitated from solution, secreted by organisms, or transported by air, ice, wind, or water and deposited.

SEICHE—A *standing wave* oscillation of an enclosed or semienclosed water body that continues, pendulum fashion, after the cessation of the originating force, which may have been either seismic, atmospheric, or wave induced.

SEMIDIURNAL—*semidaily.* Actions that recur twice each 24 hours. When considering lunar tides, tides that recur twice each lunar day.

SESSILE—1. Attached directly by base, without stipe or stalk. 2. Permanently attached; not free to move about.

SHELF BREAK—(or *shelf edge.*) The line along which there is a marked increase of slope at the outer margin of a *continental shelf.*

SILL—A submarine ridge that separates two basins.

SILT—An unconsolidated sediment whose particles range in size from 0.0039 to 0.0625 millimeter in diameter (between clay and sand sizes).

SLIP VECTOR—The direction in which relative motion occurs along a fault.

SOLSTICE—One of the two points in the sun's orbit (the ecliptic) farthest from the celestial equator; the instant when the sun's declination is maximum.

SOLUBILITY—The extent to which a substance (solute) mixes with a liquid (solvent) to produce a homogeneous system (*solution*).

SPECIES—The smallest grouping of entities that preserves their common attributes. Refers to biological organisms and chemical entities.

SPECTRUM OF WAVES—An array of the components in a mixture of waves. The components can be distinguished on the basis of their energy, power, or direction of propagation to form a *wave energy spectrum*, a *wave power spectrum*, or a *directional wave spectrum*.

SPRING TIDE—Tide of increase range which oc-

curs about every 2 weeks when the moon is new or full.

STANDING WAVE—A type of wave in which the surface of the water oscillates vertically between fixed points, called *nodes*, without progression. The points of maximum vertical rise and fall are called antinodes. At the nodes, the underlying water particles exhibit no vertical motion.

STEADY STATE—A state of a system such that all processes leading to change in the system are in balance so that no net change occurs.

STENOHALINE—Capable of existence only within a narrow range of *salinity.*

STENOTHERMAL—Tolerant of only a very narrow range of temperature.

STRIKE—The line of intersection of a horizontal plane and another plane oriented differently in space.

STRIKE-SLIP FAULT—(rift). A fault having predominant relative motion parallel to its strike.

SUBDUCTION—The underthrusting action occurring when one lithospheric plate collides with another.

SUBLITTORAL—The benthic region that extends from the low water mark to the *shelf break.*

SUBMARINE CANYON—A relatively narrow, deep depression with steep slopes, the bottom of which grades continuously downward.

SUBTROPICAL HIGH—(or *subtropical anticyclone, oceanic anticyclone, oceanic high*). One of the semipermanent highs of the subtropical high pressure belt. They lie over oceans, and are best developed in the summer season.

SUPRALITTORAL—The benthic zone above high tide level periodically moistened by waves and spray.

SURFACE WAVE—A seismic, or earthquake, wave that travels along boundary surfaces of the earth. Such surfaces separate regions of distinctly different mechanical properties.

SURF ZONE—The area between the outermost *breaker* and the limit of wave *uprush*.

SUSPENSOID—That particle which forms the solid or nonaqueous phase of a suspension. Suspensoids are usually lithic or biological in origin.

SWASH—(or *uprush, run-up*). The rush of water up onto the beach following the breaking of a wave.

SWELL—Ocean waves which have traveled out of their generating area. Swell characteristically exhibits a more regular and longer period and has flatter crests than waves within their *fetch*.

SYZYGY—The two points in the moon's orbit when the moon is in *conjunction* or *opposition* to the sun relative to the earth; time of new or full moon in the cycle of phases.

TABLEMOUNT—A *seamount* having a relatively smooth, flat summit.

TEST—The hard covering or supporting structure of many invertebrates, it may be enclosed within an outer layer of living tissue.

THERMOREMANENT MAGNETISM—Magnetism received by a magnetic material at the time it cools below its Curie temperature.

TIDAL CONSTITUENT—(also called *tidal component, partial tide*). One of the harmonic components comprising the tide at any point. The periods of the partial tides are derived from various combinations of the angular velocities of earth, sun, moon, and stars relative to each other.

TIDE—In the oceans, the periodic rise and fall of sea level due to the gravitational interaction of the sun, moon, and earth.

TIDE RANGE—The difference in height between consecutive *high* and *low waters*. Where the type of the tide is diurnal the mean range is the same as the diurnal range.

TOMBOLO—A bar or spit connecting or "tying" an island to the mainland or to another island.

TRACER—A substance or property that identifies a quantity of seawater and permits knowing the pattern of motion of the water.

TRACTIVE FORCE—The horizontal resultant of the tide-producing force over the earth.

TRADE WINDS—The wind system, occupying most of the tropics, which blows from the *subtropical highs* toward the equatorial trough: a major component of the general circulation of the atmosphere.

TRANSFORM—(also called *transform fault*). Large faults having dominantly lateral motion and whose trace follows a great circle.

TRENCH—A long, narrow and deep depression of the sea floor, with relatively steep sides.

TROPHIC LEVEL—A successive stage of nourishment as represented by links of the food chain. Primary producers *(phytoplankton)* constitute the first trophic level, herbivorous *zooplankton* the second trophic level, and carnivorous organisms the third trophic level.

TROPIC TIDE—The tide that occurs twice monthly when the effect of the moon's maximum declination north or south of the equator is greatest.

T-S CURVE—The plot of temperature versus salinity data from a water column. The result is a diagram which identifies the water masses within the column, the density, and the stability of the column.

TSUNAMI—(or *tunami, tidal wave, seismic sea wave*). A long-period sea wave produced by a submarine earthquake or volcanic eruption. It may travel unnoticed across the ocean for thousands of miles from its point of origin and builds up to great heights over shoal water.

TURBIDITY CURRENT—(or *density current*). A highly turbid, relatively dense current carrying large quantities of clay, silt, and sand in a suspension that flows down a submarine slope through less dense seawater.

TURBULENCE—The state of motion of a fluid characterized by the random fluctuation, in time and space, of the speed and direction of the motion.

TYNDALL SCATTERING—The separation of sunlight into spectral components by aggregates of air molecules or by particles having diameters equal to or smaller than about one-fourth the wavelength of the light.

UPWELLING—The process by which water rises from a lower to a higher depth, usually as a result of *divergence* and offshore currents.

Upwelling is most prominent where persistent wind blows parallel to a coastline so that the resultant wind-driven current sets away from the coast. It constitutes a distinct climatogenetic influence by bringing colder water to the surface.

The upwelled water, besides being cooler, is richer in plant nutrients, so that regions of upwelling are generally also regions of rich fisheries.

VARVE—A sedimentary deposit, bed, or lamination deposited in one season. It is usually distinguished by color or composition and used as an index to changes in the depositional environment.

VISCOSITY—(or *internal friction*). That molecular property of a fluid which enables it to support *tangential stresses* for a finite time and thus to resist deformation.

WAVE—1. A disturbance which moves through or over the surface of the medium (here, the ocean), with speed dependent upon the properties of the medium. 2. A ridge, deformation, or undulation of the surface of a liquid.

WAVE AGE—The name given to the ratio of the celerity of a wave to the speed of the wind generating the wave.

WAVE DECAY—The loss of wave energy by friction causing the wave height to diminish if wind energy is not supplied.

WAVE STEEPNESS—The ratio of the height of a wave to its length.

WEST WIND DRIFT—(sometimes called *Antarctic Circumpolar Current*). The ocean current with the largest volume transport (approximately 110×10^6 cubic centimeters per second); it flows from west to east around the Antarctic continent and is formed partly by the strong westerly wind in this region and partly by density differences.

WIND-DRIVEN CURRENT—(sometimes called *wind drift, drift current*). A current formed by the force of the wind. Theoretically, currents produced by the wind will set to the right of the direction of the wind in the Northern Hemisphere and to the left in the Southern Hemisphere.

WIND SET-UP—The vertical rise in the *still water level* on the leeward side of a body of water caused by wind stresses on the surface of the water.

WIND-WAVE—Wave motion that results from the interaction of the wind and the sea surface.

ZOOPLANKTON—The animal forms of *plankton*. They include various crustaceans, such as copepods and euphausiids, jellyfishes, certain protozoans, worms, mollusks, and the eggs and larvae of benthic and nektonic animals. They are the principal consumers of the *phytoplankton* and, in turn, are the principal food for a large number of squids, fishes, and baleen whales.

index

500

Heat capacity, 152, 354, 478–480
Heat exchange across the sea surface, 152
Heat flow, 48–51
Herbivore, 357
Hermit crabs (*see* Decapoda)
Herring:
    food web, 381, 382
Heterotrophic nutrition, 326, 356
History of the ocean basins from deep-sea
    drilling, 416–417
Holdfast, 327, 329, 372
Holocene Epoch, 417, 418
Holocene marine transgression, 303, 304, 310
Holoplankton, 362
Holothurian (*see also* Echinodermata):
    floating adaptation, 369
Holozoic nutrition, 356
Horse latitudes, 173, 174
Hudson Bay, 12, 13
Humic substances in seawater, 98
Hydration, 95
Hydrogen sulfide:
    anoxic condition, 109, 314
    in Black Sea, 109, 314
    at bottom of basins, 109, 314
    exclusion of animals by, 109, 314
    in sediments, 262
    and sulfate reduction, 380
Hydroid polyp (*see also* Coelenterata), 335,
336
Hydrostatic pressure, 143
Hydrozoa (*see also* Coelenterata):
    figure, 337
    synopsis, 335
Hypsographic curve, 14, 15

Ice:
    composition, 163
    distribution, 163
    formation, 163
    types of, 161
Ice age (*see also* Pleistocene epoch), 8
Iceland, 29
Igneous rocks:
    composition of, 486
    definition, 487
Indian spring low water, 269
Intermediate water mass:
    characteristics, 219, 221
    origin, 221–222
Internal waves, 248, 249
Interstitial water of sediments, 396, 407
Intertidal zone:
    classification of, 360, 361
    organisms in, 372
Ion:
    definition, 484
    exchange processes in desalination, 6
    pair, 96

Island, 35–37, 41, 54–55
Island arc, 13, 47, 49, 85, 86
Isostasy, 20, 21, 56, 58, 303
Isotope:
    definition, 482
    of oxygen, 110, 417, 419

Japan, Islands of, 13, 85, 302
Japan Trench, 33
Java Trench, 13
Jellyfish (*see* Coelenterata)

Katmai eruption, 404
Kelp (*see* Brown algae)
Kelvin temperature scale, 478
Kerogen in marine sediment, 98
Kinetic energy, 468, 473
Knolls, 35
Knot, 275
Krakatoa:
    ash, 404
    explosion, 247
Krill (*see* Euphausiacea)
Kurile Trench, 33
Kuroshio Current, 197, 213

Labrador Sea, 80
Lake Superior, 256
Lamellibranchia (*see* Pelecypoda)
Landslide surge, 251
Latent heat energy of evaporation, 153
    definition, 479
Latent heat energy of fusion, 153
    definition, 479
Laws of motion, 171, 265, 472
Libya, 152
Light penetration in the sea, 153
Limpet (*see also* Gastropoda), 341
Linnaeus, Karl von, 321
Lipid, production of, 98
Lisbon, Portugal, 268
Lithosphere, 39
Lithothamnion (*see* Red algae)
Littoral:
    currents, 285
    drift of sediment, 286–290
    environment, 361, 363
    organisms, 371
Littorinid snail (*see also* Gastropoda), 372
Lituya Bay, Alaska, 251
Lobsters (*see also* Decapoda):
    phyllosoma larvae, 369
Longhurst-Hardy plankton sampler, 462
Longshore current, 285
Longshore drift of sediment, 286
Lunar day, 261

510

512